Return to Pleasant Valley

Return to Pleasant Valley

**Louis Bromfield's best from *Malabar Farm*
& his other country classics.**

**Including special selections by
Ellen Bromfield Geld
and E.B. White**

Edited by George DeVault

CHILLICOTHE, ILLINOIS
The AMERICAN BOTANIST, Booksellers
1996

Return to Pleasant Valley

New material for The American Botanist edition
© 1996 George DeVault

An earlier version of the chapter Bromfield's Brazil appeared in
Successful Farming, March 1996

FIRST EDITION

Front cover illustration of Louis Bromfield with his dogs by the
late Kate Lord is taken from *Malabar Farm* (HarperCollins, New
York, 1948)

Back cover photos © 1996 George DeVault

ISBN 0-929332-06-7

Contents

Acknowledgments

Although Louis Bromfield wrote most of the material in this book, it took a lot of other people to bring him back into print. Chief among them are Joanne Fallert in the Adult Permissions Dept. at HarperCollins in New York; Herb Chaise, attorney for the estate of Louis Bromfield; Grace Darby in the Permissions Dept. at *The New Yorker* magazine for her assistance in obtaining the rights to reprint E.B. White's review of Malabar Farm; D. Keith Crotz of The American Botanist in Chillicothe, Illinois, for finding the impossible on a regular basis, especially all those signed first editions; Loren Kruse, editor of *Successful Farming* magazine in Des Moines, Iowa, who first published an earlier version of Chapter 15, Bromfield's Brazil; Jane Potter Gates and Ray Stevens of the National Agricultural Library in Beltsville, Md.; my old friend Ed Courrier, who designed the cover and helped get us started so we could produce these pages electronically on PageMaker on our old Macintosh computer; Steve Bulkley, my first night city editor who still balances constructive criticism and praise for his "kids" like a good teacher; computer guru Jeff Kause at McNaughton & Gunn printers for his technical assistance; Duane Dailey of the University of Missouri; Louis Andres, manager of Malabar Farm State Park in Lucas, Ohio; Max Drake, the man Louis Bromfield first hired to manage Malabar Farm; the Ohio Ecological Food & Farm Association; my wife, Melanie, who delayed her spring seed-starting to spend countless hours typing and repeatedly proofing the entire manuscript; my children Donald and Ruth, who also helped with the reading and now know a little more about the Ohio country where their parents were born; and, last but not least, Ellen Bromfield Geld and Carson Geld of Fazenda Pau D'Alho in Tietê, Brazil, for their warm and gracious hospitality, sage advice and personal inspiration, new friends who we hope to see more of now that, as they say in Brazil, "we know the way." Thank you all.

Dedicated to the memory of Ward Sinclair,
"a good farmer" in anyone's book.

Introduction

When it became certain that this book project would soon take me to Brazil to visit Louis Bromfield's youngest daughter at her cattle ranch outside of São Paulo, I mentioned the upcoming trip in a note to an old friend. She is the editor of a national farm magazine. And, as most roving reporters have a habit of doing whenever writing to an editor, I asked whether she might be interested in an article from Brazil, something to bring her readers the very latest chapter in the Bromfield legacy. At best, I thought, that would at least help cover some of the cost of the trip. At worst, I expected a polite, "Thanks, but no thanks." Free-lance writers get used to rejection letters. But nothing could have prepared me for the answer that finally arrived:

"Who is Louis Bromfield?" said the editor.

Who indeed? He is only a contemporary of Ernest Hemingway, Sinclair Lewis, F. Scott Fitzgerald, Pearl S. Buck, Thornton Wilder, Margaret Mitchell, Willa Cather, James Thurber and John Steinbeck. The list goes on and on. A small-town Ohio boy who dropped out of Columbia journalism school in 1917, Bromfield ran away from home to drive an ambulance in World War I. He served in seven major battles and was awarded the *Croix de Guerre*, the French military medal for bravery in action. Back in the United States after the war, Bromfield settled in New York City where he variously worked for the City News Service, the Associated Press and *Musical America*. He even wrote a column for *The New Yorker* and music reviews for *TIME*. He married Mary Appleton Wood, a native New Yorker of old New England stock, in 1921. He wrote — and discarded — three novels before publishing his first novel in 1924. That book, *The Green Bay Tree*, won the approval of the reading public and critics, alike. It was a story of the clash of generations in a small American town. One critic went so far as to favorably compare Bromfield to Voltaire, the French satirist. The next year, after publishing his second novel, *Possession*, Bromfield, his wife and their infant daughter Anne went to France for what was supposed to be a one-month vacation. They spent the better part of the next 12 years living outside of Paris, where their daughters Hope and Ellen were born. In 1927, Bromfield won the Pulitzer Prize for literature for his third novel, *Early Autumn*. He was only 30 years old and already one of the brightest American stars in a literary universe full of intense suns. While spending the winter of 1929 in New York City, he wrote screenplays for movie mogul Samuel Goldwyn. Even though he was being paid $2,500 *a week*, Bromfield hated the work so much that he paid $10,000 to get out of his contract and returned to France to work on his own writing. But such fame is fleeting. After all, how many of us can even name one winner of last year's Pulitzer without rushing for *The World Almanac*?

That's why I was not completely surprised when Bromfield's name again drew something of a blank the other night as I was talking on the phone with Melinda Ingalls, my sister in Ohio. Mindy had fallen on the ice and broken her kneecap while going out to feed the five horses -- four Percherons and one quirky quarter horse -- that she and Jim have on their Copper Rose Farm near Cardington. I just called to see how she was doing. She asked how this book was coming along.

"Almost done," I sighed with relief. Then something made me ask, "Have you ever *read* any Bromfield?" She hadn't. She said she *knew* of Malabar Farm, had even seen some signs for it once when out driving with Jim. After all, it's not *that* far from Cardington, just in the next county to the north. "They have plowing matches and things like that, don't they?"

Yes, they do. But there is more to Malabar Farm than the Sugar Maple Festival, trail rides and other special events put on by the Ohio Parks Department, which now runs the farm. A lot more. Much of what is euphemistically known these days as sustainable, re-generative or even organic farming began more than half a century ago when Bromfield tired of writing fiction and bought three worn-out farms in his native Ohio in 1939.

He named his place Malabar after the Malabar Coast and hills near Bombay, India, where in the early '30s he hunted tigers with royalty and gained the inspiration for some of his finest novels (*The Rains Came*, 1937, and *Night in Bombay*, 1940). Those books provided much of the money needed to buy his farm. Using only methods that he said were affordable for the average "dirt farmer," Bromfield doubled, then tripled yields on 1,000 badly abused acres, turning "Poverty Knob" into one of the most productive spots in Richland County in just a few short years.

Malabar was also a magical place. Its inhabitants included a galaxy of visiting movie stars — Bogie and Bacall were married there — and a zany bunch of animals, led by a pack of rambunctious boxers that really ran the place. A war-weary nation soon fell madly in love with Malabar and its offbeat crew through Bromfield's most popular books. *Pleasant Valley* started it all in 1945. The critics went wild.

- "A thrilling reading experience."—*Cincinnati Enquirer*
- "He has something to say to everyone who loves the good earth."—*Chicago Daily News*
- "This is a book for thoughtful people who love America."— *Chicago Tribune.*
- "A crusading book? Certainly it's a crusading book — and an important one. A book that every countryman and every gardener should read and get excited about. This book will become a classic."—*New York Herald Tribune Book Review*
- "One of the most important books written within the past 25 years."—*Nashville Tennessean*

But it was *Malabar Farm*, which the author humbly described as "no more than a second volume of *Pleasant Valley*," that won Bromfield the hearts of Americans once and for all.

"Malabar Farm is the farm for me," crowed E.B. White in reviewing the book in *The New Yorker* magazine in 1948.

"A book like his is a very great boon,
And what he's done, I'd like to be doon."

E.B. White wasn't the only wannabe farmer to fall under the spell of Malabar's magic. Young and old, in cities and on farms throughout America and around the world, countless people were captivated by Bromfield's passionate prose about returning home and living the good life on the land.

"*Malabar Farm* was one of the books that my mother read to us as we sat around the woodstove on winter evenings," recalls my friend Duane Dailey, who grew up on a farm in Mercer County in the Green Hills area of northern Missouri next door to Iowa. "This was major entertainment before rural electrification. It was only long after college that I learned, browsing the library stacks, that Bromfield had written much more."

Bromfield wrote 31 books in all. The total includes 19 novels, five collections of short stories and seven non-fiction books concerned mainly with his farming, experiments, observations and adventures on his Ohio farm. That handful of farm-related books outsold all of his fiction combined. Parts of *Pleasant Valley* and *Malabar Farm* first appeared as magazine articles. In book form, finally, each quickly sold hundreds of thousands of copies in dozens of printings.

The book you hold in your hands is made up of my personal favorite chapters and quotes, mostly from Bromfield's later works. It is not meant to be the last word on the author or his rich writing on widely diverse subjects. It is simply what I like about Bromfield as a storyteller. If you read a Bromfield book long ago, maybe this book will "spark" you to read another of his titles. For those of you who have never read anything Bromfield wrote, this is a sampler of what you've been missing. It's just a taste of what earlier generations of Americans grew up on because in the 10 years following World War II, Bromfield was everywhere.

For example, every Saturday morning, NBC radio broadcast his "Voice from the Valley" program. Bromfield wrote scads of magazine articles. His newspaper column was widely syndicated. He soon became the best known and most loved American farmer since Thomas Jefferson. Bromfield's fame was such that long before his death from bone cancer complications in early 1956, Malabar was drawing 20,000 visitors a year. In fact, on a single Saturday in the early '50s, some 8,000 farmers and their families from 27 states turned Malabar Farm and the tiny village of Lucas, Ohio, into a mini-Woodstock for *Successful Farming* magazine's field day on "building topsoil."

"The back country roads were filled with traffic, the cars running bumper to bumper," Bromfield wrote in *From My Experience* in 1955. "The demonstration was scheduled for 1:30 p.m., but there were hundreds of cars already parked in the rolling meadows by eight in the morning. As visitors were not expected until the afternoon, no provision was made with local churches or granges to provide food, so the visitors were forced to forage for themselves. By evening the stores in the surrounding villages were depleted of everything from breakfast foods and tinned soups to cigarettes. The demonstration took place on a Saturday afternoon but many visitors were still there on Sunday and the following Monday."

T oday, Malabar Farm is an Ohio state park. It attracts more than 180,000 visitors a year from all over the United States and many foreign countries. What's all the fuss about?

There is the Hollywood mystique, of course. Bromfield's writing resulted in 12 motion pictures released from 1930 through 1956. The stars included W.C. Fields and Mae West, making her film debut in 1932 in *Night After Night,* Vincent Price, Zasu Pitts, Greer Garson, Richard Burton, Fred MacMurray and Lana Turner. To help finance building of his 32-room Big House at Malabar, he wrote screenplays in California during the winter of 1939-1940. So it was no surprise that many of Hollywood's most glittering stars soon became as common a sight around Malabar as Bromfield's brigade of boxers. The box office galaxy included:

• Tough guy James Cagney, who sold vegetables for days on end at Bromfield's vegetable stand while staying at the Big House.

• Kay Francis, behind dark glasses and a cigarette holder dangling out of her mouth, stirring apple butter with a wooden hoe.

• Joan Fontaine hurrying out to the barn in a negligee and slippers to watch a calf being born.

• Errol Flynn, Shirley Temple, Tyrone Power, Dorothy Lamour, Myrna Loy and Fay Wray, who were among the guests at the wedding of Humphrey Bogart and Lauren Bacall at Malabar Farm on May 21, 1945. He was 44, and starting his fourth marriage. She was 19. Bromfield was best man.

Behind all the glitter, there were deeper, much more serious sides to Bromfield. These were the really important things that drew people to Malabar from around the world. On the purely practical side, Bromfield, his books and his farm provided a wealth of good, new "how-to" information that farmers and gardeners had a hard time finding anywhere else. He was the father of what he liked to call the "New Agriculture," in which all the "good farmers" of the world not only conserve but actually improve our precious topsoil and groundwater resources, while producing ever more abundant crops that are nutritionally balanced and superior, fresh and free of pesticide residues. Years before Rachel Carson wrote *Silent Spring,* Bromfield saw the danger signs of chemical-intensive farming. He warned of potentially dire environmental, economic and human health problems. Instead of spraying more and deadlier poisons year after year, he advocated crop rotations, the use of green manures and micronutrients, championing the belief of his good friend Dr. Hugh Hammond Bennett, first head of the U.S. Soil Conservation Service, that only a healthy soil can produce healthy crops capable of sustaining truly healthy people. He studied the link between deficient or unbalanced soils and human disease, birth defects and poor livestock nutrition, while advocating a preventive approach to medicine and health care.

But even more important than chisel plows, vitamins and foliar fertilizers, was the deeply spiritual, almost mystical side of Bromfield. His farm writing, unlike his fiction, was full of substance, bursting with life and awe at the excitement of creation itself. By laying a finger squarely on the pulse of the universe, Bromfield's passionate prose let us renew ourselves — physically, mentally and spiritually — by repotting humanity's severed agricultural roots in the living soil from which we were born.

It was a spiritual journey that Bromfield began himself about the time he wrote *The Farm* in 1932 in a fit of homesickness while living in Europe. He had both fame and fortune aplenty by then. But they were empty rewards. Ohio, the hills, valleys and fields of his youth, kept calling him back, tugging at his soul from across the wide ocean. It was then that he began talking more and more seriously about buying a farm in America.

"I wanted peace and I wanted roots for the rest of my life," he said of his return to Ohio and the farm in *From My Experience* the year before his death. "Fiction writing is simply a way of making a living and for my money not a very satisfactory or even self-respecting one. There are better and more satisfying things to do."

Today, many of us are stuck in much the same rut. We spend long days staring at computer screens in climate-controlled offices, worrying more than anything about whether we will still have jobs tomorrow in this era of corporate downsizing and restructuring. We're so busy rushing here and there, doing this and that to "stay fit," "relieve stress" or "relax" that we have little time left for living. In the long run, money does not buy health, happiness or security. And material possessions, especially those bought on credit, quickly become burdens and financial liabilities. It truly is an "Age of Irritation," as Bromfield described modern life in *A Few Brass Tacks* in 1946. That's why, I believe, we can all benefit greatly from even a brief return to Pleasant Valley.

George DeVault
Pheasant Hill Farm
Emmaus, PA
March 16, 1996

1

The Farm

From *The Farm*, 1933

Although classified as a work of fiction, Louis Bromfield's book The Farm *is no mere flight of fancy. Written in 1932 during what Bromfield later described as "a fit of homesickness" while he was living in Europe, the book draws heavily on his early years in Ohio, the lives of his parents and their hardy ancestors who helped clear the forest and settle the Buckeye State. In his introduction to* The Farm, *Bromfield explains why all that is so important. His explanation takes the form of a letter to his three daughters, the youngest of whom was born earlier in the year:*

Dear Anne and Hope and Ellen:

"The Farm" is written for you, who were all born long after the war ended, so that you may know a little what it was like to have lived before 1914. Something came to an end about that year and I fancy it was the nineteenth century. You will never know what it was like first hand, and you will never know the country from which your father came, because even if you ever went to visit it, you would fail to find it. You might discover a stream or hill which you would recognize from hearsay and legend, but that is all. The rest has vanished.

"The Farm" is the story of a way of living which has largely gone out of fashion, save in a few half-forgotten corners and in a few families which have stuck to it with admirable stubbornness in spite of everything. It was and is a good way of life, and although you live to be as old as the Colonel, I doubt that you will find a better way. I counsel you to cherish it as most of the descendants of the Colonel and the stalwart Elvira van Essen have done. It has in it two fundamentals which were once and may be again intensely American characteristics. These are integrity and idealism. Jefferson has been dead more than a hundred years and there is no longer any frontier, but the things which both represented are immortal. They

1

are tough qualities needed in times of crisis.

"The Farm" was written for the three of you and for your children and grandchildren. If anyone else likes it, so much the better.

Louis Bromfield
Gstaad, Switzerland
Dec. 23, 1932

Bromfield begins The Farm *in the spring of 1815 when, at age 52, Revolutionary War hero Colonel MacDougal leaves his comfortable home in Maryland to start a new life in the Ohio wilderness. The chapter reprinted here picks up the story nearly three-quarters of a century later, describing the ideal farm of Bromfield's dreams as seen through the eyes of Johnny, the Colonel's great-grandson. In reality, it is the first draft of a plan for what Bromfield will later call Malabar Farm.*

W hen Johnny was three or four years old the life of the Farm began to make an impression upon his consciousness. After that first moment of illumination when he was carried in out of the softly falling snow to be placed in the Colonel's Chair and surrounded by giantesses, he began slowly to understand it all and to attach himself to it with a strange tenacity, as if the Farm, instead of the house in the town where his parents lived, was really his home.

It came into his consciousness in flashes isolated, and yet in their separateness curiously distinct — the sound of the primitive gramophone, the delicious smell of food when he crawled or toddled into the east wing, the barking of the old sheep-dog, Beattie, the smell of the spice pinks and the red of the strawberries on a dewy Sunday morning in May. Slowly the impressions built themselves up, growing together into warm unity about the central figure of the little thin old lady who had long ago given birth to the giants and giantesses who were his mother, his uncles, and his aunts. Jamie and Maria were Johnny's grandparents, for his mother, Ellen, was one of their eight children.

In all her life the Colonel's daughter Maria never weighed more than a hundred pounds and after she had borne eight children she was always frail, so that there were times when the strength of her body gave out and she no longer had the force to stand. On these occasions she stayed in the bedroom with the picture of Pocahontas saving John Smith, lying in the great bed, small as a leaf on an autumn bank, sometimes for days and sometimes for weeks; but if the body failed in strength, the will remained alive, and even in her bed the old lady refused to cede even the smallest of her rights as head of the big household to any of her strapping daughters. Lying weak and ill, she saw to it that her menfolk were properly clothed and fed; she superintended, too, the making of pickles and jellies, and managed to spoil her grandchildren. Until the very end when she grew helpless and her wits wandered in the abyss of illness, she remained the force which kept the household and the garden and the kitchen and the dairy running as no one else could run them.

Johnny saw her for the last time when he was seven or eight years old and she asked that her grandchildren be brought in to her. A dozen times before that she had been near to dying, but on this occasion she must have sensed a difference, for she asked to see those she loved. Some of them were far off in the West and never saw her again, but of the others there were aplenty. They came and went all one day, and with all of them she was merry. She made no farewells and said nothing of death, and when Johnny's turn came he found her sitting propped up among the pillows, a little tired but very bright and with the look in her blue eyes (which were the Colonel's over again) of teasing and gentle mockery which she always had for the grandchildren. It was the sort of teasing they did not mind, since they knew that it was always the prelude to a treat. A little while after Johnny had gone, she fell asleep, and when she wakened her wits were dimmed and in her weakness she had gone back again into her childhood, and as she died she fancied that she was a girl again and that the Colonel had come to fetch her on a journey. She rose up a little in bed and cried out in a strong young voice, "It's all right, Pappy. I'm ready," and then she died.

There was something about her, as there was about her sisters — a dry quaintness, subtle and indefinable — which always set her apart from the other old ladies of the Town and County. As a small boy, Johnny was aware of it, but he did not know it then as the faint lingering aroma of the eighteenth century. She had been born when the Colonel was nearly seventy, and upon her, as upon the other children of the old gentleman, there descended the spell of his personality, his humor which was light and dry, his wits so unlike the wits of the clumsy human century into which he survived.

With his whimsies and his speech, his beliefs and even his language, she brought his century into the lives of his great-grandchildren. She called her husband, the rugged Jamie, Pa, and whenever she spoke of the Colonel it was as Pappy. She knew old songs which other women her age had never heard, and in her own household she used words which were passing or gone from the English of her time and country — words like crock and stillroom and buttery.

After the 'eighties she never changed her style of dress, and because hers was a tradition of good stuffs, expensive and durable, her clothes never wore out. On weekdays she wore dresses of black stuff made with a very full skirt which descended from a tight basque fastened at the front by innumerable tiny buttons. On Sundays, when she went to weddings, funerals, and christenings, she had a dress made of some stiff rich material brocaded in satin and covered with tiny embroidered flowers. She always wore a little bonnet, like the one in her wedding daguerreotype, tied coquettishly at one side under the chin. Her Sunday bonnet had a slightly-worn aigrette which sprung from a little wreath of pansies. She had never, like her sister Jane, had a taste for horses, and fiery animals gave her no pleasure, so she had a horse of her own different from Jamie Ferguson's other animals, that was pure white, plump, and docile. His name was Doctor and he drew a phaeton which also belonged to her, and it was behind him that she rode when she went visiting or to parties and funerals, trying the patience of her big husband, who could not abide Doctor's comfortable disregard of all noises and strange vehicles capable of throwing an ordinary horse into a fine display of rearings, buckings, and prancings.

For Johnny, the memory of his grandmother was forever associated with the buttery. This was a big dark cupboard in the very center of the old house near the dark room and at the top of the stairs which led down into the cellar. Here were kept the pies and cakes, crocks full of cookies or apples, cider, maple sugar, butter, and stone crocks of buttermilk in which little bright gold globules of butter hung suspended. Here it was that she led her grandchildren when they arrived. Sometimes there was a whole procession of greedy little monsters who clung to her full skirts while she opened the door. And the small mouths watered at the complicated perfume of cider and pies and cookies and apples which swept over them as the door was opened. It was an aroma which Johnny never smelled again for the rest of his life, an odor which has disappeared in a world where foods come in tins or wrapped in sanitary paper, yet years after his grandmother had died he could not think of her without sensing faintly the ghost of that delicious complicated perfume. She would stand there, surrounded by clamoring children, and sometimes she would tease them by pretending that, to her astonishment, the cooky-jar was empty or that some tramp must have broken in and stolen all the maple sugar, but they came to understand her teasing, and the delay only made the treat the more delicious. And sometimes toward the end of her life, when she had mellowed and abandoned even her old-fashioned ideas about the feeding of infants, she would slyly and with a mischievous look dole out pieces of pumpkin pie or maple cake. The wicked act was in itself a pledge of secrecy, and none of her grandchildren ever betrayed her, even when a pain in the stomach was a penalty. When she sinned thus the children had to remain in the dark room until they had finished the poisonous offering and had their mouths wiped, and when all was in proper order the procession with its stomachs filled with pie would emerge, with the Colonel's daughter Maria bringing up the rear, all as innocent as cherubs.

By the time Johnny was old enough to notice the bobolinks in the hayfields and hear the jangle of sleigh-bells, the Colonel had been dead for half a century and the green locust shoots which he had planted with Jed and Henry to make an avenue leading to the cabin were great shaggy trees with trunks three times as thick as a man's body. They stood in a double line on either side of the long lane, and in late spring their small scraggy branches, out of all proportion to the ruggedness of their trunks, broke out in garlands of white and pale yellow flowers, and as one bumped along the lane over the roots the air above was filled with the humming of thousands of bees swarming down from the hives near the farmhouse to gather honey against the winter.

From the highway, long before you turned in at the lane, you caught a glimpse of the rambling low white house spread over the top of the hill and enveloped by big trees, as if it had grown there and not been built at all. At the front of it, so dark that it appeared almost black against the fresher green of cottonwoods and lindens and lilacs, appeared the long hedge of pruned Norway spruce which served in winter as a windbreak and in spring sheltered from the late storms little flocks of nuthatches and crossbills and the patches of

5

daffodils, crocuses, narcissis, and grape hyacinths which drifted across the lawn.

High above the shingles of the gabled roof rose a huge cottonwood tree. It had the air of protecting the house from the elements, and twice at least it had been wounded by lightning of a midsummer thunderstorm. It was a great burden to Johnny's grandmother, for from late August onward it began shedding its leaves, twigs, and branches and little tassels of cotton wool over the neat pattern of her lawn and garden, but although Jamie proposed it nearly every spring, she would not consider cutting it down, because it had been planted by Pappy when the forest was cleared away.

If the cottonwood tree was the bane of Maria's existence, the lane was the curse of Jamie's. It was built in the soft rich clay soil of the countryside, and as it went up hill and down, the torrents made by midsummer thunderstorms were forever washing gullies and ruts in its surface. The roots of the locust trees, ancient, tough, and gnarled, came through the surface and sent up tough green shoots which no amount of traffic was ever able to kill, and in spring, when the snow broke up, the brook became for a time a torrent which threatened the foundations of the little bridge and sometimes swept over the roadway itself.

Yet it was the pleasantest of lanes, wild and a little disordered, with here and there a big locust tree scarred by lightning which countryside legends said such trees attracted. On either side the elderberry bushes spread panicles of white blossoms and black fruit, and underneath grew tiny wild strawberries which were white and almost transparent and very sweet.

In those days the County had not yet been invaded by Czechoslovak and Silesian peasants, nor by ideas of "scientific" farming, and the farms had less the feeling of orderly checkerboards imposed upon the earth than of little colonies which had grown out of the earth and belonged to it. There were no straight bare fences of galvanized wire. The fences of pickets or rails seemed to be a part of the earth, and in summer they stood half-hidden by the growth of blackberries and bracken, hazel bushes and hawthorn, which grew up about them. For children the fencerows were jungles filled with excitement where rabbits hid and thrushes built their nests, and for Johnny's grandparents they provided elderberry wine, nuts for the cellar, and jams and jellies made of wild blackberries and strawberries. They sheltered coveys of quail and occasionally gay-colored pheasants which destroyed the insects in the cornfields. And in autumn, when they turned crimson and gold and purple and the little husks of the hazelnuts began to burst open, they had a romantic beauty which disappeared when Czechs began to cultivate every inch of fields and allowed no clod of earth to go without producing.

Near the bridge, leaning over the brook, there was a colossal ancient willow in which tramps had once set a fire. The tree did not burn, but inside the hollow trunk there was a great charred cavern big enough to conceal three or four children, and there Johnny and his cousins played at robbers on hot summer days when the cows stood knee deep in the pool beneath the drooping branches, chewing and swishing their tails. They were Jersey cows, small, sleek, and golden, with enormous udders and shadows of deep brown about their big brown eyes and their silken dewlaps. In spring the willow tree furnished shoots from which whistles were made on which one could play real tunes by pushing the wood up or down inside the slippery bark. Beyond the bridge the lane mounted upward on the steep slope which led to the house, the great barn, and the outbuildings clustered about them. In the spring when the mud was deep the shining rumps of the horses went into little ripples as they plunged forward to drag the carriage up the hill.

At the top you arrived precipitously in the quadrangle surrounded by linden trees which the Colonel had planted to feed his bees when the locust blossoms had faded and which in June filled the air on the hilltop with their odor. The whole of the quadrangle, save for those parts inclosed by the buildings themselves, was surrounded by a fence made of chestnut staves woven together with wire. On one side, where the fence separated the quadrangle from Maria's dooryard and garden, the pickets were of pine, carefully planed, neat and coated each spring with whitewash. In the fence there was a lych gate garlanded with roses which swung closed with the aid of a heavy weight made from the worn cog of an old cider press. It was Maria's invention against the irresponsibility of her grandchildren, who might leave the gate ajar and admit calves and colts to wander among her choicest plants. Opposite the white fence stood the bulk of the great barn.

It was a vast barn, wide and solid and high, with enormous lofts above and stables and stalls for the cattle below. It had a roof of shingles, and for some reason, despite the advanced ideas of Jamie, it had never been painted, but for that same reason it had a beauty, and above all a dignity, which neatly painted barns never achieve, and there was about it none of the toylike appearance of the classic red-painted barn. Beneath the assaults of the violent Middle Western climate it had long since turned silver gray. The sides and the shingled roof were spotted with golden lichen, and over one end of it there sprawled a Concord-grape vine of fabulous age from which the fruit was stolen every year before it ripened by the birds which nested in the eaves and on the big hand-hewn rafters of the mows. From the crannies in the sides of the mows wisps of hay protruded, giving the old barn an air of bursting with plenty. It had the beauty of an ancient barn in the fertile Ile-de-France. It seemed to have been there forever and to have grown out of the earth itself, and about it there was a legend. Because it stood on the watershed, people in the County said that if a bird stood on the rooftree and shook the water from its wings, the water which fell on one side of the roof would flow into the Ohio River and from the other side into the Great Lakes. When Johnny was a little boy learning geography he traced with fascination the progress of those drops of water from one side into the vast Mississippi and the hot Gulf of Mexico, and on the other into the St. Lawrence and the North Atlantic haunted by whales and icebergs. It was fascinating to follow the journey of drops of water shaken from the wings of a swallow on the rooftree of your own grandfather's barn.

Near the barn, so near that one could step from the roof of one to the other, stood the fruit-house, a great, blind, windowless structure whose eaves were frequented by clouds of pigeons. It was the father of cold storage in all the state, having been the idea of the Colonel and carried out after his death by Jamie Ferguson. They were both curious about new things and were forever trying them.

The upper part of the structure was a single loft half filled with sawdust. Its walls were double, and in the space between was packed the ice which was cut during the winter in the woodlot pond to last until it disappeared at length beneath the heat of an August sun. Under the loft there were three or four big rooms lined with bins filled with apples and pears and hubbard squashes, which, inclosed by walls of ice, lasted each year until the new crops were gathered. Always just inside the door hung a kerosene lantern, by whose light you found your way about the windowless interior. On the hottest of summer days you could enter the cool darkness and bring forth a basket of apples still bearing the bloom of last year's harvest. The fruit-house had an unforgettable smell of plenty and it had a great deal to do with the vast feasts which came out of Maria's kitchen.

In another corner of the quadrangle stood a gray unpainted structure known as the wagon-shed. It sheltered the farm wagons and machinery, and on the upper floor there was a workshop with a vast tool-chest filled with planes and saws and other more complicated tools. It smelled of paint and clean pine wood, and in one corner were stored broken bits of furniture to be repaired during the long months of winter. Among them stood the spinning-wheel and carding-machine, long since abandoned, which had been brought over the mountains from Maryland by the Colonel. Just beneath the windows of the wagon-shed stood the corncrib, a slatted, V shaped structure mounted upon stilts made of hollow tiles to prevent the raid of hungry rats. All the year round the golden corn peeped through the slats, growing lower and lower as the spring and summer advanced, until in November it was filled again to bursting with the new crop. It gave a sense of richness to that small landscape and of a life which went on and on like the earth itself. When he was small Johnny would go to the corncrib with his grandmother to fetch in a basket of corn and turn the handle of the sheller which was too heavy for Maria's frail arms, and at the sound of the sheller stripping the yellow grains from the ears, the chickens and ducks, the geese and the guinea-fowl and turkeys, would come running from the fields and the barn, the poultry-houses and the wagon-shed, to crow and gobble, quarrel and quack, while she scattered the corn about her on the ground.

All the year round the quadrangle bordered by linden trees was a scene of noise and activity, for through it passed all the whole life of the Farm. The farm beasts crossed it on their way to and from the fields, stopping on the way in the shade of a big Norway spruce to drink at the wooden trough made of a single hollowed log filled with cold well water and covered with moss. In the mornings and evenings there was a clamor of cows and horses, pigs and colts and sheep, running before the excited barking of the big dogs. At harvest-time the huge wagons, creaking under the weight of timothy and clover hay or sheaves of wheat and oats, crossed it on the way to the mows. At threshing-time it was filled with engines and farm teams, buggies and wagons, and the whole life of the Farm became disordered and exciting. The farm animals found their inclosure occupied by a great snorting engine attached by a whining belt to another engine standing on the floor of the mows, sprouting straw for winter bedding into a great stack in the middle of the barnyard on the other side. And when the cows entered the barnyard on the evening of threshing-day, it took all the dogs to force them into their stalls for milking, for at the sight of the mountain of new straw they seemed to go mad, running round and round it, rubbing their backs and sides against it, to scratch themselves and drive off the worrying flies.

Beyond the house lay more fields like those which bordered the lane from the highroad. The "back" lane ran from the quadrangle between fields and orchards to the woods and the sugar-camp and Finney's thicket, and for a child it was a path which led from all that was peace and security to all that was mystery and adventure. Again and again in his childhood Johnny escaped to run away down the "back lane," for in him there was, even then, a wild desire to know what lay beyond the next gate, the next fence, and the next hedge.

On the way one passed the big orchard which was Jamie's pride, and beyond one came to the field where the big hickory stood. It was a memorable tree, famous in the countryside for bearing enormous nuts with shells so soft that the faintest tap of a rock or a hammer would lay open the bisque-colored kernels. It had been there forever and, like the old willow tree, it served as a shelter for the cows against the angry sun of August. In each field there were big trees left to shelter them against sun and tempest, and hedgerows against which they might brush themselves to drive off the flies.

At the end of the lane one came to the woods, a patch of many acres where the Colonel had left the trees of the primitive forest when he cleared the rest of the land for cultivation. They were enormous trees, mostly beech, oak, and maple, and beneath their thick shade grew the dogwood which in spring turned to cloud-drifts of white. In the very midst of the wood, on the edge of the pond where the ice was cut in winter, stood the sugar-house where in March, while the melting snow still littered the earth, the boiling down of the maple sap took place. For the grandchildren this was a season of festival when they were allowed in pairs to spend a whole night beneath the blankets of the bunk in one corner while Jamie sat up tending the fires and watching the sap which boiled in big iron tanks. You went to sleep only when you could no longer keep your eyes open, and sometimes in the night the hooting of an owl wakened you, terrified, to find that you were safe and warm, with your grandfather sitting in a big chair by the table, reading farm reports by the light of the kerosene-lamp. And in your nostrils was the scent of burning hickory logs and of maple sap boiling in the vats. In the daytime the fat horses dragged up the sap in the hogsheads on a sled and sometimes you made the round of the trees, helping to collect the buckets of sap which hung against the trunks. When the sap at last had boiled into thick syrup, Jamie would throw a ladleful of it on a snow bank outside, where it hardened into thick tooth-some candy.

Beyond the woods lay Finney's thicket, a big abandoned jungle of a place which did not belong to Johnny's grandfather, but to a neighbor who long ago had cut down the forest and allowed the saplings and underbrush to take possession. In parts it was a tangled jungle of willows and wild grape vines and birch trees, and in it, two miles or more from any highroad, the shrubs and wild flowers, the wild birds and animals, lived unmolested either by Jamie, who was no hunter, and by the children of old Job Finney, who was a Quaker and would permit no one to shoot the birds on his land. In the thickest part the grandchildren built cabins and played at Indians, dividing into two parties in a game the goal of which was for one side to discover, surround, and capture the camp of the other; but so thick was the underbrush and so vast the thicket that more than once the game ended at evening without discovery of the camp.

In the big sprawling white house the only rooms which had a fixed and sacred character were the dining-room, the kitchen, and the bedroom of Johnny's grandparents. They remained unchanged from the day Jamie and Maria were married until the day they died. The others were always in a state of change, due to the number of relatives "visiting" at the moment, so that sometimes you arrived to find what had been a common living-room occupied by two or three beds filled with cousins. Because the house consisted almost entirely of "wings" growing out of the ancient central cabin, it was in reality three or four small houses and sometimes it housed two or three families. The restless sons of Maria and Jamie had a way of departing suddenly for the West to look over some new country with an eye to settling there, and when they left the wives and all the children were deposited at the Farm, and sometimes one of the eight sons and daughters would suddenly return from the West with a whole family to "visit" indefinitely. There were moments when even the parlor was occupied by sleeping children and when it was necessary even to consign an unfortunate sleeper or two to the stuffiness of the big dark room with the Colonel's collection of fossils.

The furniture was an odd mixture, ranging from patent rocking-chairs upholstered in plush and crude split-hickory chairs to the fine clocks and rosewood chairs which the Colonel and Susan had managed to bring across the mountains from the East. When Johnny was small there were two pictures in the house which had for him a sinister fascination. One was the oleograph hanging in his grandparents' bedroom, which antedated the days of Currier and Ives and depicted Pocahontas in the act of saving the life of John Smith. The Indian princess was an extremely buxom young squaw wearing a headdress of ostrich plumes and attired in what appeared to be a coat of mail like those worn by Roman legionaires, and she knelt by the side of John Smith, equally stalwart but heavily bearded, encircling his neck with a pair of the mightiest arms ever bestowed upon woman. But her gaze was turned away from John and directed a little upward toward the raised tomahawk of one of Powhatan's menials, who, like the redskins in the plays of Voltaire, was decorated with the plumes of the ostrich. It was scarcely a tomahawk, but rather a spiked bludgeon such as the Crusaders carried in their combats with the Infidels. John Smith's head rested upon a huge boulder, and Johnny, before the candle was put out at night and in the morning when the sound of cowbells at the watering-trough wakened him and the sunlight came through the shutters, lay in the big bed speculating upon the horrible mess which would result if the raised bludgeon ever fell. When the bliss of spending a night at the Farm descended upon him, he begged permission to sleep in the Pocahontas room, where he occupied a kind of trundle-bed in an alcove a dozen feet from the great bed of Jamie and Maria's. Until he was eight or nine years old the picture exerted over him a fascination compounded of mingled delight and horror.

The other print was a huge engraving depicting all the stages of Pilgrim's progress. It had the fascination of a picture which was always new, for in a way there was so much of it that you were always discovering details which you had never seen before — imps and devils, strange plants and fat cherubs. It was composed of a series of small pictures in each of which Christian appeared in one of the stages of his long journey through Vanity Fair and the Slough of Despond, past the cave of the giant Despair, to the glory of the gate where he was received by hosts of angels all blowing upon trombones. It hung on the wall of the dining-room above an old and massive Victorian sofa upon which the grandchildren were allowed to stand while Maria explained the horrors and delights of the story. The sofa long since had been abandoned to the children and was upholstered in carpet so that they might slide and jump on it until exhausted.

The "Pilgrim's Progress" was a companion piece to Fox's Book of Martyrs which stood on the shelf among the other books of the Colonel's library in the dark room. This horrible tome was forbidden the children, and was at last destroyed by Maria in the kitchen stove when she discovered that it had been stolen by Johnny and his cousin Sam and removed to the hayloft, where they might study its dreadful engravings undisturbed. Among them one remained forever stamped on the two childish minds; it was a picture of "Maria Henshowe being delivered of a living child while being burned at Smithfield with two other women."

For half a lifetime after the Colonel's death his daughter succeeded in preserving intact the little museum of fossils and arrowheads and glacial stones in the cabinet in the dark room. Valiantly she managed to protect it from the raids of her own children, but by the time her grandchildren began to arrive in force, her strength gave way and she allowed them to take the arrowheads and make arrows with them and the round stones to play with at bowls or duck-on-a-rock, always exacting a promise from them that the things would be returned to the cabinet; but one by one the arrowheads were lost and the round stones left in the quadrangle before the barn until at length nothing remained but the dried botanical specimens pasted to leaves of brown paper. One by one, like the Colonel himself, they returned to the earth of the Farm.

The children of the Colonel went to the Congregational church. None of them, brought up with the Colonel's philosophic ideas stamped upon them, was really religious. They went to the Congregational church for social reasons, because that was where they met their friends; but none of them was troubled as to beliefs. They were inclined, like their father, to accept a natural world which they found good and full of pleasures. But Jamie had been brought up as a Presbyterian, and when he married Maria there still lingered in his youthful soul the ghosts of Calvinistic superstitions regarding heaven and hell and predestination and original sin, and so Maria had yielded to his desire and abandoned the easy-going Congregational church for the sterner delights of violent sermons thundered out Sunday mornings by the Reverend McPherson from the pulpit of the Presbyterian church. The thunderings neither convinced nor frightened her, and for four or five years she endured them, sometimes dozing quietly while the Reverend McPherson shouted and shook his fist. But it all came to end abruptly one Sunday morning when in a wakeful moment she heard the preacher roar out that "the floor of hell was paved with the skulls of unbaptized infants." This, she told herself, had passed the borders of nonsense into idiocy, and being the Colonel's daughter, she rose quietly in the midst of the sermon and walked out of the church, never to enter it again.

Nor did Jamie ever go into a church again until the day he was buried, when they carried him in, dead. Somehow, perhaps because some power of the Colonel's and of the eighteenth century still lingered in the farmhouse as it lingered in all his children, the old Calvinist superstitions died out of him and in their place there came a sense of rebellion and a conviction that although parsons as individuals might be good men, parsons as an institution were a plague. His attitude toward the church as he grew older was both less intellectual and less indifferent than the Colonel's. He had a simple conviction that no priest or parson knew any more about God than himself, and so could tell him nothing, and he believed that Sunday morning spent in going about his farm did more good to his soul than sitting in any church. Yet he always had a genuine religious feeling compounded of a delight in nature and a respect for God as the mystery which stood behind nature. It was almost a pagan feeling which was associated with his fields and his cattle and which caused him to offer up a prayer of thanksgiving vaguely directed toward the heavens when he sat down to a vast meal surrounded by his children and grandchildren. With his prize cattle and sheep, his orchards and vineyards, grafted by his own hands, and all his experiments with new plants and varieties of grain, he was nearer to God than most priests and did more good for man than most parsons.

The garden of flowers and herbs which lay on the gentle south slope between the farmhouse and the brook was, next to the grandchildren, Maria Ferguson's great delight in life. For her it was what theater and clothes and parties were to most women. It was her great amusement, and working in it, even when she was a bent old lady, after a day of hard work, seemed not to tire her, but to refresh her spirit and charge her frail body with new strength. She had the strange tenderness for plants which any good gardener must have, and she never allowed anyone to work in her garden save under her supervision, for she was unwilling to see her plants mauled by clumsy hands. For her, it was as if she saw her own children being tormented before her eyes. Her gardening differed from that of the Colonel because she cared more for the beauty and color of her garden than for the variety and strangeness of its specimens.

Some of the plants had long, long histories. The Colonel had left her a great collection, most of them unique in that part of the world, and from these she was forever giving seeds and cuttings to the wives of other farmers who liked flowers. Long after she was dead and the Farm was no longer the Farm, her great-grandchildren had in their gardens dwarf irises which were the descendants of roots brought from Scotland the year Lord Baltimore came to Maryland. There were new plants, too, for Johnny's grandfather as well as his grandmother had an interest in new plants and shrubs. They came from all parts of the world and few of them survived long the bitter winters and the ferocious summers of that Middle Western County. There were two cedars of Lebanon which managed to struggle through one winter, wrapped in straw and burlap, but did not survive a second. And the big catalpa tree which shadowed the front stoop was the first tree of its kind in the County. But most of the plants were old-fashioned flowers like bleeding-heart and grape hyacinth. There were armies of daffodils and a ragged hedge of lilacs separating the flowers from the vegetables, and beneath the window of her bedroom a bed of small white English violets whose perfume scented the air on blue evenings in May. And there were, of course, stock and spice pinks and countless varieties of campanulas. And in the midst of the lawn, away from the flower-garden, there were beds of begonias and geraniums grown from the slips of the plants which she had cherished all through the cold months.

In winter in the warm rooms of the house there were wire stands covered with rows of pots which contained geraniums and begonias, amaryllis, wandering-jew and saxifrage, and a dozen other tender plants. There were geraniums of an immense age with wooden stalks which climbed with tropical exuberance up and up toward the ceiling. Something in the delicacy and the ardor of Maria's thin, veined hands made her flowers grow fantastically. Under the hand of one gardener the strongest plant will wither and

15

die, and beneath the touch of another the frailest seedling will grow into a great hardy plant. The bungler has no place in a garden, and only those with a passion for plants ever succeed with them. It was said in the neighborhood that Maria Ferguson could plant a splinter and it would burst into bloom.

Because the Colonel chose a hill for his cabin, there was no spring near the house, and so its place was taken by an immensely deep well. It was no mere shaft sunk by a gasoline drill, but a great tunnel, five feet across, which to a child seemed to pierce the center of the world. If one stood on tiptoe it was possible to look down it and see far at the bottom a mirror of cool water that reflected the sky and the clouds and the silhouette of a small head. Its walls were made of uncut field stone and in the chinks moss and ferns grew luxuriantly. They were always dripping with moisture, for the bucket on its way up splattered water over them. The well pierced one of the subterranean streams with which the country was crossed and recrossed, and the water was always changing, cool and fresh. It served not only as a well, but as a refrigerator, for there was, besides the bucket for drawing water, a great wooden bucket on a rope which could be raised and lowered just to the cool level of the water. In very hot weather the meat and butter and the cream were kept there. From this well Johnny's grandmother watered all the young plants she set out.

Beyond the borders of the flower-garden lay the vegetable-gardens, with their rows of sweet corn, carrots, beets, and crisp celery and the neat little hills where muskmelons and cantaloups grew far separated from the spot where their incestuous cousins, the cucumbers, grew. And at the edges, sprawling luxuriantly against the picket fence, grew the enormous rambling vines of the Hubbard squash with their big rocky fruits ripening, to be put away in the fruit-house against the long winter. And there was always at least half an acre of strawberries with their runners each summer put symmetrically into place to make a little circle about the parent plants. The strawberry-patch was always weedless and the berries ripened on a thick carpet of yellow wheat straw. In summer Maria allowed her grandchildren to go out in the morning and select their own dishes of strawberries, fresh with the dew still on them. Always she gave instructions that the berries were to be picked as they came, but she never said anything when the children returned boldly bearing a bowl filled to the rim only with dark-red prize berries.

The work in the vegetable-garden was done by her sons or by the men who worked on the Farm, but she supervised it all and selected the prize melons and ears of sweet corn which were to be kept for seed. The vegetable-garden was of the greatest importance. Out of it came not only all the vegetables for the summer, but for the winter as well, for Maria would have considered it a disgrace to have bought food of any sort. It had been part of the Colonel's dream that his farm should be a world of its own, independent and complete, and his daughter carried on his tradition. The Farm supported a great household that was always varying in size, and in winter the vegetables came from the fruit-house or from the glass jars neatly ticketed and placed in rows on shelves in the big cellar. The sweet corn was dried in the sun instead of being preserved, pasty and insipid, in tins, and not only did it retain much of its own delicious flavor, but took on something from the sun itself. And the strawberry jam never knew a vulgar kettle. It too was made by cooking it on the roof of the woodshed in the glare of the hot July sunlight.

At the far end of the garden on a little mound beside the brook there was the graveyard grown over with ivy and periwinkle. There were ten or twelve graves in all. Beneath the blanket of periwinkle lay two old men, a little girl of three, and a woman of thirty-seven who, her tombstone said, had gone out of the world in bringing a child into it. The rest of her story was not recorded on the tombstone. Her name, I remember, was Hannah Wells.

Here beneath an old apple tree, perhaps one of those planted by Johnny Appleseed on his demented wanderings, lay Susan and the Colonel, buried side by side. They had the most imposing tombstones of all. They were of white marble, and the others were only of poor sandstone and were slowly crumbling away with age. In Johnny's childhood most of the inscriptions had become illegible. By the time he was a man they were gone forever, chipped and melted by the frosts of a hundred winters.

It was a perfect grave for the Colonel. He lay in the very heart of the land which he had wrested from the wilderness, only a little way from the house which he had built with Jed and Henry. All around him his grandchildren and great-grandchildren worked and played, stirring the fertile soil each spring not a half dozen feet from his head. And his daughter had only to cross her garden to tend his grave.

If it was a Sunday in summer, the buggy stopped in the

quadrangle carpeted with pigweed at the front gate (the one weighted with the cog of the worn-out cider-press) and all the family climbed down there to enter the garden and walk along a path made of moldering bricks sunk deep in the grass. Johnny's father, aided by one of the uncles or by old Jamie himself, left the buggy under the linden trees, unharnessed the horses and turned them loose to run madly round and round the great pasture. They were town horses and a day in the country grass was as much a lark for them as coming to the Farm for any of the younger generation. The arrival was always announced by the welcoming barks of the farm dogs, who ran down the hill as far as the bridge to greet all visitors. Sometimes if you arrived early you got down from the buggy in the midst of an animal bedlam, to discover the cows, having been milked, were being turned out again to grass. The barking of the dogs warned Johnny's grandmother of the arrival, and sometimes, if the breakfast was well in hand, she would come out of the house and halfway down the path to greet you. She was always dressed in her full-skirted black partly hidden beneath a spotless gingham apron. If it was a Sunday in winter when the snow covered the ground, she stood waiting for her grandchildren in the doorway of the dining-room with her delicate hands, clasping a corner of the apron, folded at her waist.

The dining-room was a large room with four big windows and in one corner an old-fashioned cast-iron range which kept it warm in winter and was put out of sight during the summer months. In the front of it, surrounded by a nickel frame, there was a big piece of isinglass which permitted you to watch the flames inside. At two of the windows stood wire contrivances covered with pots of begonias, geraniums, amaryllis, and wandering-jew. Almost the whole room was taken up by a great dining-table. The number of chairs varied according to the number of offspring in the County at the moment. Sometimes there were as many as twenty or twenty-five chairs and never were there less than ten.

The kitchen always seemed a very small place, considering the quantity and the quality of the food which came out of it. Like the dark room, it had its disadvantages because it, too, was part of the original log house which had come to be hidden as the house grew wing after wing. It was dark, with only a door and a small window which did not give into the open air, but into the big woodshed where the wood, carefully split to fit exactly her stove, and thoroughly dried to give the best of heat, stood neatly piled. All around the edge of the shed was a platform, and in the center an open space a foot lower, where the chipping and splintering was done in bad weather. The center part was always filled with dried chips which were used for starting fires.

In the little dark kitchen there was a colossal iron range with a great tank of hot water at one end and an oven which swallowed up two fat turkeys at a time. It was always scented with the faint, delicious odors of cloves and cinnamon, and at one side there was a door which led down to a cellar fabulously stocked with pickles, sauerkraut, preserved peaches, quince jelly, and Damson-plum jam, all of which had been made in the little kitchen abovestairs.

With Maria and with her grandchildren Sunday was a great day when the house was filled to overflowing and the odors of turkey and sausage, waffles and coffee, filled the whole east wing, and after the Sunday dinner the beds were filled with grandchildren taking their "naps." On Sunday the children and grandchildren came from every part of the County. At dawn Johnny rose with his brother and sister in order to arrive at the Farm in time for breakfast, for in the small frame of their grandmother was a determination that Sunday should be a long day. For this the grandchildren had no regrets, since on Sundays they were never told, when they wakened, that they must be quiet and good until the grown-ups were stirring, and at eight in the evening they were never told that it was long past their time for being in bed. They fell asleep at last, one by one, out of weariness brought about by a surfeit of delights, and when the time came for the family gathering to disperse, they were dressed, still half asleep, for the homeward journey. And the next morning they wakened at home in their own beds.

Sundays at the Farm had a special glow and excitement which nothing else — not even the arrival of the circus — ever surpassed. It happened Sunday after Sunday, year in and year out, but the sense of excitement endured. Always, it seemed, there was something new. Sometimes it was a calf or a litter of puppies, sometimes a rat-hunt with the big sheep-dogs among the standing shocks of corn, sometimes it was maple-sugar-making, and sometimes a whole troupe of new cousins appeared suddenly from the West on a visit. There was about those Sundays something splendid and matriarchal brought down from Scotland, and after the grandmother died they were never the same and presently they came to an end altogether.

In spring and summer and autumn Johnny and his family made the journey to the Farm in a buggy drawn sometimes by one, sometimes by two, horses, according to the state of the family fortunes, which were always up and down, or the quality of the horses his father was forever buying and selling and trading with a passion which amounted to a mania. They drove along the yellow clay roads at an hour when the meadow larks were swinging on the elders and the fat thrushes rustled in and out of the dry leaves in the fencerows. In the early mornings of summer the bobolinks haunted the fields of timothy, filling all the air with their friendly cries. In winter, when the frozen ground lay hidden beneath a foot or two of snow, the buggy was abandoned and the journey made in a sleigh where you were tucked in with blankets and old fur robes, with your feet resting on hot bricks placed in ankle-deep clean straw. The bells jingled and the horses trotted and the snow fell, melting upon cheek and nose and lips, and in the evening when the moonlight struck the banks of snow they were no longer banks of snow, but of diamonds.

The winter journeys were the best of all. There was excitement even in the preparations for departure, with a great hubbub and laughing and chatter. There were mufflers and overcoats and mittens and caps, and if you were very small and the night very cold, a soft Shetland scarf had to be tied across your face so that you did not breathe too deeply of the frosty air. And there were the hot bricks and buffalo robes to be arranged while Johnny's father held the impatient horses and the bells jangled and sang. Old Jamie, the grandfather, was always there, standing coatless and vigorous in the snow, to see that everyone was tucked in properly; and at last the horses sprang off down the lane under the locust trees, and the last thing you saw on looking back was your grandfather standing at the gate, waving farewell.

In those days there was not a road of concrete or asphalt in all the County, and in summer the hoofs of the horses beat not harshly against a hard slippery surface, but softly against the good yellow clay. In the ditches and along the edge of the road the wild sweet clover grew waist-high, giving off a thick perfume and a sound of humming. By the time you had arrived at the end of the long lane which led from the highroad to the farmhouse, the dew had begun to disappear from the glistening spider webs in the cloverfields and the appetite grew colossal.

On arrival there was always a great deal of kissing and greeting, and on the occasions when the family gatherings were larger than usual, Johnny had the sensation of being lost in a forest of long legs and big bosoms, for all his aunts and uncles and grown cousins were very big men and women with emotions in proportion to the size of their bodies. They did everything with violence. They were like Jamie in their size and their violence, and not at all like the Colonel. In the midst of them, Maria, so tiny and frail, the mother of them all, seemed preposterous and comic.

When the hubbub had subsided a little, Johnny's grandmother would emerge from the emotional disorder of her gigantic offspring and kiss each of the grandchildren delicately. Then Johnny's father would arrive from the barn, dressed in city clothes and bearing the Sunday papers, for he was a city man and the Sunday papers were his classic contribution. He always got them late Saturday night so that the early-morning start would not be delayed. There were bundles and bundles of them wrapped in the bright-colored comic sheets, damp and stained by the melting snow, which became at once the possessions of the clamoring children — the *Cleveland Plain Dealer*, the *Chicago Inter-Ocean*, the *Chicago Tribune*, the *Cincinnati Enquirer* and the *Columbus Dispatch*. They were always filled with political news which provided material for wild arguments and denunciations among the men and some of the women during the rest of the day, for the family was as violent in its opinions as in its emotions, and at times, especially during the Bryan campaigns, the arguments achieved the quality of bitter denunciations.

When all the wraps had been put away in the dark room, the grandmother returned to the kitchen and, aided by her daughters, prepared to serve the breakfast, while the men and the children seated themselves at the table.

When the breakfast was ready the food was brought on the table — sausages, waffles, and maple syrup from Jamie's own maple-grove, fresh strawberries or peaches if it were summer, coffee, hot fresh rolls, and sometimes chicken and mashed potatoes, home-dried corn, and an array of jams and preserves. Everything on the table came from the Farm itself, and it was only the beginning of a day spent in high feasting. On Sundays Jamie suspended all labor except the milking of the cows, and spent the day walking over his land, examining the fences and the state of the crops. Johnny's father, released from city life, wandered about vaguely, starting up rabbits and pheasants which his dogs never captured. After lunch there were a great many sleepers scattered through the house or beneath the trees on the grass in grandmother's garden. It was a day of festival given over to plenty. It began with old Jamie's prayers to the Deity of plenty and over it all presided Maria, a kind of priestess who stood apart with a queer little smirk of pleasure and satisfaction at the sight of her offspring eating the things she had prepared.

More often than not there was a stray tramp or two seated in the woodshed, enjoying what was borne away untouched from the over-laden table in the dining-room. Less than a mile from the Farm the main line of the Erie Railroad climbed a long hill where all east-bound freights slowed down, and tramps could leap on and off with ease. In time Maria had become a marked woman, and in the mysterious gastronomic guide of hoboes her kitchen was three-starred. They came and went on their way from the East. Sometimes one of them stayed a week or a month or a season to work on the Farm. There were among them some remarkable characters. But most of them were a bad lot who came to eat and run. She never turned them away. It was her way of giving thanks for the plenty she had always known.

The place had no name of its own. Among all the descendants of the Colonel it was known simply and regally as The Farm. In that rich county there were hundreds of other farms, but for the Colonel's children, grandchildren, and great-grandchildren, for a great many neighbors and friends, and perhaps even for the tramps, there was only The Farm.

2

The Return
Of The Native

From *Pleasant Valley*, 1945

The year is 1938. Europe, where Louis Bromfield has now lived with his family for 15 years, is on the verge of erupting into a second world war. And Senlis, the small French town where the Bromfields have a 50-year lease on an eighteenth century stone house and a few acres, is directly in the path Germany has twice used to invade the city of Paris. In fact, the ancient chapel on the family's property was converted into a stable by German cavalry in 1870 and 1914.

"And about that house, much as we loved it, there was no sense of real permanence, no feeling that one day grandchildren and great-grandchildren would return there to ride the pony and fish and go swimming in the little river. There was always about it a sense of living upon borrowed time in a dream which one day would come abruptly to an end," Bromfield writes years later in Pleasant Valley. *"During all those years there was in every one of us, even the smallest of the children, I think, the hunger for a house of our own outside the doomed world of Europe.*

"In the end Mary and the children left that lovely old house as refugees. Most of the books, furniture and pictures were shipped out to safety a little while before the Germans came in."

While his family goes to live with his parents in Mansfield, Ohio, Bromfield stays in France to do whatever he can to help. French friends implore him to return to America — and stay there — to alert his countrymen to the growing Nazi threat. Finally, in November of that year, Bromfield joins his family in Ohio and they begin looking for a permanent home of their own in the countryside of his boyhood.

As the car came down out of the hills and turned off the Pinhook Road the whole of the valley, covered in snow, lay spread out before us with the ice-blue creek wandering through it between the two high sandstone ridges where the trees, black and bare, rose against the winter sky. And suddenly I knew where I was. I had come home!

All the afternoon we had been wandering through the southern part of the county trying to find the Pleasant Valley Road. It was not as if I had never been there before. Once I had known it very well, as only a small boy can know a valley where the fishing and swimming is good, the woods are thick and cool and damp, and filled with Indian caves. I had known every turn of the creek, every fishing hole, every farm, every millrace, every cave. But that had been a long time ago — more than thirty years — and now finding my way back through the hills was like trying to find one's way back through the maze of a vaguely remembered dream. There were places I remembered when I came upon them, places like the village of Lucas, and the bridge over the Rocky Fork and the little cross-roads oddly called Pinhook and another called Steam Corners, no one has ever been able to say why. But like scenes and places in a dream these were isolated landmarks, disconnected, with the roads that lay between only half-forgotten mysteries. In those hills where the winding roads trail in and out among the woods and valleys, I can lose myself even today after I have come to know the country all over again as a grown man. On that first day I was utterly lost.

I might have asked my way. In the village there was the little bank of which one day I was to become a director, and the village post office where one day I was to do what I could, as an amateur politician, to get Hoyt Leiter appointed postmaster. As I write this I am struck again by the curious dreamlike quality of the whole adventure in which the elements of time and even of space seemed confused and even suspended. It was as if the Valley had been destined always to be a fiercely dominant part of my existence, especially on its spiritual and emotional side. It has always existed for me in two manifestations, partly in a dreamlike fashion, partly on a plane of hard reality and struggle. Perhaps these two manifes-tations represent the sum total of a satisfactory life. I do not know. I think that some day when I am an old man, it, like many other mysteries, will become clear, and that clarity, as one of the rec-ompenses of old age, will become a part of the pattern of a satisfactory life.

I could have stopped and asked my way at the bank or the post office, or I could have stopped the car and asked one of the three or four people who passed us trudging along on foot in the snow. Once we passed a boy in a Mackinaw and ear-muffs riding on a big blue-roan Percheron mare. He raised his hand in greeting. As I passed each one I thought, "That might be a Teeter or a Berry or a Shrack or a Darling or a Tucker or a Culler."

Those were all names which had belonged among these hills since Indian times. The young ones I couldn't know because all of them had been born during the thirty years I had been away. But I peered into the faces of the old ones trying to find there something that I remembered from the days when, as a small boy, I had driven over the whole of the county in a buggy behind a team of horses, electioneering for my father or for some other good Democrat.

Then, as a small boy, I had known all the Teeters, the Cullers, the Berrys and all the others for sometimes we had had midday dinner with them. Sometimes we had tied the horses to the hitching rail and got out and gone into the fields to help ring hogs or husk corn. Sometimes, if the roads were deep with mud or an early blizzard came on, we unharnessed the steaming horses and put them in a stall deep with straw and ourselves spent the night in a big bed with a feather quilt over us. I think my father was welcome in the house of any farmer or villager of the county, Republican or Democrat. They all knew him as "Charley" Bromfield. He was a kindly man, who was a bad politician because he didn't pretend to like people; he really liked them. I think he liked politics, in which he never had much success and in which he lost a great deal of money, principally because it brought him into close contact with nearly all kinds of people. He was one of the fortunate people who liked the human race despite all its follies and failings.

And so the faces of the people I saw in the village streets and on the country roads were very important to me on that first day. I was coming home to a country which I had never really left, for in all those years away from the Valley it had kept returning to me. It was the only place in the world for which I had ever been homesick. More than half of the time I had spent away from Pleasant Valley was passed in France, a country where I had never been a stranger, even on that first night when I stepped ashore at Brest at the age of eighteen and tasted my first French cheese and French wine in the smoky, smelly little bars and cafés of the waterfront. Often in distant parts of the world, among strange peoples, I had wakened to find that I had been dreaming of Pleasant Valley.

There have been moments in my experience when I have been sharply aware of the "strange intimations" of which Dr. Alexis Carrel writes — intimations which have scarcely been touched upon in the realms of science — "strange intimations" of worlds which I had known before, of places which in the spirit I had touched and heard and smelled. France was one of the places I had always known. From the time I was old enough to read, France had a reality for me, the one place in all the world I felt a fierce compulsion to see. Its history fascinated me, its pictures, its landscapes, its books, its theaters. It was, during all my childhood and early youth, the very apotheosis of all that was romantic and beautiful. And finally when, the morning before we were allowed ashore, the gray landscape of Brittany appeared on the horizon, there was nothing strange about it. I had seen those shores before, when I do not know. And afterward during all the years I lived there, during the war when I served with the French army and in the strange, melodramatic truce between wars, it was always the same. Nothing ever surprised or astonished me; no landscape, no forest, no chateau, no Paris street, no provincial town ever seemed strange. I had seen it all before. It was always a country and its people a people whom I knew well and intimately.

I have had a similar feeling about the austere, baroque, shabby-elegant quality of Spain and about the subcontinent of India. Germany, under any regime, has always been abhorrent, a place where I was always depressed and unhappy and a hopeless foreigner, even in a city like Munich which many people accept as beautiful and warm and gemütlich — a feeling which was not improved by spending my last visit there in the Vierjahreszeiten Hotel with Dr. Goebbels. And although, save for a little very remote Swedish blood, I have no blood that did not come from the British Isles, England was always a strange, although very pleasant country, more exotic to me than Spain or India. I do not begin to understand these things, these "strange intimations."

The point I wish to make is this — that during all those thirty years, sometimes in the discomfort of war, sometimes during feelings of depression engendered by Germany, but just as often during the warm, conscious pleasure and satisfaction of France or India or the Spanish Pyrenees, I dreamed constantly of my home country, of my grandfather's farm, of Pleasant Valley. Waking slowly from a nap on a warm summer afternoon or dozing before an open fire in the ancient presbytère at Senlis, I would find myself returning to the county, going back again to the mint-scented pastures of Pleasant Valley or the orchards of my grandfather's farm. It was as if all the while my spirit were tugging to return there, as if I was under a compulsion. And those dreams were associated with a sensation of warmth and security and satisfaction that was almost physical.

It may have been because in all my waking hours, during most of those years, I was aware of insecurity and peril, conscious always that in the world outside my own country, a doom lay ahead. During the last few years before the end of Europe, the feeling of frontiers, hostility and peril became increasingly acute, and distant Pleasant Valley, fertile and remote and secure, seemed more and more a haven, hidden away among the lovely hills of Ohio. I think no intelligent American, no foreign correspondent, living abroad during those years between the wars, wholly escaped the European sickness, a malady compounded of anxiety and dread, difficult to define, tinctured by the knowledge that some horrifying experience lay inevitably ahead for all the human race. Toward the end the malady became an almost tangible thing, which you could touch and feel. Many doctors had a hand in the attempt to check it, most of them quacks like the Lavals and the Daladiers, some untrustworthy like Sir John Simon, later honored by a title for his follies and deceptions, some merely old-fashioned practitioners with quaint nostrums patched and brewed together like Neville Chamberlain. One saw the marks of the malady on every face, from the hysterical ones whose follies became even more exaggerated, to the dull or unscrupulous ones who became each an individual thinking only of himself, and rarely of his country.

Toward the end I found myself spending more and more of my sleeping hours in the country where I was born and always what I dreamed of was Ohio and my own country.

And at last when Mr. Chamberlain debased the dignity of the British Empire, took his umbrella and overshoes and went to Munich to meet a second-rate adventurer, I, like any other moderately informed and intelligent person in Europe, knew that the dreadful thing was out of hand, and that nothing now could stop it. I sent my wife and children home to America on a ship crowded with school-teachers and businessmen and tourists whose pleasure trips or business had been cut short by orders from the State Department for all Americans traveling in Europe to come home.

My wife said, "Where shall we go?" and I replied, "To Ohio. That is where we were going anyway sometime."

I myself stayed on, partly out of a novelist's morbid interest in the spectacle, however depressing, and partly because, loving France, I wanted to be of help if there was anything that I could do. I stayed for weeks, more and more depressed, and it was Louis Gillet who persuaded me at last that I could do more for France at home in my own country than I could ever do by remaining in France.

I remember that we talked it all out beneath the great trees and among the magnificence of the ruins of the Abbaye de Chaalis where Louis Gillet held the sinecure of curator. The leaves were falling from the trees in the long gentle autumn of the Ile de France. His four boys were all mobilized. His widowed younger daughter was there on a visit from her quiet farm in Perigord. A second daughter, wife of the head of the Institute de France in Athens, and her two small children, had not returned to Athens at the end of the summer because of the malady, of that doubt and dread which crippled the will and the plans of everyone in Europe, in homes in Poland, in Norway, in Italy, in England.

And as we walked about the great park among the lagoons and the seventeenth century gardens, surrounded by the evidence of all the glorious history of France, Louis Gillet talked, brilliantly, humanly as he could talk when he was deeply moved.

At last he said, "You must return home. There is nothing you can do here that a Frenchman could not do. You can go home and tell your people what is happening here, what is bound to come. Tell them they will not be able to escape it — to be prepared and ready. We in France and in England too have already lost half the battle by complacency and bitterness and intrigue. The Hun is preparing to march again down across the face of civilized Europe. Go home and tell your people. You can help France most by doing just that."

That night after dinner all of us went out into the moonlit forest of Ermenonville to listen to the stags call. It was the mating season and the stags made a wonderful roaring noise to attract the does. Sometimes in a patch of moonlight you could, if you were down wind and sat quite still, catch a glimpse of a big stag calling, his head raised, his muzzle thrust straight out, sick with love. And if you were very lucky you could witness the magnificent spectacle of two stags fighting over a doe. The deer were the descendants of those deer which François Premier and Henry Quatre had hunted in these same forests. It was the fashion in the autumn on moonlit nights to go out from the provincial towns in the Oise to listen to their calling — *entendre bramer les cerfs.*

It had been the fashion perhaps as far back as the days when our town of Senlis was a Roman city.

Sitting there in the warm sand and lanes of the forest on a moonlit night, surrounded by a family which represented all that was finest in France and therefore in our Western civilization, I experienced a faint sickness in the pit of my stomach. In a day or two I would be leaving all this — the forest, the old town of Senlis, the good people who lived there. I would be saying farewell to France which I had loved and known even before I had ever seen it. And if one day I returned it would never be the same. It would live, because an idea, a civilization never wholly dies but goes on living in some altered form as a contribution to all that follows, but it would be changed, dimmed and dissipated by the violence of war and decadence. I would never again find the France I was leaving.

I was aware too, quite suddenly, of what it was that attracted me to Europe and most of all to France; it was the sense of continuity and the permanence of small but eternal things, of the incredible resistance and resiliency of the small people. I had found there a continuity which had always been oddly lacking in American life save in remote corners of the country like parts of New England and the South which were afflicted by decadence, where permanence and continuity of life existed through inertia and defeat. In the true sense, they were the least American of any of the parts of America. They had stood still while the endless pattern of change repeated itself elsewhere in factories, in automobiles, in radio, in the restlessness of the rich and the nomadic quality of the poor.

The permanence, the continuity of France was not born of weariness and economic defeat, but was a living thing, anchored to the soil, to the very earth itself. Any French peasant, any French workingman with his little plot of ground and his modest home and wages, which by American standards were small, had more permanence, more solidity, more security, than the American workingman or white-collar worker who received, according to French standards, fabulous wages, who rented the home he lived in and was perpetually in debt for his car, his radio, his washing machine.

Sitting there it occurred to me that the high standard of living in America was an illusion, based upon credit and the installment plan, which threw a man and his family into the street and on public relief the moment his factory closed and he lost his job. It seemed to me that real continuity, real love of one's country, real permanence had to do not with mechanical inventions and high wages but with the earth and man's love of the soil upon which he lived.

I knew that the hardest thing for me to bear in leaving France and Europe was not the loss of the intellectual life I had known there, nor the curious special freedom which a foreigner knows in a country he loves, nor the good food, nor even the friends I would be leaving behind. The thing I should miss most, the thing to which I was most attached were the old house and the few acres of land spread along the banks of a little river called the Nonette — land, earth in which I had worked for fifteen years, planting and cultivating until the tiny landscape itself had changed. If I never saw it again a part of my heart would always be there in the earth, the old walls, the trees and vines I had planted, in the friendships that piece of earth had brought me with horticulturists, farmers, peasants, market gardeners and the workingmen whose communal gardens adjoined my own.

They had liked and respected me, not because I was by their standards fabulously rich or because on Sundays Rolls-Royces and automobiles labeled *Corps Diplomatique* stood before my door. They liked and respected me because I grew as good or better cabbages with my own hands than they were able to grow. And it occurred to me that the honors I valued most out of all those I had received was the diploma given me by the Workingmen-Gardeners' Association of France for my skill as a gardener and the medal given me by the Ministry of Agriculture for introducing American vegetables into popular cultivation in the market garden area surrounding the city of Paris.

All of these things had to do with a permanence, a continuity which one seldom found in America. When I returned home, I knew that permanence, continuity, alone was what I wanted, not the glittering life of New York and Washington, not the intellectual life of universities. What I wanted was a piece of land which I could love passionately, which I could spend the rest of my life in cultivating, cherishing and improving, which I might leave together, perhaps, with my own feeling for it, to my children who might in time leave it to their children, a piece of land upon which I might leave the mark of my character, my ingenuity, my intelligence, my sense of beauty — perhaps the only real immortality man can have, so people would say long after I was dead as they would say in Senlis long after I was gone, "Yes, the American did that. He planted that tree and built that bridge. He made the garden below the river in the old orchard." I cannot see that man could wish a better afterlife than the peace of oblivion and the immortality that rests in houses and trees and vines and old walls.

But on the floor of the forest the November fog had begun to settle down and the first chill of winter had begun to slip in about us. The stags, satisfied, had quit calling. Quietly we walked back to the Abbaye under a waning moon, past the canals built six hundred years before by the monks of Chaalis who were also the first millers of that rich wheat country.

Inside the pleasant house under the pompous bourgeois portrait of the Gillet ancestor who had been a marshal under Louis Philippe, we had a glass of good vin rose and I drove home at last through the forest back to Senlis. It was the last time I ever saw Louis Gillet, with his long, sallow, bearded face and blue eyes. Afterward, week after week, I had letters from him when he was a réfugié, proscribed by the Germans, living in Montpellier with one son gravely wounded, another a prisoner in Germany and a third with the Free French in Syria. He kept on fighting with his pen and voice against the Nazis, against German kultur, against the defeatism and treason of Vichy. And then we entered the war and the Germans occupied all of France, a steel curtain came down, and I heard from him no more.

By some curious chance on the day I began to write this book, I had word through the French Underground that Louis Gillet was dead, away from the Abbaye which he loved, a réfugié in Montpellier. I do not know whether the Germans imprisoned him, or how he died, but I do know now, six years after we walked beneath the trees in the Abbaye gardens, that all the advice he gave me was wise advice, that all the things he feared and predicted have come true. I know that he was a wise and good man. My only regret is that he never came to see me in Pleasant Valley, to see the land to which I had returned because we both believed it was my destiny and a good destiny. I would have liked him to know, to understand through his own senses, the rightness of all he said that November evening in the forest of Ermenonville before what must have been for him — the end of the world.

All along, all through the years of homesickness and even after I had come back to America, I had never said to anyone that the county in which I was born was one of the beautiful spots of the earth. I had kept the belief to myself, a little out of shyness, a little because there were times when I, myself, had doubts, knowing that all too often when later in life you revisit scenes you have known and loved as a child, something strange has happened to them. Somehow, mysteriously as you grew into manhood and swallowed the whole of the world, they have become shrunken and different. The houses that you remembered as big and beautiful have dwindled and become commonplace, the stream on which you once played pirates is no longer a lovely gleaming river but has turned into a small and muddy brook.

On that winter afternoon while I searched for Pleasant Valley among the hills and winding roads, I was a little afraid that when I came suddenly upon it, I would find that it had changed, that all the while I had been dreaming of something that no longer had any existence in reality.

With me in the car were Mary, my wife, and George who had been my friend and managed my affairs for a great many years. You will hear of them again in the course of this story, so it is just as well to explain them now. Mary was born on Murray Hill in New York City, a New Yorker of New Yorkers, and George was born on Long Island. Neither had ever known Ohio — my Ohio — save for the flat uninteresting country south of the lakes where Mary had taken the children on her flight from the doomed maneuvers of Chamberlain and Hitler.

All that afternoon as the car drove southward out of the flat lake country into the rolling hills of Wayne and Ashland County they kept saying, "This is beautiful country, why didn't you tell us about it?"

I had never really talked about it but once. Years earlier during a fit of homesickness in Switzerland, I had written a whole book about it called *The Farm*. I knew now that until the car turned into the wooded hill country, they hadn't really believed what I had written then. They had thought the county and the people I described were imagined as in a book of fiction. Their exclamations encouraged me; perhaps, after all, the Valley would be exactly as I had remembered it.

And then we turned the corner from the Pinhook Road and I

knew that I was right. Nothing had changed. It lay there in the deep snow, wide and pleasant between two high sandstone ridges covered by forest. Halfway up the slopes on each side, in the shelter of the high ridges, stood the familiar houses and the great barns, unchanged after thirty years — houses with the old names of the Pennsylvania Dutch and old English stock which had settled the country long ago — the Shrack place, the Mengert place, the Berry place, the big white houses and barns of the Darling settlement set in the wide flat rich end of the Valley where Switzer's Run joined the Clear Fork.

And then far away, a mile or more on the opposite side of the Valley, I saw a small house with an enormous cupolaed barn. The building sat on a kind of shelf halfway up the long sloping hill that turned its back on the north winds. It was already twilight and the lower Valley was the ice-blue color of a shadowed winter landscape at dusk and the black, bare trees on the ridge tops were tinted with the last pink light of the winter sunset. There were already lozengers of light in the windows of the distant house. Like Brigham Young on the sight of the vast valley of Great Salt Lake, I thought, "This is the place."

I heard my wife saying, "What a lovely, friendly valley!"

On that late winter afternoon, one had a curious sense of being sheltered from the winter winds, from the snow, from the buffetings and storms of the outside world. My wife and George saw a snow-covered valley. They could not see what I was seeing for the Valley had no place in their memories. What I saw was a spring stream in summer, flowing through pastures of bluegrass and white clover and bordered by willows. Here and there in the meanderings of the stream there were deep holes where in the clear water you could see the shiners and bluegills, the sunfish and the big red-horse suckers and now and then a fine smallmouthed bass. On a hot day you could strip off your clothes and slip into one of these deep holes and lie there in the cool water among the bluegills and crawfish, letting the cool water pour over you while the minnows nibbled at your toes. And when you climbed out to dry in the hot sun and dress yourself, you trampled on mint and its cool fragrance scented all the warm air about you.

I saw, too, fields with fat cattle and wild marshy land where the cattails grew ten feet high and the muskrats built their shaggy round houses in the autumn, marshes which in April were bordered and splashed with the gold of one of the loveliest of all wild flowers, the marsh marigold. A little later in summer from among the rich tropical green of its spade-shaped foliage the arrowroot threw up long spikes of azure blue. And I saw the old mills, high, unpainted silver-gray with the weathering of a hundred years, the big lofts smelling of wheat and corn and outside the churning millrace where fat, big carp and suckers lay in the deep water to feed on the spilled grain and mash.

And I saw not the winter-naked woods, all snow and ledges of pink sandstone rock, but whole fields of dogtooth violets and trillium and Canadian lilies and Dutchman's-breeches and blood-root. And in summer the same woods were waist high in ferns and snake-root and wild grapes hung down from among the branches so that the whole woods seemed a tropical place like Brazil and Sumatra. As a boy in these woods I had pretended that they were tropical forests and that I was lost in them, as very often I was. And now I knew I was right. I had been far in the years between. I had seen tropical forests in Malabar and Macassar which held the same feeling of dampness, of fertility where, as in these Ohio woods, the leaves and tendrils and fresh green shoots were so thick that the whole air seemed green as if one were under water.

And I saw the woods in late February and March when there were no leaves on the naked trees and here and there in damp hollows the first lush green of the skunk cabbage was thrusting through the dead leaves and marsh grass of the year before. For me there is always something exciting and especially beautiful about the skunk cabbage. Boldly it thrusts its tropical green leaves into the frosty air of dying winter, the first of all plants to herald the awakening and rebirth of life with each spring.

That time of bareness when the skunk cabbage first appeared was the time of making maple syrup and I saw the sugar camp with its roaring fires and the woods streaked with the last melting snow and the fat horses steaming as they drew the sled which carried the great hogshead of fresh sap taken from the budding trees. And the long nights when the run was good and I was allowed to sit up all night with my grandfather and boil syrup while the fire made shadows on the oaken walls of the sugar camp and the wind howled outside.

I was seeing all this which the two others could not see. My heart was crying out, "Wait until spring comes! If you think it is nice now, you will see something you cannot even imagine when this country awakens."

We crossed the Valley and the little river half frozen over, with the swift-running clear spring water fringed with ice and rime, and up the hill on the opposite side of the wide sheltered ledge where the small house sat with its little windows blocked with light.

We followed the Hastings Road, a narrow, insignificant township road which led back and forth through woods and up and down low hills to the casual crossroad settlement called Hastings; and halfway up the hill we turned across a ravine with a small spring stream flowing down it, showing blue where the living water, green with cress, ran clear of ice between the dead leaves of last year's sweet flag.

At the house no one answered the knock. I knew it was chore time and so I went to the big barn to find the owners.

It was a big, red barn built in the days when farmers were rich and took pride in their barns. Ohio is filled with them, barns which are an expression of everything that is good in farming, barns in which their owners took great pride. Nowadays one sees often enough great new barns on dairy farms owned by great corporations, or stock farms owned by millionaires; but these new barns have no character. They express nothing but utility and mechanized equipment, with no soul, no beauty, no individuality. Already they appear on any country landscape commonplace and standardized without beauty or individuality — in fifty years they will simply be eyesores.

The old barns built in the time of the great tradition of American agriculture when the new land was still rich and unravaged by greed and bad farming, had each one its own character, its special beauty born of the same order of spirit and devotion which built the great cathedrals of Chartres or Rheims or Salzburg. They were built out of love and pride in the earth, each with a little element of triumphal boastfulness — as if each barn was saying to all the rich neighboring countryside, "Look at me! What a fine splendid thing I am, built by a loving master, sheltering fat cattle and big-uddered cows and great bins of grain! Look at me! A temple raised to plenty and to the beauty of the earth! A temple of abundance and good living!"

And they were not built *en série*, like barracks. Each rich farmer had his own ideas, bizarre sometimes, fanciful with fretwork and cupolas and big handsome paintings of a Belgian stallion or a shorthorn bull, the main cupola bearing a pair of trotting horses bright with gilt as a weather vane. They were barns with great, cavernous mows filled with clover hay, two stories or three in height with the cattle and horses below bedded in winter in clean straw, halfway to their fat bellies. Perhaps there was waste space or they were inconveniently planned for doing the chores, but there was a splendor and nobility about them which no modern hip-roofed, standardized, monstrosity can approach. Ohio is filled with them — Gothic barns, Pennsylvania Dutch barns with stone pillars, New England barns attached to the house itself, the stone-ended barns of Virginia and even baroque barns. There is in Ohio no regional pattern of architecture as there is in New England or the Pennsylvania Dutch country. Ohio was settled by people from all the coastal states each bringing his own tradition with him, and so there is immense variety.

In my boyhood nearly all these barns had a rich, well-painted appearance. Those owned by farmers with an ancient Moravian background outdid the barns which only had a single stallion or bull painted on them; they had painted on the big sliding barn door a whole farm landscape for which the farm itself had served as a model and in it appeared bulls and cows, calves and stallions, hens and ducks and guinea fowl, horses and sheep and hogs. They were hex-paintings and their roots lay, not in Ohio or even in the coastal states, but far back in the darkness of medieval Germany, in a world of Bald Mountains and *Walpurgisnächte*. They were painted there on the big barn doors as a safeguard against the spells of witches, against vampires or incubi for it was believed and it is still believed among the old people that the spell cast by any malicious neighboring witch on the cattle in one of these great barns would fall not on the cattle themselves but upon the representations painted on the barn door. Always they were painted artlessly by someone on the farm and some of them had a fine primitive quality of directness and simplicity of conception.

Usually over the doors of these painted barns there hung a worn horseshoe, for it was believed that witches had an overweening passion for mathematics coupled with a devouring curiosity. If a witch sought during the night to sweep through the barn door on her broomstick and found herself confronted by a used horseshoe, she was forced to turn about and have no peace until she had retraced and counted all the hoofprints made by the shoe. The more worn the shoe the better, for it would take her all the longer to satisfy her compulsion, and she would not have completed her impossible task before morning arrived and she had to return whence she came. If the shoe had been worn long enough, the prints it had made would be so numerous that she could never count them all in a single night. As each night she had to begin afresh, she would never be able, even in the long nights of winter, to get through the door to do evil to the cattle.

As a boy I had seen in the early mornings little heaps of corn or cornmeal outside each door of a barn owned by some old man whose Moravian blood took him far back into the mists and shadows of Germany. They were placed before the doors for the same reason as the omnipresent horseshoe. A witch confronted by a heap of corn could not go on with her evil purpose until she had satisfied her curiosity by counting every grain. If the corn were ground into meal, so much the better for the task became a thousand times more difficult.

All these memories came flooding back during the short walk from the house to the great barn. Then I pushed open the door and walked into the smell of cattle and horses and hay and silage and I knew that I had come home and that never again would I be long separated from that smell because it meant security and stability and because in the end, after years of excitement and wandering and adventure, it had reclaimed me. It was in the blood and could not be denied. But all of that story I told long ago in *The Farm*.

Return to Pleasant Valley

3

"Malabar Farm"

By E.B. White

Malabar Farm is the farm for me,
It's got what it takes, to a large degree:
Beauty, alfalfa, constant movement,
And a terrible rash of soil improvement.
Far from orthodox in its tillage,
Populous as many a village,
Stuff being planted and stuff being written,
Fields growing lush that were once unfitten,
Bromfield land, whether low or high land,
Has more going on than Coney Island.

When Bromfield went to Pleasant Valley,
The soil was as hard as a bowling alley;
He sprinkled lime and he seeded clover,
And when it came up he turned it over.
From far and wide folks came to view
The things that a writing man will do.
The more he fertilized the fields
The more impressive were his yields,
And every time a field grew fitter
Bromfield would add another critter,
The critter would add manure, despite 'im,
And so it went — ad infinitum.
It proves that a novelist on his toes
Can make a valley bloom like a rose.

Malabar Farm is the farm for me,

A place of unbridled activity.
A farm is always in some kind of tizzy,
But Bromfield's place is *really* busy:
Strangers arriving by every train,
Bromfield terracing against the rain,
Catamounts crying, mowers mowing,
Guest rooms full to overflowing,
Boxers in every room of the house,
Cows being milked by Brahms and Strauss,
Kids arriving by van or pung,
Bromfield up to his eyes in dung,
Sailors, trumpeters, mystics, actors,
All of them wanting to drive the tractors,
All of them eager to husk the corn,
Some of them sipping their drinks till morn;
Bulls in the bull pen, bulls on the loose,
Everyone bottling vegetable juice,
Play producers jousting with bards,
Boxers fighting with St. Bernards,
Boxers fooling with auto brakes,
Runaway cars at the bottom of lakes,
Bromfield diving to save the Boxers,
Moving vans full of bobby-soxers,
People coming and people going,
Everything fertile, everything growing,
Fish in the ponds other fish seducing,
Thrashing around and reproducing,
Whole place teeming with men and pets,
Field mice nesting in radio sets,
Cats in the manger, rats in the nooks,
Publishers scanning the sky for books,
Harvested royalties, harvested grain,
Bromfield scanning the sky for rain,
Bromfield's system proving reliable,
Soil getting rich and deep and friable,
Bromfield phoning, Bromfield haying,

Bromfield watching mulch decaying,
Womenfolks busy shelling peas,
Guinea fowl up in catalpa trees.
Oh, Bromfield's valley is plenty pleasant —
Quail and rabbit, Boxers, pheasant.
Almost every Malabar day
Sees birth and growth, sees death, decay;
Summer ending, leaves a-falling,
Lecture dates, long distance calling.

Malabar Farm is the farm for me,
It's the proving ground of vivacity.
A soil that's worn out, poor, or lazy
Drives L. Bromfield almost crazy;
Whether it's raining or whether it's pouring,
Bromfield's busy with soil restoring;
From the Hog Lot Field to the Lower Bottom
The things a soil should have, he's got 'em;
Foe of timothy, friend of clover,
Bromfield gives it a going over,
Adds some cobalt, adds some boron.
Not enough? He puts some more on.
Never anything too much trouble,
Almost everything paying double:
Nice fat calves being sold to the sharper,
Nice fat checks coming in from Harper.
Most men cut and cure their hay,
Bromfield cuts it and leaves it lay;
Whenever he gets impatient for rain
He turns his steers in to standing grain;
Whenever he gets in the least depressed
He sees that another field gets dressed;
He never dusts and he never sprays,
His soil holds water for days and days,
And now when a garden piece is hoed

You'll find neither bug nor nematode,
You'll find how the good earth holds the rain.
Up at the house you'll find Joan Fontaine.

Malabar Farm is the farm for me,
It's the greenest place in the whole countree,
It builds its soil with stuff organic,
It's the nearest thing to a planned panic.
Bromfield mows by any old light,
The sun in the morning and the moon at night;
Most tireless of all our writing men,
He sometimes mows until half past ten;
With a solid program of good trash mulch
He stops the gully and he stops the gulch.
I think the world might well have a look
At Louis Bromfield's latest book;
A man doesn't have to be omniscient
To see that he's right — our soil's deficient.
We've robbed and plundered this lovely earth
Of elements of immeasurable worth,
And darned few men have applied their talents
Harder than Louis to restore the balance;
And though his husbandry's far from quiet,
Bromfield had the guts to try it.
A book like his is a very great boon,
And what he's done, I'd like to be doon.

4

"My Ninety Acres"
From *Pleasant Valley*, 1945

There really was an old man named Walter Oakes. He was a farmer and a good one. He lived not far from Malabar Farm. Ellen Bromfield Geld was only a little girl, but she recalls her father rushing in from the field to invite Oakes and other neighbors to the Big House the next night after chores.

"The first time they came, they sat on the edge of the old Valois furniture, self-conscious and not a little suspicious, stiff as Grant Wood's proud, wooden plains people until George passed the punch, personally spiked to stir boldness in the most hesitant breast," she recalls in her book The Heritage. "Then these upright figures began to unbend, lined faces crinkled into warm, outlandish smiles, as gradually they remembered how Charlie Bromfield and his son Louis used to roam the countryside at election time, sometimes stopping for an evening meal or to spend the night in the loft above the stable. And, watching my father's own smile in a face every bit as sun-creased and burned as their own, they began to discern that he had not changed much after all, inspite of his 'fancy living,' and that, further, he invited them that evening because he hoped that they would still find him one of them.

"Toward eleven o'clock, for there were chores to be done at dawn, they would don their tweed coats and leather jackets and depart, scattering heart-warming fragments of approval which could be heard through the door.

"A lot like the old man — got the same smile." "Full of queer ideas, but by the looks of his hands he's a dirt farmer."

"Ain't high and mighty like I expected."

"The Mrs. seems downright nice. I wonder, do you s'pose she'd think it funny being asked to come to a sewing circle?"

"The next time they came, Grant Wood wouldn't have found a subject among them. Punch was accepted at the door, the folks sat back in the French furniture, and crop talk and politics flowed as freely as a cocked barrel of cider at apple-picking time."

Ihad a friend, a little old man, who lived over the hill in Possum Run Valley in a small white house on a farm which is known as "My Ninety Acres." It has never been given that name as farms are named "Long View" or "Shady Grove." The name is not painted on the red barn nor on a fancy sign hanging at the end of the lane leading up to the house; nevertheless throughout the Valley everybody always refers to Walter Oakes's farm as "My Ninety Acres." At first, years ago when Walter was still a young and vigorous man, they used to speak of "My Ninety Acres" with a half mocking, half affectionate smile, especially the big farmers who owned a lot of land, because Walter always talked about that ninety acres as if it were a ranch of many thousand acres like the vast King Ranch in Texas, or a whole empire, as if he were Augustus Caesar or Napoleon referring to "My Empire." Some of the old farmers, I think, believed Walter a bumptious and pretentious young man.

But at last as time passed, and Walter turned into a solid middle-aged farmer and later into an old man, the smiles and mild sense of mockery went out and "My Ninety Acres" became simply the name of the place the way a farm was known as the Ferguson place or the Anson place. People said, "I'm going over to 'My Ninety Acres'" or "If you want to see a nice farm, go and have a look at 'My Ninety Acres'." Nobody in the Valley any longer finds anything confusing or absurd about the name. I think this is so partly because in places like the Valley, people come to accept the name that is natural to a place and partly because as the years passed old Walter earned the right to say "My Ninety Acres" as Augustus Caesar might say "My Empire."

He had a right to speak of it with pride. It wasn't the conventional Currier and Ives farm one expects from the long tradition of American farming — a bright, new place with new wire fences, and cattle standing like wooden animals in a pasture that was more like a lawn than a pasture. There was, indeed, a certain shagginess about it, a certain wild and beautiful look with that kind of ordered romantic beauty which was achieved by the landscape artists of the eighteenth century who fell under the influence of Jean Jacques Rousseau's romantic ideas regarding Nature. The white house was small but always well painted and prosperous in appearance, and there was no finer barn than Walter's with its fire-red paint, its big straw shed and its ornate shutters and cupolas painted white and there were no finer cattle in the whole county than those which stood behind the white-painted wooden fences of the barnyard staring at you, fat and sleek and contented, as you drove past "My Ninety Acres."

The romantic shagginess appeared too in the garden around the small white house with its green shutters that stood beneath two ancient Norway spruces. The patches of lawn were kept neatly mowed but surrounding them grew a jungle of old-fashioned flowers and shrubs — lilacs, standing honeysuckle, syringa, bleeding heart, iris, peonies, tiger lilies, day lilies, old-fashioned roses like the Seven Sisters and the piebald and the Baltimore Belle. At the back the little vegetable garden was neat enough with its rows of vegetables and its peach and pear and quince trees in a row inside the white picket fence. But beyond the borders of the garden, the shagginess continued. There weren't any bright, new, clean wire fences. The wire along the fence rows was hidden beneath sassafras and elderberry and wild black raspberry and the wood lot on the hill above the creek was not a clean place with the grass eaten short by cattle. The cattle had been fenced out and the trees, from seedlings to great oaks, grew rankly with a tropical luxuriance.

But despite the shagginess of the farm's appearance no fields in the Valley produced such big crops or pastured such fine cattle and hogs. At "My Ninety Acres" the shagginess didn't exist, the neighbors came to understand, because Walter was lazy or a bad farmer — there was no more hard-working man in the whole Valley. They were that way because Walter wanted them like that — Walter and Nellie.

I never saw Nellie Oakes. She died before I was born, but my father told me about her. In his time she had been the prettiest girl in the Valley and she taught school at the Zion School house until when she was twenty-two she married Walter Oakes. People wondered why she chose him when she might have married Homer Drake whose father owned four hundred and fifty acres of the best land in the county or Jim Neilson whose family owned the bank and the feed mill in Darlingtown. She could have had her choice of any of the catches of the Valley and she chose Walter Oakes, who had no more than ninety acres of poor hill land he had just bought because he didn't have money enough for anything better.

In the parlor of the little white house on "My Ninety Acres" there hangs an old enlarged photograph of Walter and Nellie taken at the time of their marriage. It is hand-colored and the bride and bridegroom are standing like statues, each with a clamp obviously fastened at the back of the heads in order to "hold the pose," but even the stiffness and artificial coloring cannot alter or subdue the look of youth and health and courage that is in both of them. Walter, the thin, tough old man who was my neighbor and friend, stands there in the photograph, stalwart and handsome and full of courage, one big muscular hand on Nellie's shoulder. He was blond with blue eyes and the gentle look which big, strong men often have because there is no need for them to be pugnacious or aggressive.

On a chair, beside and a little in front of him, sits Nellie in a white dress with leg-o'-mutton sleeves and a full flounced skirt — dark, more beautiful than pretty — with big dark eyes, holding in her small hands a lace handkerchief and a bunch of lilacs. I think Nellie was beautiful rather than pretty because of the look of intelligence. Even today, you sometimes hear old people say, in the Valley, "Nellie Oakes was a mighty smart girl — the only woman I ever knew who was as smart as she was pretty."

Nellie, so far as I can discover, never told anybody why she chose to marry Walter instead of one of the catches of the Valley, but I know from all the long story that it was because she was in love with him. As it has turned out, she was right because the big four hundred and fifty acre Drake place which Homer inherited has gone down-hill ever since Homer took possession of it and today, with its worn-out fields and decaying buildings, it won't bring as much as "My Ninety Acres" and Jim Neilson died long ago as a drunkard, having lost both the bank and the feed mill. But "My Ninety Acres" is the richest, prettiest farm in all the county, although Nellie isn't there to enjoy its beauty and prosperity. I say she isn't there because she died a very long time ago. But sometimes when I walked about the fields of "My Ninety Acres" with old Walter, I wasn't at all sure she wasn't there, enjoying its beauty and richness as much as old Walter himself.

I am forty-eight years old and Nellie died before I was born when she gave birth to her second son, Robert.

My father was a gentle man. He never went through the Valley without stopping at "My Ninety Acres" and usually I was with him. Sometimes when we stopped at "My Ninety Acres" for a meal or for the night, I stayed and played about the barn with Robert Oakes who was two years older than I and his brother John who was two years older than Robert. Sometimes if it was a Sunday we went fishing or swimming. Sometimes I simply trudged behind my father and Walter Oakes and his two sheep dogs as they walked about "My Ninety Acres," and as I grew a little older I sometimes wondered that the two men could be together, walking side by side, perfectly happy, without talking at all. I did not know then what I came to know later that among men who were as close to each other as my father and Walter Oakes, conversation wasn't necessary. They knew without speaking what the other felt when a lazy possum, out in the middle of the day when he shouldn't have been, lumbered across the pasture and out of sight and scent of the dogs (I've seen Walter call the dogs and keep them by his side till the possum had disappeared, safe in some deep hole or hollow log).

And I was always a little surprised at how often Walter would say, "Nellie wanted me to put this field into pasture but we couldn't afford not to use it for row crops," or "Nellie was smart about such things," or "It's funny how many good ideas a woman can have about farming. Now Nellie always said..." Sometimes in the warm summer heat, I'd return to the house, still trudging along behind the two grown men and the dogs, believing that I would find there the Nellie whom I had never seen, who was dead before I was born, waiting for us with a good supper on the table.

But Nellie was never there. There was only an elderly widow woman called Mrs. Ince, a distant cousin of Walter's who came to keep house and look after him and the boys after Nellie Oakes died. She was a queer old woman, very thin and very active, who was always asking Walter how Nellie had molded the butter or pickled the beets or kept a broody hen on the nest because she wanted everything to be the way Walter liked it. She could not have been more than fifty for she was still young enough to create talk in the Valley about her living there alone on "My Ninety Acres" with Walter and the boys, but to a small boy like myself she seemed immensely old. She was, as I remember her, very plain and kind and dull with the meekness which often characterized indigent widows of her generation who were grateful for a roof over their heads, something to eat and a little spending money. When she came to "My Ninety Acres" some of the old women in the Valley talked of the impropriety of her living there in the same house with Walter. I know now that anyone who had ever known Nellie must have been mad to think that Walter Oakes ever had any thoughts about poor, drab Mrs. Ince. She was at most, a convenience, someone to do the cooking and baking and housekeeping for a vigorous man and two wild, vigorous boys.

People in the Valley couldn't see why Walter Oakes didn't get married again. They said, "He's still a young man and he's done a wonderful job with 'My Ninety Acres'," or "I don't see how a man like that can get on without a woman at his age. It ain't natural." And a good many widows and spinsters past their first youth certainly set their caps for him. It wasn't only that he was doing well with "My Ninety Acres," he was, as I remember him then, a big, straight, clean good-looking fellow with his sun-tanned face, blue eyes and blond hair bleached by the sun. He would, I think, have pleased even a young girl.

But Walter never showed any signs of marrying again. He was always polite and his eyes sometimes twinkled with humor when he saw what some of the good ladies were up to. He didn't leave "My Ninety Acres" save to go into town to buy or sell something or to go to the Valley church on Sunday with Mrs. Ince and the boys. He'd come home from church and change his clothes and spend the rest of the day walking round the place. Sometimes, to the scandal of the old ladies of the Valley, he'd plow or make hay with the boys on a Sunday afternoon. I remember him saying to my father, "They talk about my working on Sunday or plowing, but when the ground is ready or hay has to be taken in, it has to be taken care of. The good Lord wouldn't like to see his beasts eating poor hay all winter because some old woman said it was wrong to work on Sunday. Nellie always said 'The better the day, the better the deed' and quoted that bit of the Bible about the ox falling into the ditch."

The two boys were nice kids and smart like Nellie. John, the older one, looked like her, with dark eyes and dark hair. Robert, the younger one, who had never seen his mother, looked like Walter. The father wanted both of them to go to college and get a good education. I think Walter always loved John, the older one, best — not because of any resentment of Robert because he had caused his mother's death but because John looked so much like Nellie.

With all my family, I went away from the county when I was seventeen and I was gone for twenty-five years. Sometimes at first my father heard from Walter, rather brief, unsatisfactory and inarticulate letters, written on lined paper torn out of a copybook, but neither Walter nor my father were very good letter writers. They were both the kind of men who could not communicate without the warmth that came of physical presence. Writing letters didn't mean much. When they met again, even after years, the relationship would be exactly the same. They were that kind of men, and that kind of friends.

I know very little of the details of what happened during those years, only a fact or two and what little I have picked up from Walter as an old man in his implications regarding the past. The war came and in it John, the older son, who Walter secretly loved best, was killed at St. Mihiel. He was twenty-one and just finished with agricultural college. Walter had counted on him returning to the farm, marrying and producing grandchildren to carry it on. Robert when he returned from the war, did not stay on the farm. He was very smart, like Nellie, but he didn't want to be a farmer.

Robert had ambitions. He had had them even as a small boy. Sometimes when the three of us, as kids, sat naked among the wild mint by the swimming hole, we talked about what we were going to do in life and Robert always said, "I'm going to be a great man and get rich and have an automobile with a man to drive it."

In the twenty-five years I was away from the Valley Robert had achieved exactly what he had planned. By the time I returned to the Valley Robert was president of the Consolidated Metals Corporation and he had made many millions of dollars. I think he must have had both Nellie's "smartness" and Walter's steadfastness.

In the first weeks after I came home I never thought about my father's friend, old Walter Oakes. Indeed, I had very nearly forgotten his existence. And then one day I heard Wayne, one of the boys on the farm, say something about "My Ninety Acres" and I remembered it all and asked, "Is Walter Oakes still alive?"

"Alive!" said Wayne, "I'll say he's alive. The livest old man in the county. You ought to see that place. Brother, that's the kind of farm I'd like to own. He raises as much on it as most fellows raise on five times that much land."

Wayne, of course, was only twenty. He couldn't know how once people had laughed when Walter Oakes spoke proudly of "My Ninety Acres." Clearly, they didn't laugh any more. Clearly, Walter Oakes was the best farmer in all the county, very likely the best farmer in all the rich Ohio country.

The next Sunday I walked over the hills to "My Ninety Acres." As I came down the long hill above the farm I saw that it hadn't changed much. The house still looked well-painted and neat with its white walls and green shutters and the barn was a bright new prosperous red. But the shrubs and flowers had grown so high that they almost hid the house. It was a day in June and as I walked down the long hill the herd of fat, white-faced cattle stood knee-deep in alfalfa watching me. I hadn't taken the dogs because I knew Walter always kept a couple of sheep dogs and I didn't want a fight.

As I walked down the hill I thought, "This is the most beautiful farm in America — the most beautiful, rich farm in the world — 'My Ninety Acres'."

The corn stood waist-high and vigorous and green, the oats thick and strong, the wheat already turning a golden yellow. In the meadow the bumblebees were working on clover that rose almost as high as a man's thighs. In all that plenty there was something almost extravagant and voluptuous. The rich fields were like one of the opulent women painted by Rubens, like a woman well loved whose beauty thrives and increases by love-making.

I pushed open the little gate and walked into the dooryard with the neatly mown grass bordered by lilacs and peonies and day lilies. The door stood open but no one answered my knock and thinking the old man might be having a Sunday nap, I stepped into the house and called out, "Walter! Walter Oakes!" But no one answered me.

I hadn't been in the house for twenty-five years and I didn't remember very well my way about it so when I opened the door which I thought led into the long room that had once been used both for eating and living, I found that I was mistaken. I had stepped into the parlor instead.

It had that musty smell of country parlors and the shutters were closed but there was enough light for me to see the enlarged hand-colored portrait of Walter Oakes and his bride Nellie hanging on the wall above the fireplace. Out of the stiff old picture they looked at me young, vigorous, filled with courage and hope and love. It struck me again how pretty Nellie was.

I stood for a little time looking at it and then turned and closed the door behind me. I went out through the sitting room and the kitchen where everything looked clean and neat as in the dooryard, and I thought, "He must have a woman to look after him."

By now, of course, I remembered enough to know that I should find old Walter somewhere in the fields. Sunday afternoon he always spent walking over the place. As a small boy I had followed him and my father many times.

So I went down toward the creek and as I turned the corner by the barnyard I saw him down below moving along a fence row. Two sheep dogs were with him, the great-great-great grandchildren of the pair I had known as a boy. They were running in and out of the hedgerow yapping joyously. I stood for a moment, watching the scene. The fence row bordered a meadow of deep thick hay and below among feathery willows wound the clear spring stream where I had often gone swimming with Walter's boys — John who had been everything Walter had hoped for in a son, the best loved, who was buried somewhere in the Argonne, and Robert who had gone away to become rich and powerful. There was something lonely about the figure of the old man wandering along the fence row filled with sassafras and elderberry. For no reason I could understand I felt a lump come into my throat.

Then I noticed that there was something erratic in the progress of the old man. He would walk a little way and then stop and, parting the bushes, peer into the tangled fence row. Once he got down on his knees and for a long time disappeared completely in the thick clover.

Finally, as he started back along the far side of the field, I set off down the slope toward him. It was the barking of the dogs as they came toward me that attracted his attention. He stopped and peered in my direction shading his eyes with his big hands. He was still tall and strong, although he must have been well over seventy, and only a little stooped. He stood thus until I was quite near him and then I saw a twinkle come into the bright blue eyes.

"I know," he said, holding out his hand. "You're Charley Bromfield's boy. I heard you'd come back."

I said I'd been trying to get over to see him and then he asked, "And your father? How's he?"

I told him my father was dead. "I'm sorry," he said, very casually as if the fact of death were nothing. "I hadn't heard. I don't get around much." I explained that my father had been ill for a long time and that death had come as a release.

"He was a good man," he said. "A fine man. We sort of dropped out of writing each other a good many years ago." He sighed, "But after all writing don't mean much." The implication of the speech was clearly enough that friends communicated without writing, no matter how great the distance that separated them.

Then suddenly he seemed to realize that I must have seen him for a long time, ducking and dodging in and out of the fence row. A faint tinge of color came into his face and he said shyly, "I was just snoopin' around my ninety acres. I like to see what goes on here and I don't get time during the week."

He looked down at his big hands and noticed, as I did, that some of the black damp loam of the fence row still clung to them. He brushed them awkwardly together. "I was just digging into the fence row to see what was going on there underground. A fellow can learn a lot by watching his own land and what goes on in it and on it. My son John — you remember the one that was killed in the war — he went to agricultural school but I don't think he learned more there than I've learned just out of studying my own ninety acres. Nellie always said a farm could teach you more than you could teach it, if you just kept your eyes open ... Nellie ... that was my wife."

"Of course," I said, "I remember."

Then he said, "Come with me and I'll show you something."

I followed him along the fence row and presently he knelt and parted the bushes and beckoned to me. I knelt beside him and he pointed, "Look!" he said, and his voice grew suddenly warm, "Look at the little devils."

I looked and could see nothing at all but dried brown leaves with a few delicate fern fronds thrusting through them. Old Walter chuckled and said, "Can't see 'em, can you? Look, over there just by that hole in the stump." I looked and then slowly I saw what he was pointing at. They sat in a little circle in a tiny nest, none of them much bigger than the end of one of old Walter's big thumbs — seven tiny quail. They sat very still not moving a feather, lost among the dry, brown leaves. I might not have seen them at all but for the brightness of their little eyes.

"Smart!" he said, with the same note of tenderness in his voice. "They know! They don't move!"

Then a cry of "Bob White!" came from the thick, fragrant clover behind us and Walter said, "The old man's somewhere around." The whistle was repeated, again and then again.

Old Walter stood up and said, "They used to laugh at me for letting the bushes grow up in my fence rows, but they don't any more. When the chinch bugs come along all ready to eat up my corn, these little fellows will take care of 'em." He chuckled, "There's nothing a quail likes as much as a chinch bug. Last year Henry

Talbot, down the road, lost ten acres of corn all taken by the bugs. Henry's a nut for clear fence rows. He doesn't leave enough cover along 'em for a grasshopper. He thinks that's good farming, the old fool!" and the old man chuckled again.

We were walking now up the slope from the creek toward the house, and he went on talking, "That fence row beside you," he said, "is just full of birds — quail and song sparrows and thrushes — the farmer's best protection. It was Nellie that had that idea about lettin' fence rows grow up. I didn't believe her at first. I was just as dumb as most other farmers. But I always found out that Nellie was pretty right about farmin'. She was hardly ever wrong ... I guess never."

As we reached the house, old Walter said, "Funny how I knew you. I'd have known you anywhere. You're so like your father. I've missed him all these years, especially when anything happened he would have liked..." he chuckled, "like these baby quail today. Come in and we'll have a glass of buttermilk. It's cooler in the sittin' room."

I went with him into the springhouse. It was built of stone with great troughs inside cut out of big blocks of sandstone and the water ran icy cold out of a tile that came through the wall. Cream, milk and buttermilk, stood in crocks in the icy water, each covered by a lid held in place by an ancient brick with velvety green moss growing on its surface. Coming out of the heat into that damp cool spot was like coming into another world.

He picked up a pitcher with buttermilk in it and I asked, "Who does your churning for you?"

He grinned, "I do it myself," he said. "Of an evening. I kinda like it."

We went and sat in the living room and he brought glasses and two white napkins. It was buttermilk such as I had not tasted in thirty years — creamy, icy cold with little flakes of butter in it.

I said, "What became of Mrs. Ince?"

He said, "Oh, she got old and sick and went back to live with her sister. I just didn't get anybody to take her place."

"You mean you're living here all alone?" I asked.

"Yes."

I started to say something and then held my tongue, but old Walter divined what it was I meant to ask and said, "No. I ain't lonely. I've always got the dogs. Jed Hulbert comes down and helps me with jobs I can't do alone and his wife takes care of my laundry and cleans up once a week. Jed and his wife like the money and they're nice people." He smiled, "It doesn't seem to me like a farm is a lonely place. There's too much goin' on. Nellie used to say she didn't understand the talk of these women who said they got lonely. Nellie said there was always calves and horses and dogs and lambs and pigs and that their company was about as good as most of them women who talked that way. And she always had her posy garden. Did you notice it coming in? It's mighty pretty right now. Nellie planted everything in it ... just the way they are today." He was about to say something else but checked himself and looked at me strangely. A secretive, almost sly look came into his eyes and he turned away to stare at the glass he held in his hand.

After an awkward pause I said, "Well, Robert did all right by himself. He always said he wanted a big automobile and a driver and a lot of money and he got it all right."

Then old Walter looked up at me and grinned, "Yes, I guess he got just about what he wanted. He's a good boy, but he's got some funny ideas." The old man chuckled. "He's been trying for years to get me to retire and live in the city where I could take it easy or go down and live in Florida. What'd I do with these big ugly hands in a place like that? I wouldn't know what to do with myself. And what would become of 'My Ninety Acres'? Or he's always wantin' to buy me a bigger place with a house full of gadgets or to buy me a lot of machinery. What would I want with a bigger place? Ninety acres is enough for any man if he takes care of it right, like he should. And anyway it wouldn't be the same as 'My Ninety Acres'. And I don't want machinery bought with his money. 'My Ninety Acres' ought to buy its own machinery and it does."

A fierce note of pride came into his voice. "All the machinery it needs. Robert wants me to hire a couple to live here and do the work for me, but I wouldn't like that. Yes, Robert's got some crazy ideas and he doesn't understand how I feel. I guess he thinks I'm a little crazy."

It was getting late and I rose but the old man went on talking. "It's a pity about Robert not having any children. I guess his wife is all right. I don't see much of her. We don't have much in common. But it's a pity Robert couldn't have found a woman he could have loved."

That was the first and last time I ever heard him speak of his daughter-in-law but out of the meager speech and the look in his eye and the sound of his voice I divined what she must be like. Indeed, I gained a very clear picture of her.

"Robert comes to see me about once a year and stays for a day or two, but he's a pretty busy man with all the big affairs he has to manage."

"Tell him to drive over and see me the next time he comes," I said, "And you come over too."

He opened the screen door for me. "I'm afraid I don't get off 'My Ninety Acres' very often any more. You'll understand if I don't get over soon. The place takes a lot of time when you're working it alone."

I left him and the dogs at the gate and set out over the hill across the pasture with the fat, white-faced cattle, for home.

It wasn't the last time I saw old Walter. There was enough of my father in me to make the friendship between myself and the old man before long very nearly as warm as their friendship had been. And after all, between them, they had taught me many of the things I had come with experience to value most in life. The Sunday afternoon visits to "My Ninety Acres" became very nearly a habit, for I found gradually that old Walter was in himself an education. He knew more of the fundamentals of soil, of crops, of livestock than any man I have ever known. Some of them he had read in books and in farm papers but he didn't trust the things he read until he tried them out and many of them he didn't even attempt to try out since out of his own wisdom he understood at once that they were rubbish. Instinctively and out of experience he rejected things which ran counter to the laws of nature.

"Nellie," he would say, "always said that Nature and the land itself was the best answer to all these questions. If it wasn't natural it wasn't right, Nellie would say, and I've never found that she was wrong. She used to say that there were two kinds of farms — the 'live' farms and the 'dead' ones and you could tell the difference by looking at them. A 'live' farm was the most beautiful place in the world and a 'dead' farm was the saddest. It depended on the man who worked them — whether he loved the place and saw what was going on or whether he just went on pushing implements through the ground to make money. Nellie was awful smart about a lot of things."

Sunday after Sunday we would make a round of the small

empire while old Walter told me the history of each field and what had happened to it, what he had learned from this field or that one, and why his alfalfa and clover were thicker than those of his neighbors, his corn higher and sturdier, his Herefords bigger and fatter. And after a time I began to understand how old Walter and my father could walk side by side half the afternoon without speaking to each other, communicating by a smile or a nod or without any visible or audible sign. There are times when speech is a poor, inadequate business.

One afternoon I arrived to find old Walter in the garden, standing quite still, staring at something. He did not speak when I came near him but only raised his hand in a gesture which clearly prohibited any speech or violent movement. Then he pointed at a male cardinal, very handsome in his red coat, moving restlessly about the lower branches of a magnolia and chirping anxiously. In a low voice he said, "The poor fellow is looking for his mate. I found her dead yesterday on the ground under that pine over there. He was staying around, trying to bring her back to life and make her fly away with him. I took her and buried her. I hoped he'd forget and fly away and find another mate. But he didn't. He keeps hanging around, trying to find her. It's funny about birds and animals that way."

Then a farmer and his wife came in the gate and interrupted our quiet. We were not always alone on those Sunday walks because neighbors and even farmers from a great distance came sometimes on Sundays to see his farm and hear him talk about "My Ninety Acres." I knew he took pride in his prestige but he never showed it. He kept his simple, modest manner when he talked of this field or that one, a kind of fire would come into the blue eyes, like the fire in the eyes of a man talking of a woman he loves passionately. He never came to see me but he always welcomed me warmly on "My Ninety Acres" and when I missed a Sunday, he was disappointed.

And then one brilliant day in October I saw a big, shiny black car coming up the long lane to our house. I knew at once who was in it. I knew by the size and importance of the car, and as it drew nearer, by the cut of the driver's uniform. It was Robert. He had come on his annual visit and had driven over to see me.

I went down the path to meet him and as he stepped out of the shiny car, it was hard for me to remember him as the boy I had seen the last time when he was sixteen, slim, muscular, towheaded and athletic. He still looked a little like old Walter, yet in a strange way he appeared older than the old man. He was plump and rather flabby with pouches beneath the eyes which looked through the shining lenses of steel-rimmed spectacles. He stooped a little and there was a certain softness about his chin and throat.

He said, "I'm Robert Oakes. My father told me you had come back to live in the Valley."

"Yes, I know. I'm delighted to see you. Come in."

I found him rather as I had expected him to be, an intelligent fellow, with a good deal of dignity and authority. He was, after all, the child of old Walter and Nellie and their qualities could not be altogether lost in him. After thirty years the going was a little stiff at first but after a drink we got together again, mostly by talking about "My Ninety Acres" and the old swimming hole in the creek and maple sugar making time and the other boyhood experiences we had shared.

He laughed once and said, "The old gentleman has certainly made good on his ninety acres."

I asked him to stay for lunch and he accepted the invitation so readily that I suspected he had counted on it from the beginning. I said, "I know it's no good sending for your father. He won't leave the place."

"No, he and Jed were in the field by the creek husking corn when I left." Robert laughed, "He told me if I sat around long enough over here I'd get a drink and be asked to lunch. He said it was worth it to see the house and the place. Privately, I think he wanted to get rid of me for most of the day so he could get on with his work. He doesn't know what to do with me. I get in his way and take up his time."

We had lunch at a table crowded with noisy children with four dogs on the floor beside us. I think, at first, that Robert didn't know quite how to take it, but he warmed up presently and said to me, "You have a mighty good life here. I envy you."

After lunch we sat for a time on the porch overlooking the Valley. The sky was the brilliant blue of an Ohio sky in October and the trees were red and gold and purple with the green winter wheat springing into life in the fields beyond the bottom pasture where the Guernseys moved slowly across the bluegrass. He kept watching the Valley, so intently at times that he did not seem to hear what I was saying.

And presently he came round to what was clearly the object of his visit. "I really wanted to talk about my father," he said. "He's quite a problem and stubborn as a mule. I know your father was a great friend of his and that he accepts you nowadays exactly as if you were your father. And I thought you might have some influence on him. You see, I offered him almost everything — I've offered him a fruit ranch in Florida or Southern California, or a bigger farm, or a flat in New York. I've tried everything and he doesn't want any of it. He won't even let me hire him a couple or buy him an automobile or any machinery that might make life easier for him. This morning he was up at daylight and down husking corn in the bottom field with Jed by seven o'clock."

I grinned for I could see the whole picture and could understand how the old man's rich, famous, successful son got in his way.

"When I got up," said Robert, "I found some eggs and pancake batter laid out for me and coffee on the stove, with a note to my driver about how to get breakfast for me. In the note he said to come down to the bottom when I'd finished breakfast. What can you do with a fellow like that?"

"What do you want me to do?"

"I want you to persuade him to let me do something for him. He's seventy-five years old and I'm afraid something will happen to him alone there in the house or barn."

"I'm afraid it's no good," I said. "I couldn't persuade him any more than you."

"I've tried everything even to saying 'What would it look like if it came out in the papers that my father had died suddenly alone on his farm in Ohio?' That's pretty cheap, but even that didn't move him. All he said was, 'You're rich enough to keep it out of the papers and anyway the dogs would let people know if I was sick.'"

We were both silent for a time and then I said, "Honestly, Bob, I don't think there's anything to be done and to tell the truth I don't see why we should do anything. He's as happy as it's possible for a man to be. He's tough as nails and he loves that place like a woman." Then hesitantly, I said, "Besides, Nellie is always there looking after him."

A startled look came into the son's blue eyes and after a moment he asked, "Do you feel that way, too?" Nellie, who died when Robert was born, must have been as unknown and strange to Robert as she was to me.

I said, "I think Nellie is everywhere in that ninety acres. He's never lonely. She's in the garden and the fields and his famous fence rows. She's out there husking corn with him now in the bottom forty."

Robert lighted another cigar. "It's the damnedest thing," he said. "Sometimes I've felt that he had some resentment because I killed my mother when I was born or that he liked John better because he looked like her, but I know that isn't true. That's not in the old gentleman's character. I think it's more because Nellie is always there and I just get in his way. It's funny," he added, "I always think of her as Nellie — somebody I would have liked knowing because she was so pretty and kind and gay and 'smart' as they say here in the Valley. Sometimes I think the old gentleman gets Nellie and the ninety acres a little mixed up."

We talked some more and then Robert called his driver, got in the shiny car and drove off. We had agreed that there wasn't anything to be done about old Walter and Nellie. I said I'd keep my eye on him and go over myself or send somebody once every day to see that he was all right. Of course on Thursdays it wasn't necessary because that was the day that Jed's wife came to do the washing and clean up. And so every day for two years I, or somebody from the place, went over. Sometimes we'd have an excuse but more often we didn't even let him know that he was being watched. One of us would drive past at chore time, or I'd walk over the hills and watch until he appeared in the barnyard or the garden. I knew how much he'd resent it if he suspected that anyone was spying on him, and I didn't want to risk breaking our friendship.

I continued to go over every Sunday and each time I went over I learned something about soil, or crops or animals, for the knowledge and experience of the old man seemed inexhaustible. And then one Sunday afternoon in early September when we were walking alone through one of old Walter's cornfields, I made a discovery. It was fine corn, the whole field, the best in the whole county, and as we came near the end of a long row, he stopped before a mighty single stalk of corn which was beautiful in the special way that only corn can be beautiful. It was dark green and vigorous and from it hung two huge nearly ripened ears and a third smaller one. Old Walter stopped and regarded it with a glowing look in his blue eyes.

"Look at that," he said. "Ain't it beautiful? That's your hybrid stuff." His hands ran over the stalk, the leaves and the ears. "I wish

Nellie could have seen this hybrid corn. She wouldn't have believed it."

As I watched the big work-worn hand caressing that stalk of corn, I understood suddenly the whole story of Walter and Nellie and the ninety acres. Walter was old now but he was vigorous and the rough hand that caressed that corn was the hand of a passionate lover. It was a hand that had caressed the body of a woman who had been loved as few women have ever been loved, so passionately and deeply and tenderly that there would never be another woman who could take her place. I felt again a sudden lump in my throat, for I knew that I had understood suddenly, forty years after the woman was dead, one of the most tragic but beautiful of all love stories. I knew now what Robert's strange remark about Nellie and the ninety acres getting mixed up had meant. Robert himself must once have seen something very like what I had just seen.

It happened at last. I went over one Sunday afternoon a few weeks later and when I could not find old Walter or the dogs anywhere I returned to the house and went inside. I called his name but no one answered and in a little while I heard scratching and whining in the ground floor bedroom and then a short, sharp bark and when I opened the door the sheep dog bitch came toward me. The other dog lay on the hooked rug beside the bed his head between his paws, looking at me mournfully as if he knew that I understood. On the bed lay old Walter. He had died quietly while he was asleep.

I telegraphed to Robert and he came with his wife for the funeral. The wife was exactly as I expected her to be and I understood what old Walter had meant when he said it was a pity Robert had never found a woman he could love. As I listened to the service, I knew how much feeling lay behind old Walter's simple observation.

He was buried beside Nellie in the Valley churchyard. The dogs came over to join my dogs and after awhile they got on together. Robert wouldn't sell "My Ninety Acres" but I undertook to farm it for him and one of our men went there to live. But it will never be farmed as old Walter farmed it. There isn't anybody who will ever farm that earth again as if it were the only woman he ever loved.

5

Why Didn't Anyone Tell Us?

From *Out of the Earth*, 1948

"Out of the Earth," according to its first edition dust jacket, *"is about the New Agriculture and the incredible worlds which have opened up with the scientific discoveries of the past few years. A cubic foot of productive soil is an organism in itself in which every law of the universe is in operation. 'It is probable,' says Mr. Bromfield, 'that we have learned more about agriculture and the soil in the past generation or less than in all the history of the world. It is also probable that what we have discovered up to date is only about one tenth of what there is to know.' These discoveries have to do not only with increased production of food and fiber, but with increased quality as well. 'Poor land makes poor people,' and, improperly used, unproductive land annually causes Americans an incalculable loss in terms of bad health and bad living conditions. The science of the New Agriculture offers a way to bring to millions of people a new meaning in their lives. To taxpayer and farmer alike, it offers new independence and freedom from costly, unnecessary, and eventually ruinous government interference and subsidies."*

There are many hundreds of thousands of good farmers in the United States and many more hundreds of thousands of bad or indifferent farmers. It would be difficult to imagine any one factor more important and more beneficial to the whole of our economy and even of our civilization than a population of farmers who were all good and intelligent husbandmen, independent in character and prosperous and secure in life through their own efforts. It is immensely encouraging that the breed of farmer is constantly improving, away from the indifferent farmer of the frontier and the vaudeville "hick" who inherited the declining or "run-down" land wrecked by his predecessors during the end of the nineteenth and the beginning of the twentieth centuries. It is immensely encouraging to discover everywhere young men and women growing up in the warm new tradition of the 4-H Clubs, the Future Farmers of America and the Vocational Agriculture classes.

One of the most stimulating experiences in a lifetime fairly rich in stimuli has been the contacts we have had at Malabar with countless G.I. training classes. These are the "on-the-job" training classes set up under the Veterans Administration to give the G.I. both instruction and practice in the profession of farming. I use the word "profession" advisedly, for the atmosphere surrounding these groups of G.I.'s, sometimes several to a single county, is one of dignity and of stimulation on a higher level than that known in the past in American agriculture save among the limited number of naturally intelligent and persevering husbandmen. For the most part, the veterans are in their late twenties and early thirties, with a seriousness of character and purpose which is, at times, very moving.

The level of teaching, from men selected by the G.I.'s themselves and approved by the Veterans Administration, is singularly high, not necessarily in the academic sense because there is no specification of advanced college degrees, but because most of the instructors are close to the earth and to animals, love their jobs, are proud of their boys and are more often than not successful, practicing farmers themselves. This is immensely important in the teaching of agriculture and immensely important in relation to the things I have to say further on in this chapter. These instructors have their hands in the earth.

One does not learn about soils and animals exclusively in a classroom and one does not maintain the vitality and sparkle of the great teacher by passing years in an armchair and working out formulas without ever putting foot on God's good earth.

The farmer eternally believes what he sees and learns from the reality of the world around him and from his own observation. Merely to teach a farmer how to observe and what to look for is, in itself, the greatest possible achievement and one which is far too greatly neglected in our present system of agricultural education. I have found few things more humanly encouraging and satisfactory than the light which comes into the faces of some of the farmer instructors of the G.I. training classes as their "boys" see and hear new things about farming and animal husbandry. It is a light I have seen too rarely in the faces of the agricultural college instructor or even in the visages of many county agents.

There is in the faces of these farmer-instructors none of the boredom or condescension that I have encountered sometimes in other fields of agriculture education. There is none of the smugness that too often accompanies a university degree acquired through "cramming" with a minimum of inspiration. In the face of the instructor there is respect for the intelligence of his "boys" and their eagerness to be good farmers and to get ahead in the world. He is not merely holding down a job, for his payment is ridiculously small in relation to the amount of time and energy he expends. He is really trying to do a job and as often as not has the spirit of a crusader. He understands, sometimes without knowing, what it means to "spark" a young fellow so that he will carry on for the rest of his life with a lively interest in all the phases of soil and agriculture long after his "on-the-job" training is finished.

The spark, I think, is the thing that is most overlooked in our agricultural training. The lack of it, and the lack of capacity for producing it, marks the greatest failure in our agricultural education, and this failure I think arises partly from the fact that the average teacher in agriculture does not sufficiently respect the profession to which, somehow or other, he has attached himself. There is nothing sadder or more discouraging than the agricultural college professor or instructor, sitting in his office with his feet on the desk, killing time between classes of young people who bore him because he has never found his profession exciting or has never bothered to learn anything new since he received his degree.

My maternal grandfather, of whom I have written many times, and who died at eighty-six one of the best educated people I know although he never went to school after the age of eighteen when he ran away to the Gold Coast, once said to me, "If a person really wants an education, there is nothing on earth that will keep him from getting it. If he doesn't want it, nothing on earth can impose it upon him. But the fact is that the great majority of the human race lies in between. They are average and they don't know whether they want an education or not and all they need is a sparking. It's like striking a spark from a flint to tinder. Start the fire and it will go on and on opening up constantly new excitements, new curiosities, new stimuli for the rest of an existence."

What he said applies more to the potential farmer than perhaps to the men and women of any other profession. A little "sparking" is what is needed rather than a cramming with many facts which are frequently of little use to him and many times are obsolete or proven unsound by the time they get to him.

It need not always be young people who need the sparking. I have seen middle-aged and even elderly farmers who had been practicing an indifferent kind of farming listlessly and without interest in the "grandpappy" pattern until suddenly a county agent or a neighbor or a son or daughter made apparent to them that they were practicing the most exciting and satisfactory profession in the world without ever knowing it.

I have never forgotten the look in the eye of a sixty-five-year-old hill farmer in the poorest county in Tennessee, who could neither read nor write, as he showed us the rich grass and legumes that had replaced the broom sedge and poverty grass on his steep fields, and made us, in his excitement, scramble down and climb back up a half-mile hill in order to see the fat white-face cattle which were lost somewhere in the brush of his bottom pasture. He had been sparked at the age of sixty when, through some quirk (perhaps because he thought he couldn't be any worse off), he had volunteered to work with the Agricultural Agents of the T.V.A. in setting up a pilot farm. There was no doubt that the last remaining years of his life would be richer and more exciting than all the rest of his life put together. His bright blue eyes had a light in them that was never there even when he was a boy of eighteen. Some T.V.A. agricultural teacher had set a spark to the tinder.

Although no exact figures are available, it is probable that the nation, including federal and state colleges and agencies of all sorts, spends in the neighborhood of $3,000,000,000 a year in aid and education for farmers. No other group in our society benefits in anything like the same degree and the reader might well ask, "If so much money is spent every year, why has so little progress been made in improving our agriculture?" The answers are, I think, almost endless.

There are in the nation forty-eight agricultural colleges more or less controlled and financed by the states themselves and there is the vast Department of Agriculture, until the recent war our most expensive department of government, and the Extension Service, operating more or less jointly between the Department of Agriculture and the various state colleges. And there are many other agencies of

education such as the Soil Conservation Service and the rather
political Triple A, now become the even more political and bureaucratic Producing and Marketing Association, and there are Farmers'
Institutes held locally in winter and short courses for farmers at
many state colleges during the winter months. And there are thousands of truckloads of pamphlets upon every subject from agronomy
to teaching the farmer's wife how to make a bed. And there are
numerous agricultural foundations privately endowed and films
made by industrial companies and private foundations and distributed free of charge in an enlightened self-interest.

Out of all this, it is astonishing what a small trickle of information, much less of inspiration, finally comes through to the average
farmer. The tragedy is that the poorer the area, the poorer the
farmer, both in knowledge and economic status, the less the information that reaches him. This is particularly true of the 60 per cent
of our farmers who produce very little more than they consume and
acutely true of the poorest regions of the South and the Southwest
where actually there exists suspicion and hostility of most agents
associated with government of any kind. In such areas the local
church is a potent factor, and if every local preacher, most of them
of the "shoutin'" evangelistic variety, could be enlisted as a force
for good agriculture, good diet and good soils, the advances made
both in health and in economic terms in such areas would be
tremendous.1

The good, intelligent farmer, the "sparked" farmer will somehow find the information he wants, but often enough he has to dig
for it.

Part of the answer lies probably in the old and classic statement
that "teachers are born and not made" and that there are all too few
real teachers in the field of agricultural education, or any other field

1 In recent years there has actually come into existence an organization
known as The Friends of the Soil which works with the local preachers in
bringing new agricultural ideas to the people of backward areas. It has even
developed a ritual dealing with the soil, its meaning and its potentialities
which is used in church services. The ritual, of course, is sprinkled with the
innumerable and beautiful quotations relating to husbandry and the soil
which abound in both the Old and the New Testaments. The Friends of the
Soil is not the same organization as The Friends of the Land, a society which
has done much invaluable work in propagandizing the importance of our
natural resources and their conservation throughout the country during the
past ten years. The two organizations, however, work closely together.

for that matter, with the capacity for "sparking" the students working under them.

At top, of course, the principal cause of the failure is bureaucracy and red tape and politics, all of which demonstrate their evil operations in a hundred ways. Sometimes the dean of an agricultural college is appointed politically by a board of college directors who in turn were appointed politically and none of whom have much knowledge concerning agriculture or agricultural economics. I have known one dean, so harassed and preoccupied by politics and administration (campus politics as well as party politics) that he did not even know what was being grown on his own farm. It is obvious, I think, that he had small contact with farmers and small time to devote to directing the kind of education which would be profitable to both individual farmer and nation.

And there is the kind of "gentleman" dean who is more concerned with speaking at dinners of industrialists and bankers than with the farmer and the soil from which he becomes eventually so remote that his contribution is virtually nullified. And the kind of dean who does not want to extend his various departments or enter new fields of research because it will cost money which he has to beg from a frequently agriculturally illiterate board of college trustees or directors, or because, in the interdepartmental jealousies and politics, any action in a progressive sense is likely to raise too may rows. I know one dean who, when asked what the college was doing regarding the study of trace elements, responded, "Well, we haven't done anything yet but we're being forced into it." Forced into it by whom and by what? By the good farmer, the privately financed agricultural foundation, the medical profession and the agricultural magazines which do a heroic job in helping the farmer, and even by the fertilizer companies. "Forced into it" when an agricultural college should have been leading the way to prove either the virtues or the fallacy of the effects of trace elements. Then he added lamely, "But if I authorize any special research, it will make an awful row because some of my professors don't believe in trace elements." A fine basis for advancement of science or education!

In the same field I recently heard a professor say, when asked concerning a trace-element product marketed by one of our large industrial corporations, "Oh, there's nothing to that! No use spending money on that stuff," and then almost immediately catching himself, he added, "Oh, maybe there is after all. That company is paying for three fellowships here at the college!" When asked how he knew whether the stuff was any good or not or whether he had ever tested it, he answered, "No, of course not. We haven't time for things like that."

Meanwhile, Johns Hopkins University, a non-agricultural institution concerned mostly with medicine and one of the first-ranking universities in the world, has allotted $500,000 to the study and coordination of already existing information, in the same field, and Cornell University, with perhaps the greatest agricultural school in the world, last year set up a whole new School of Nutrition with one department dealing with the relation of minerals to the health of plants, animals and people.

Missouri University and the State Agricultural College are also making valuable contributions to the field of minerals and nutrition and crop yields, largely under the leadership of Dr. William Albrecht, one of the great authorities on the subject.

Recently another college, when requested by the state Wildlife Commission to compile information regarding the relation of poor and depleted soils to wild-life population, requested ten years and $40,000 to set up a research project although the information already existed and much of the work had already been done by other colleges and the Wildlife Service. The problem was merely one of coordination of already known material with no need whatever for going over the whole field again in an expensive process of the wholesale duplication so widespread under our disorganized system of agricultural education.

To date most of the information in the whole field of minerals and nutrition has come from industrial foundations, medical colleges and good farmers endowed with powers of imagination and observation. The medical profession as a whole has displayed a steadily increasing interest in the so-called trace elements, especially in relation to the endocrine system, as medicine has moved increasingly toward the philosophy of preventing disease and physical breakdowns rather than sitting by until they have occurred and then trying to patch up the patient.

Successful Farming, one of our best agricultural magazines, has recently published an illustrated booklet called *Getting a Better Living from Your Soil* which is in itself an agricultural education with all of the nonsense removed. It is streamlined and provides within its hundred pages the fundamentals of a good and modern agriculture. Virtually every article is written by individual specialists and members of the faculties of agricultural colleges and the level is uniformly and remarkably high in intelligence, in scientific value and in readability. Indeed, any layman could read the whole booklet with great interest. Yet the remarkable fact is that somewhere along the line, owing to deficiencies and handicaps of bureaucratic education, very little of the same information ever finds its way through the intricacies of a system down to the level of the farmer. It is as if, in order for these admirable men to reach the farmer, they are forced to escape from the system and write for magazines or to talk to the farmer personally.

The same high level of sound education holds for all of our best agricultural publications in which very often the farmer can find much more information of a fundamental and valuable quality than he is able to get from the state colleges or through the Extension Service. Perhaps the great difference is that in the magazines, the editors respect the intelligence of the good farmer and explain to him actually what happens in the earth and even in his livestock, presenting it in a way which makes the material not only interesting but fascinating and stimulating. Of course it is not filtered through endless offices and bulletins and the censorship and prejudice of many small men, but goes direct from the scientist to the farmer through the medium of the magazine. One often gets the impression from reading our farm magazines that the editors and contributors, who frequently include top-level dirt farmers, are far out in advance of many of our state colleges, yet, curiously enough, the best articles are sometimes written by scientists from the very staffs of the colleges which seem most backward.

What is true of the *Successful Farming* booklet is true also of the excellent Yearbooks put out by the Department of Agriculture each year, where the individual professor writing direct to the farmer does the kind of job which is needed. It would appear in the case of the colleges that too much of the writing, too much of the instruction, is left in the hands of bored or limited bureaucrats or instructors and little men all the way down the line or in some cases these things have suffered from the limited abilities and prejudices of deans and directors. The same excellent qualities exhibited in the books mentioned above hold true of another book which no real farmer should be without. It is *Hunger Signs in Crops*, published by the

National Fertilizer Association of Washington, D.C. Again the professors write brilliantly on their own when writing directly to the farmer. It would appear that the college campus enveloped them in a fog of mediocrity, dissension and apathy.2

And what happens to the individual teacher or research expert with the brilliant mind and the capacity to "spark"? More likely than not one or two things happen to him. In a welter of campus politics and jealousies, the armies of mediocrity and laziness gang up on him, or his brilliance and his achievements are recognized by some industry or privately endowed foundation or perhaps by a better agricultural school and he is hired away at much more money than that provided by his existing inadequate salary. In too many of our agricultural colleges the faculty, under such combined pressure, eventually becomes a standard of mediocrity but of little else, staffed by men who are able to remain there only through an untroublesome conformity and mediocrity, teaching on and on year after year, frequently out of textbooks and theories long obsolescent or enveloped in a haze of academic monotony and boredom.

Certainly the costs and the inconvenience of prescribing new textbooks is one factor in the general mediocrity of agricultural education. There are books being used in some of our agricultural colleges which not only became obsolete long ago but are actually teaching methods and ideas long since proved not only false but actually destructive to a good agriculture. It has been too much trouble or no one has cared enough to eliminate such books or bring them up to date and in line with the fabulous discoveries made in the whole field of agriculture within the past few years. And, of course, there are still a good many professors and instructors, as out of date as the textbooks, who have never learned a new fact nor asked an imaginative or scientific question of themselves or of the students they teach since the day they achieved their college degrees.

And occasionally the dean, who is frequently subject to the politically appointed, agriculturally illiterate board of directors, cannot get the appropriations he wants to run a real college of agriculture. Such a college, and even education itself, frequently becomes wholly unimportant to the directors in comparison with the

2 The University of Oklahoma Press, under the direction of Savoie Lottinville, deserves special praise for the fine list of stimulating and valuable books on all phases of agriculture which it brings out from time to time.

new $3,000,000 stadium or the bargaining with the Peanut Bowl or the Soybean Bowl or some other commercially managed athletic field over how much they will get for the appearance of the Siwash team in a contest with the Freshwater team.

And our federal Department of Agriculture, even after a fairly thorough housecleaning by Milton Eisenhower, is still an incredible monstrosity with one division and bureau overlapping another and creating in the process all kinds of duplications, feuds and jealousies. Even the Hoover Report understated a confusion which ranges from the divisions of research through the endless economic agencies set up all too often merely to buy the farmer's vote. Feuds, jealousies and name-calling arise out of the muddled and conflicting authorities which not only nullify the purposes for which they were set up but frequently create actual harm for the whole of our agriculture and economy.

Certainly these difficulties are of little help to the farmer looking for information. More often than not the spectacle of one bureau or one individual feuding with another merely confuses him and turns him cynical regarding the whole department. The very pamphlets sent out to him are frequently unreadable because of their dullness and lack of clarity and frequently enough they contain information actually contradicted by the next pamphlet that comes along. The purpose for which the Department was set up — that of research and instruction to benefit the profession of agriculture — has at times become lost altogether in propaganda for or against this or that political issue, for or against this or that division or service or bureau. Indeed, no Department of our government (and only the Defense Department is more expensive to the taxpayer) is so riddled with the evils that increase as bureaucracy mounts and mounts. Moreover, the post of Secretary of Agriculture, set up originally to direct research and agricultural science, has become increasingly merely an office for disseminating party political propaganda to buy the vote of the farmer.

The Extension Service, operating jointly with the state agricultural colleges to bring information and benefit to the farmer, again suffers from the evils of red tape and of bureaucracy. The county agent, often ill paid and devoted and able, working in the individual county, is forced to do acres of paper work, filling in reports and questionnaires which are forwarded eventually to those vast archives in Washington so costly to the taxpayer and so handicapping to the farmer, where they repose without even having been looked at to gather dust as more and more buildings are erected to house them. Some perhaps are never used for any purpose whatever.

This red tape, demanded by the Federal Government and sometimes by the state colleges, is one of the greatest barriers between the farmer and the information he desires and needs. It occupies many hours a week of the county agent's time which otherwise could be spent in the fields on the earth with the farmers of a county. This, oddly enough, was the original purpose for which the county agent came into existence but it is a purpose which sometimes seems to be utterly forgotten by the bureaucrats in their dusty cells. The county agent was designed to be the most direct link between sources of agricultural information and the farmer but, as such, the county agent is handicapped in many ways of which bureaucracy and red tape is but one. He is subject to the censorship of the state college and sometimes to the authority of a fire-eating, unscientific, political dean or Director of Extension who sets up his own prejudices rather than scientific fact or research as the measure of information which should reach the farmer.

Many a county agent, in his practical and even scientific approach to agriculture, is far more advanced and accurate than some of his superiors. And frequently he becomes the victim of feuds and jealousies occurring on higher levels. Not the least example is the kind of feud which exists in certain states between the Extension Service and the Federal Soil Conservation Service, a feud promoted by certain state Farm Bureaus, agencies which have no legal standing whatever in government but which in certain states have actually used unscrupulous pressures to turn the Extension Service, paid for by the taxes of all of us, into a recruiting service for increasing their memberships. The feud, needless to say, thrives most in the states where, generally speaking, there is a high proportion of the absentee landlordism which has been for long so costly not only to the natural resources of the nation but to the individual taxpayer as well.

All of these difficulties, vices and failures are perhaps not more than the results of the human failings of mankind, aggravated and magnified when bureaucratic government increases, but the farmer and the taxpayer are the victims of them all — the farmer in terms of the partial failure of a system to help him and the taxpayer in the huge sums he must pay for the working of a machinery which is faulty and confused and duplicating in its operation. Many excellent results come out of it but, as often as not, the results come by accident or through the outstanding qualities of the individual, from county agent to director or college dean, who manages somehow to survive his infinite restrictions and handicaps and break through to the farmer himself and to that agriculture upon which so much of our economic salvation, health and vigor as a nation depend. Somehow, in all the red tape, in all the jealousies and feuds, duplications and human weaknesses, the capacity for "sparking" the farmer becomes dimmed and often lost. It survives only with the officials who have courage and intelligence and perhaps the diplomacy to carry out their purpose despite the weaknesses both of system and of individuals, but under a bureaucracy which tends to reduce all human talent to utter mediocrity, they do so at a decided risk.

They do fortunately exist — these individuals who manage somehow to carry through with the purpose to which they are dedicated. They exist among the deans, the professors, the county agents, but almost without exception they are able to accomplish their high purposes not because of but in spite of the politics and bureaucracy and feuds and prejudices and red tape of a system. They are the heroic ones and they do carry the spark. One of them is worth fifty of the bureaucratic or academic conformists both in character and intelligence and in dollars and cents to the taxpayer and the farmer.

In the services of the Department of Agriculture and in the Extension Service and the state colleges there exist men of the highest ability and devotion, frequently serving for salaries representing a fraction of what they are worth in terms of intelligence, character and training. To them the farmers and the nation owe a very great debt. Some have attained recognition in the areas in which they work and some even beyond the limits of those areas. In one sense the vast Extension Service is as good as the local overworked county agent on whose shoulders fall an increasing number of duties and obligations, many of them conceived and imposed by some dusty statistician in an office hundreds or even thousands of miles away. I have known county agents who have made over the whole economy of their counties through their own personal efforts, and they have done so frequently at the risk of losing their ill-paid jobs because they have paid more attention to soil and agriculture and the farmer than to the endless silly forms and reports they are expected to fill out and turn in.

The job to be done lies in the soil and in agriculture and not merely in reporting this or that tidbit of useless information to some remote and sterile statistician.

Certainly one of the great errors of our agricultural higher education at the present time is the exaggerated emphasis placed by many state colleges on producing only technicians and specialists. The error no doubt arose out of the need a generation or more ago of more experts and more teachers to go into the field and work with the farmer. That need is long past, although the need for top-quality, inspired teachers is still very great, as indeed it probably always will be. But at the present time there is a glut of technicians, of specialists in every field of agriculture, so that many a young man or woman emerges from an agricultural college with a diploma and no place to go. Moreover, all too often the young man or woman came from a farm and would make perhaps his greatest contribution by going back to his own area and doing a first-rate job, but he has in a sense been spoiled as a good farmer by a highly technical education as an "expert" and technician and has acquired a curious kind of snobbery regarding the soil and fundamental agriculture itself. And sometimes the pressures and overemphasis on the particular field in which he has chosen to specialize have thrown him out of balance altogether so that he falls into the error of so many specialists and believes that all the answers to all the complex problems of agriculture can be found in his own narrow field.

In no field of our education, unless until quite lately in the field of engineering, has overspecialization been so rampant as in agriculture. One has only to look about in the field of agriculture to find any number of normally intelligent young men and women who might have made excellent farmers and prosperous productive citizens of the nation but have been in a sense deformed and thrown off the track into an overcrowded field of activity where it is becoming increasingly difficult to find a good job.

At one of our greatest state agricultural colleges only 4 per cent of the 1948 graduating class expressed the intention of going back to the farms from which they came. The others were all technicians and specialists setting out into an already overcrowded field.

This same system of attempting to force young people to become technicians and specialists rather than good farmers shows up throughout the study plans of most state colleges. On the assumption that every student wishes to become a specialist, the tendency is to impose upon each and every one the necessity of choosing a major subject and then directing his education in that direction. As a result, many young people who want to learn the fundamentals of good agriculture as quickly and as efficiently as possible are forced to spend countless hours on higher mathematics, on advanced chemistry, even on foreign languages which will never be of the faintest use to them, and to spend much time and money taking a four-year course of which 50 per cent is unnecessary and often without value. I have, indeed, known many young people of great intelligence and much valuable experience as farmers who after a year or two became utterly discouraged and left college because of the long hours and schedules designed for "specialists."

Here again the question of "sparking" is of the utmost importance. What is crammed into a young head out of books is of no importance if it is unaccompanied by inspiration and it will be more quickly and easily forgotten than learned. The student trained in fundamentals and "sparked" will find out during the rest of his life all he needs to know regarding his profession and he will continue to find out until the day he dies. The "short courses" offered by some state colleges during the winter months have been apparently the only concession made away from this tendency to force down the throat of every student a mass of stuff which is both meaningless and valueless, however much it may please the individual professor teaching it. Many a young person cannot afford four years of expensive agricultural education in terms of money, but many more, impatient to get started in life, cannot afford the fancy work in terms of time and discouragement.

In some cases the Extension Service has been guilty of pushing contests and projects into the field of the unsound and even of the absurd, especially in terms of sound regional agriculture and livestock raising. Certainly one instance is that of feeding animals for prize 4-H awards far beyond the limits of economic soundness. One outstanding example, pertinent because of the exaggeration, occurs occasionally in the fat stock contests conducted in some of the Gulf Coast counties where young people bring in calves from other areas and then feed them on a regional basis suitable to Iowa but wholly unsuited to the cattle industry in a warm, humid, insect-ridden country where corn is not a profitable crop. Quite obviously the prize should go to the young person who raised a Brahma or a cross-bred Brahma in the terms of the community in which he is living, rather than bringing in a breed unsuited to the climate and the forage of the area and then raising him as if he were being raised on a feedlot in the rich corn-belt area of the Middle West where corn may be raised efficiently and cheaply. The winner sells his prize steer for several thousand dollars of businessmen's money and the rest of the contestants are left holding the bag unless some sympathetic oil man comes along and pays for the expensive feed which has gone into the cattle they have been raising and feeding. Fortunately for the contestants this is usually the case, but the whole procedure has little to do with efficient and profitable cattle raising in an area which essentially and continually is a breeding rather than a feeding area for cattle.

A similar error regarding the relationship between animal husbandry, pure-bred cattle and good feed and forage exists in many of our agricultural colleges which in some cases 75 per cent or more of the total money allotted to these things is spent in teaching about blood lines, registry and judging animals as against 25 per cent and less on nutrition, on good agriculture and the raising of good pasture and forage which are the fundamentals as compared with which the rest is merely dependent and accessory. The same error of course extends into the field of pure-bred cattle activities as practiced by many city farmers and some practical registered cattle breeders who should know better. In all too many cases, a whole staff is maintained to keep track of pedigrees and tests of $25,000 bulls and $5,000 cows while the animals themselves are frequently on third-grade pasture and forage or being fed unbalanced, forced grain diets. To be sure, the bad results are inevitable in shy breeding, in a variety of diseases and, in the case of many valuable dairy cows, in "burning out" the animals in a few years. Veterinarians are brought in and give the animals injections and capsules in order to cure shy breeding and other ills which should never have occurred in the first place if the owners and often the college-educated managers and specialists concerned had had the opportunity of a proper and balanced education. In the same school of thought are those "record-breaking" dairies which feed $2 a day worth of feed to get 5 cents more milk, in total neglect of that economic line which means profits for the farmer and health and longevity for valuable cattle.

Indeed, the whole emphasis on line and in-breeding has pushed in many breeds to the point of absurdity, both physiological and economic, and in many cases to the deterioration of qualities of ruggedness and high production on cheap good forage which are the essence of profit for the farmer and commercial cattle breeder. This has been increasingly so in the range of show animals in some of the beef breeds where the process has been shrewdly and brilliantly described by an experienced old rancher friend in Texas.

He says:

First you give the bull hormone injections and then aid him to breed the cow. Nine months later, you summon a midwife to deliver the calf. Once on its feet it spends half an hour trying to find the udder of the cow and when it is at last located, the calf gets a half cup full of milk and you end up by bringing in a Holstein to feed and raise the calf. A year later you help the calf to his feet, put him on roller skates and crimp his coat, shine him with oil and wheel him into the show ring where he wins first in the yearling class, and as soon as he is old enough to breed, the process begins all over again. But what in Hell has this to do with the kind of cattle which can scrounge a living and bring up a profitable calf on the range? Maybe it may please some millionaire or some judge who has never made a living raising cattle but there ain't much sense of any kind otherwise.

In this overemphasis on breeding, on pedigrees and on records I have known many a small general or dairy farmer to lose his shirt. Indeed, in some states one might gain the impression that there was something disgraceful about good, healthy, productive grade cattle operating at a good profit to the farmer. All the pressure is toward every little farmer having a registered and accredited herd, often enough regardless of whether they are feeding on weeds or on good forage. As a corollary of this, the farmer is encouraged to do heavy-grain feeding and to spend his potential profits on every kind of protein and mineral concentrate and supplement. He must go to the expense of a professional official tester and record keeper and spend hours over pedigree papers, when all the time he could be making a lot more money on high production per acre of good high-protein, high-mineral-content forage while operating a good, selected grade herd of animals.

The sad experience of many a dairy farmer lured into a registered cattle program is again best told in the words of an old-timer friend from Iowa who has been through the whole racket. He puts it thus:

To really get anything out of the registered racket you have to be in the top level. My father's herd used to average at sales $1500 and better an animal. When he got old and the operation fell into the hands of my brother it went to pieces because he didn't stay in the top level. When my father was alive he spent hundreds of thousands of dollars in showing his herd, transporting it from one fair to another. His only rival was Mr. X who had just as good a herd and they worked the racket together. One year my father would import from England with great fanfare a $20,000 bull, and breed him to his best cow. When the first bull calf was born, Mr. X would buy it from my father with great fanfare for $2000 to $3000 and give him a note in exchange. Then the next year Mr. X would bring in with great fanfare a $20,000 bull and breed him to his best cow and as soon as the first bull calf was born my father would buy it from Mr. X and give him a note for $2000 to $3000 in exchange. Then both of them tore up the notes and suckers who came to the sale bid on that level of prices for the calves and paid for the two $20,000 bulls and maybe my father and Mr. X showed a profit.

All too often the average farmer with a pretty good and profitable dairy herd is urged to go in for registered cattle, and he goes out and spends $5000 for a bull and maybe $500 or $600 apiece for heifers. The prospect, according to his advisors, is now brilliant although he has added to the expense of his production through testing, special fancy feeds and in a great many other ways, and the chances are that he has less vigor and even perhaps less milk-producing capacity in some cases than in his old grade herd. Then when his calf crop arrives, the magic seems to vanish. He has purchased heifers for $500 to $600 apiece, but when he attempts to sell such heifers back to the big registered herd buyers, the most he can get for his heifers is little more than he could get for one of his grade heifer calves.

There is no question whatever of the great value of the registered cattle of this country nor of the good and scientific work that has gone into their breeding. The question again is one of getting off on the tangent of overspecialization and of breeding lines so close in order to produce a "pretty" animal which pleases the current fashion of the show-ring judges that vigor, profitable feeding capacity and many other qualities become lost to the detriment of both dairy and beef industries. And the man who owns and operates profitably herds of registered cattle must have a certain temperament, a certain pride and even perhaps an obsession for the registered animals. It is not a business for the average farmer, and to urge him into it on the basis that grade cattle are a disgrace and that he will make more money from a registered herd is doing injury both to the individual farmer and to agriculture and the livestock industry in general, especially when the fundamental factors of a good agriculture and good and cheap forage are overlooked in the rustling of the pedigree papers under the lamp at night.

Occasionally I go on the so-called "feeding tours" through the corn-feeding lots of the Middle Western states. It is a tour usually under the direction of state college officials to observe beef feeding practices and discover which ones are the most profitable. Often enough, perhaps as much as 50 per cent of the time, the most money is actually made not by the farmer feeding pure-bred beef cattle but by the farmer feeding Holstein or Brown Swiss steers or steers of those breeds crossed with some beef breed. The reason is simple enough. The big dairy breeds and the cross-breds cost less to buy in the beginning. Because of their big frames and rapid growth they put on, in bone and meat together, a much greater poundage of meat per pound of feed or per acre of pasture than many a pure-bred beef steer bred to produce top-quality cuts of meat. When marketing time comes the dairy or cross-bred steer feeder takes less a pound for his animal at the stockyards, sometimes a lot less, but in the greater weight of his steers he gets a bigger price and a great many times bigger profit. One Kansas feeder told me, in two feedlots of steers — one cross-bred Holstein and Whiteface and one pure-bred beef cattle — his cross-bred steers brought him at the peak of the market in 1948 $80 a head more than the pure-breds.

This is, of course talking economics and not cattle breeding, and quantity not quality, but in recent years the quality beef has attained a price so high that the market has become restricted and the spread between the price of top-quality beef and that of second- or even third-grade beef has narrowed to a point where many a feeder no longer aims at the top-quality market but at the level which will make him the most money, with animals which make the most rapid efficient growth in a market which shows the greatest demand. Under such conditions we again approach the law of diminishing returns and the fact that when any agricultural product or commodity costs too much to produce or is priced too high for other reasons, the market begins to contract, and a surplus is created or prices fall to a point where demand again becomes active. It is a rule and a law on which the colleges might well place greater emphasis to the benefit of countless farmers who could make much higher profits than they are making, not from higher prices, but from more efficient and productive operations at home on their own land.

The county banker, like the county preacher, has a great role to play in the improvement of our agriculture and consequently in the improvement of the whole economy of the nation; and increasingly the county banker is carrying out his responsibility. Not always has he done so out of mere disinterested virtue but because, tardily, the banker, from the small state bank to the great banks of New York City, has come to understand how much a sound agriculture, upon which all our economy is largely based, means to the banks and to the nation. He has seen county banks die like flies for two generations and he knows out of bitter experience that when an agricultural area dies, the local bank dies with it. It no longer has either depositors or borrowers.

Today countless county banks have engaged agricultural specialists not only as advisors in making loans but as actual teachers and consultants. If a farmer is persistently a bad farmer, he will deposit no money and the bank cannot afford to loan him money; but the bank itself can aid and counsel him and even, by making restrictions on a loan, force him, sometimes against his own stupidity and stubbornness, to farm well and prosperously with proper regard for his land and his livestock.

In Tennessee, C.W. Bailey has made over the economy of seven counties from poverty to prosperity simply by his advice and his power as a country banker. In Arkansas, W.W. Campbell has made the same kind of contribution to the nation. Even banks as large as the potent Wachovia Bank of North Carolina, under the leadership of Robert Hanes, are carrying out statewide programs of farm education and aid, and the district banks of the Federal Reserve System have all instituted notable agricultural programs of which that of Chester C. Davis, President of the St. Louis Federal Reserve Bank, established the precedent. With all of these forces at work, it is only logical to ask, "Why have we so many bad farmers?"

I think that the farmer, too, must shoulder a large amount of the blame, sometimes because he is lazy, sometimes because he is overworked, sometimes because he is ignorant and chooses to remain so, sometimes because he is trying to make a wretched living on land which is not agricultural land at all but semi-desert on which

no man, however clever or informed, could make ends meet, sometimes because he belongs in that abominable tenant-absentee landlord combination in which both landlord and tenant are squeezing
from the dying soil its last traces of fertility. And sometimes the
farmer is merely too old to take any interest in improving his land
or his income. He is merely waiting to die.

Fortunately there are great changes in progress, arising principally from the younger generation which has been given a different
point of view regarding agriculture. Largely speaking, their point of
view represents the New Agriculture in which the farmer is part
businessman, part specialist and part scientist rather than the old,
wasteful, ignorant, frontier agriculture or even an agriculture in the
four-year rotation general farm pattern. This change will come
about eventually through the force of economics alone since the
older patterns are profitable neither for the individual nor for the
nation. Moreover, they imply two other defeating factors — an
overburdening investment in different kinds of machinery and long
hours of drudgery.

There is a good deal of sentimentality awash throughout the
nation with regard to "farming as a way of life," a phrase which
carries the implication that there is something especially satisfactory, at least spiritually, in farming in a primitive way as our
ancestors did upon the frontier. The truth is that "farming as a way
of life" is infinitely more pleasurable and satisfactory and profitable
when it is planned, scientific, specialized, mechanized and stripped
of the long hours and the drudgery of the old-fashioned obsolete
pattern of the frontier or general farm.

There is also much loose thinking about "the family-sized
farm" and the idea that a specialized, scientific, business-like farm
cannot be "family-sized." This is sheer nonsense, for the modern
farm may be family-sized and still infinitely more satisfactory than
the "family-sized" farm of the past in which there was no program,
no plan, no pattern but only a scurrying, planless confusion in which
a family was trying to raise a few dairy cattle, a few beef cattle, a
few hogs, a few sheep, a few chickens together with 10 acres of this
and 10 acres of that in a frontier pattern which no longer has any
justification in a highly industrialized world where markets, distribution, mechanization and many other factors which did not exist on
the frontier have altered not only the agricultural but the economic
and even the sociological picture.

The specialized, scientific, business-like farm does not mean the single-crop or even the undiversified farm. It merely means that a farmer and his family do two or three jobs well on a planned, sensible basis rather than a dozen jobs planlessly, badly or inefficiently. Such a pattern approaches that of the efficiency by which American industry produces more and better automobiles, plumbing, radios, etc., than all the rest of the world put together, sells them more cheaply to the consumer than any other nation in the world, and at the same time pays its industrial workers wages from 30 to 90 per cent higher than any other country in the world. The same pattern of planning and high production per unit, per man-hour, per dollar invested, applies to agriculture as well as to industry, but in terms of high and efficient production per acre, per man-hour, per dollar invested. And, of course, the base is always the quality and productivity of the soil and the production per acre. If the raw material represented by grain and forage is costly because the farmer spends too many man-hours, too much fertilizer and too much gasoline in relation to his yields per acre, it does not matter how many animals he owns as machines in the barns or on the pastures, he will make no money, any more than a factory with hundreds of machines can make money by purchasing raw materials at a price so high that the price for the finished product is completely out of line with his costs.

In the end such a process simply means failure and bankruptcy. Ruin approaches the farmer, whether he is in cash crops or in livestock, at an exact ratio with the decline in yield per acre because as the yield declines the costs go up. As my partner, Bob Huge, states it so well, "Too many farmers think they make their money on livestock or on the number of livestock they carry. The animals are merely the machines which process the raw materials. The amount of money the farmer makes is determined almost entirely by the amount he raises per acre."

The livestock industry in Texas is still subject to this ancient fallacy, for too many bankers and too many ranchers estimate the wealth of a rancher by the number of livestock rather than the quality and the carrying-capacity per acre of his range pasture. A 10,000-acre ranch running one steer to every 30 acres of thin, overgrazed pasture cannot make as much money as a 5000-acre ranch running one steer to 5 acres of good undergrazed pasture. Nor can the corn farmer raising 20 bushels to the acre compete with the corn farmer raising 100 bushels per acre because it costs the 20-bushel-an-acre farmer five times as much in taxes, interest, gasoline, man-hours and seed to raise a bushel of corn as it does the 100-bushel-an-acre farmer. The livestock has nothing to do with it except to process the raw material.

The fact of this changed pattern in American agriculture is one of the things rarely impressed on the farmer in all the operation of our ponderous machinery for agricultural education. The specialized, scientific, business-like operation has nothing to do with the size of a farm. The profits, prosperity and low costs of operation are determined by the program and the pattern, and the New Agriculture is not the enemy of the "family-sized" farm but on the contrary its greatest friend. As two outstanding examples, I have one friend who last year grossed $145,000 on 13 acres. He is a truck gardener and hothouse grower. I have another friend who grossed $44,000 on 160 acres but he did it by specialization and high production per acre. As a general farmer on the same acreage, even in a time of high prices, his gross could not have exceeded $8000, in addition to long workdays and man-hours spent in running about doing a dozen different things with indifferent skill and efficiency.

This revolutionary change in American agriculture, away from the frontier to the highly complicated age in which we live, a change which has been going on unnoticed for the past generation or less, is one of the factors, perhaps the key one, in a modern, successful and profitable agriculture; yet our ponderous educational system has largely failed to bring this fact to the consciousness of the average American farmer. The pattern of the New Agriculture — imposed upon the face of the nation — could vastly reduce the necessity for subsidies, parities, floor prices and other semi-political dodgings of the issue, permit agriculture to stand squarely upon its own feet, reduce taxes and living costs and greatly increase the farmer's income.

One factor which the writer finds peculiarly stupid and irritating is the condescension toward the farmer practiced throughout many of the bureaus and agencies both of the federal and the state governments. It is based, I think, upon the assumption that the average farmer, because he sometimes lacks education, is therefore stupid and incapable of comprehending the simplest scientific fact.

There are many elements in our past agricultural history which tend to lead the educational forces generally into this error. Some of them are bald facts, rarely discussed even by the historian and never by the politician. Among them is the fact that the early pioneers were by no means all splendid, heroic, courageous and intelligent characters as we are led to believe by most history books and romantic novels. Among them, perhaps in the majority, was a large percentage of the shiftless populations of the East, unable to hold their own or stand upon their own feet in the more severe competition of already heavily settled areas. Many of them were bankrupt and a few were actually running from the sheriff. Some were merely adventurers who created nothing in the new world to which they migrated but merely lived off the community.

The race of pioneers was by no means made up solely of the cream of the Atlantic seaboard communities and, indeed, as the country further and further west was opened up, the quality of the pioneer actually declined. Much of the lawlessness of the West arose wholly from the character of the emigrants. Largely speaking, the descendants of this element found themselves on the land and in many cases upon poor land which they had not the initiative and the energy to leave. Even today it is this element, isolated upon marginal or wholly non-agricultural land and in certain pockets and backwaters, which is not only our greatest agricultural problem but our greatest sociological one as well.

The failure and the gradual disintegration of this element and their descendants in intelligence, in character, in initiative and even in genes is compounded of many things — of originally inferior stock, of poor nutrition, or miserably low living standards, of exploitation at the hands of absentee landowners. Their cure, economically or sociologically, is not an easy task nor can it be accomplished rapidly, and it will not be accomplished by the crocodile tears of the "liberal" and the sentimentalist but only by better nutrition, better farming methods, better income and in some cases by wholesale migration off the marginal land upon which their ancestors, for one reason or another, unwisely chose to settle.

By no means were all the original pioneers of this category, and, inevitably, as history has proven again and again, the cream rose to the top in the opening-up and gradual development of the vast new areas of the nation. Fortunately the shiftless and lawless elements were eventually subdued, sometimes by the costly system of vigilante committees, and the nation grew and education and civilization advanced. But by the middle of the nineteenth century a new deteriorating process began in agricultural areas which continued steadily until very recently.

It was a process closely allied to the vast industrial and metropolitan development which took place from the early nineteenth century onward. Put very simply, it was no more than the slow but insistent draining away of the best stock from the farms into the great cities where opportunities for educational and material advancement were much greater. It was a simple and an understandable process in which, in most rural areas, the more intelligent, the more energetic, the more creative drifted away generation after generation from the farm into the city leaving behind the less vigorous, gifted and talented to carry on the agriculture of the nation. It was not only that this general migration was disastrous in the immediate sense; it was also cumulative, for those left behind provided, generation after generation, an agricultural population gradually but persistently declining in the qualities of energy, intelligence and ability.

Very simply it worked thus — that in a family of five children, the four most able ones migrated to the city to make their fortunes, to become presidents of banks and railroads. These left behind the fifth and least energetic and clever member of the family to marry in turn a boy or a girl who alike had been left behind. In turn, they had, let us say, five children of which the four most able in turn migrated to the city, leaving behind the least able one who in turn married the residual fifth of some other family.

This process has been going on over most of the United States for five to six generations or more, and one has only to glance through Who's Who to discover that the vast majority of our leaders in all fields have not come from the cities but were the brightest members of farm families who migrated into the cities. It is, of course, a process which has been costly to American agriculture and one which no livestock breeder would dream of following in his breeding program.

The most tragic element is that this migration of the best stock away from the farm was almost in inverse ratio to the soil fertility of given areas and to the standard of living. The poorer the area, the more complete was the migration of the better element of the stock. On better soils where living was easier, the income greater and the possibility of making a good living more favorable, much of the better stock remained. Also, tragically, the need for energetic and intelligent farmers was and is greatest in the areas least favored in terms of productive and good soils. A bad or stupid farmer can survive and prosper longer on forty-foot-deep alluvial soil in the Mississippi Delta or in the black soil belts of Texas and Iowa than on the thinner, less well-balanced soils of other parts of the country. Frequently his longer prosperity does not mean that he was or is a better farmer but merely that he had better luck in the area upon which his ancestors chose to settle.

All of these elements tended to produce, together with lack of transportation and communication, the typical "hick" type which was the butt of so many jokes in stage, vaudeville and movie theater until very recently. It is significant that in the talking picture of today the "hick" type is rarely seen save as the dreadful example of a reactionary created by a bad agriculture. The usual farmer of today in the contemporary movie, and especially the young farm boy or girl is intelligent, healthy, active and smarter than his puny, neurotic, city contemporaries. This is a great step forward and it leads to the speculation that perhaps, from now on out, under a good agriculture, the four cleverest, most energetic children of a family will stay on the land practicing the New Agriculture while the "dumbest" goes to the city to become a bank or public-utility-company president. There is even much evidence on both sides to indicate that this process is already under way.

Unfortunately this conception of the farmer as a "hick" was not confined to the theater in all its manifestations but apparently prevailed with the general public and to a surprising extent within the higher circles of our agricultural education. I would qualify the term "higher education" by defining it as the circles in which there are the most college degrees.

It is one of the failures of our fundamental American philosophy that we confuse education and intelligence as much as we confuse plumbing and civilization. One ounce of intelligence is worth a pound of education, for where there is intelligence, education will advance and follow on its own, but where education alone exists, the results can be terrifying beyond even the realms of untutored stupidity. Too many of our Phi Beta Kappas turn out to be postmen or clerks or find at middle-age resources largely confined to the comics and the pinball machines. It is the element in our agricultural educational machine which is educated without being intelligent which has taken the attitude of condescension toward the farmer, best represented by the patronizing pat on the shoulder while giving "good advice" by telling the farmer to do something because it will be good for him rather than telling how and why a certain process or practice works, stimulating his imagination and "sparking" his interest and curiosity so that he will take care of himself from there on out.

Most of our bulletins, most of the speeches made to farmers by government agents are concerned simply with giving him advice without making the least concession to his intelligence or capacity for understanding scientific facts. In the writer's own wide experience among average farmers, he has acquired the greatest respect for their intelligence, understanding and actual hunger to be "sparked." Certainly among the top-notch farmers he has found an intelligence, a curiosity, a capacity for observation and deduction, and even for scientific reasoning far above those of many a professor with a whole string of letters behind his name. Very often the farmer shows a lack of interest in a speech or a pamphlet or a lack of response to them because he already knows the information being presented to him in a childishly simple way or because the presentation is simply so damned dull. Nothing is worse than the "ready-made" speech, so common in this era of bureaucracy, which is prepared for the "important" speaker by some anonymous underling, and which the speaker has never seen until he rises to read it in a dull and uninterested voice. And nothing is more insulting to the intelligence of an audience. But it is what we get in greater and greater doses out of Washington and even from many of our college deans and presidents.

All too often the farmer is told to lime his soil without being told the faintest thing about what the effects of liming are beyond the fact that if he limes he can raise legumes. He is not told of its effect upon the ionization processes related to iron and aluminum or the wonderful catalytic properties of limestone. He is considered too stupid and uneducated to understand about trace elements, even if the speaker or pamphlet writer has himself ever heard of such things. He is treated, all too often, as if his only function was to take the advice given him without question and simply go ahead gratefully and do as he is told.

To be sure, the exceptional farmer, the bright boy or girl, the inherently good farmer, can get all the information they want and nothing will keep them from getting it. The bureaus, the divisions, the colleges all supply information, and the average agricultural magazine does an excellent job in true teaching, not simply in advising the farmer, but explaining to him the processes which take place and the reasons for the advice. In theory, there is no reason today why a bad or an unprosperous farmer should exist anywhere in the United States. Information is available on every side, most of it sound and much of it fairly up-to-date, but all too often the farmer has to go and hunt for it, and not all farmers are exceptional and not all farm boys and girls are brilliant. The average farmer is average, and as my grandfather observed, "The average ones are the ones who are important, because there are so many of them." They cannot always go and get it, sometimes because they are too busy, sometimes because they become bewildered by the overspecialization which they encounter at experiment stations and colleges, sometimes because, in fairly remote areas, the facilities are simply not at hand. Sometimes a good farm program or sound agricultural methods have to be sold and there are not enough real salesmen, or the county agent, whose job the selling is, has become swamped by red tape and forms to be filled out.

As one of the countless farmers who visit Malabar put it, "We like to visit successful farms. If we go to the college experiment station we have to go separately to the agronomist, the sheep or cattle or dairy or poultry man, the fertilizer man or a half dozen other specialists to get what we want to know. Sometimes it would take us a week or more and we haven't got the time. Nobody puts it into a working pattern for us. And an experiment plot is not the same as a farm. What works on a prepared plot does not work in a field with two or three kinds of soil. At a successful, well-managed farm we can get an immense amount of information and a lot of good ideas in just a few hours."

His remark implies no derogation of the experiment stations which were set up originally to do research and in most cases do an excellent job. Somewhere along the line there is a missing element in our education and I suspect it is the pilot farm, operated by a legitimate farmer himself in terms of the average farm, under the advice which he gets from colleges and in co-operation with them, where visiting farmers may come and go over the place field by field and animal by animal, knowing that the whole place is not operated on taxpayers' money but profitably on the farmer's own income and capital. It would be a place where he could rub shoulders with the same concrete problems he faces at home, a place where he could examine the texture of the soil and the health and vigor of the livestock and look over the fence and know he is seeing a productive and profitable field and that he can find out how it was made that way. We should remember that every farmer believes what he sees. It might be that a state college should call for volunteers among the good farmers of each county and let it be known that the volunteers were working with the college and getting all the answers and reasons and not merely being told to do this or that.

Perhaps the best solution of all would be a great Foundation, privately endowed, which would not concern itself with research but with collecting and co-ordinating all the information and the results of research which all too frequently become lost or duplicated over and over again at a great waste of energy, time and money, because there is no central agency to co-ordinate them and fit them into a pattern. It would be a center for the creation and dissemination of readable and entertaining booklets and for the distribution of the almost endless supply of good films, some of them made by the government and some by foundations and industrial corporations, which today are all too rarely seen by farmers and least of all by the farmers who need them most. It could well be established somewhere in the Great Mississippi Basin as a center where two or three farms were in actual profitable operation on different programs and where the farmer could come to find out all about the latest machinery. And possibly it could set up a series of regional pilot farms in different areas, supported not by taxpayers' money but operating independently and profitably, and these in turn could become smaller centers of information and education. It would be a national center for the dissemination of agricultural information and possibly one day even an international center for a world in desperate need of just such an institution. It should be a clearing house for all agricultural and economic knowledge and maintain a close, intimate and respectful contact with the farms of the nation, and it should recognize and establish recognition of agriculture as what it is — not merely a way of making a living or even a "way of life" but one of the most difficult, dignified and honored of professions. We shall never get such an attitude or accomplish wholly the great things which need to be accomplished from or by government institutions alone because of the many reasons set forth earlier in this chapter. The synthesis of all that is best can only be accomplished through a well-endowed, well-staffed and comprehensive Foundation, independent of academic restraints and prejudices, politics of every kind and free, above all, of the paralysis of bureaucracy and red tape which gets between the farmer and what he wants to learn.

Certainly such a Foundation, devoted to the welfare of all mankind, would be the greatest monument any rich man could leave behind him. It would be a monument that would carry his name down the ages.

Much of this chapter has been rude and even brutal, and undoubtedly the writer has stepped on as many toes as an elephant at a church supper, but he believes that much, at least, of what he has written is with few qualifications true and has long needed saying. The chapter was born out of a single remark which the writer has heard repeated dozens of times from the thousands of farmers who come to Malabar and remain talking and talking after a long day until the milking is done, the cows are turned out and the moon comes up over the lower pasture. When at last they turn to leave they ask, time after time, a simple but extraordinary question. It is: "Why didn't anyone tell us any of this?" They do not mean: "Why didn't anyone tell us to lime?" or "Why didn't anyone tell us the value of green or barnyard manure?" They have been told all that time and again. What they mean is: "Why didn't anyone tell us what goes on in the soil and what it means to our livestock and ourselves?" They really mean: "Why didn't anyone tell us how fascinating is this profession in which we find ourselves?" They are simply hungry for the spark which they are not getting. That spark, my friends, is the essence of good teaching. It is an essence of which we have, for all our $3,000,000,000 in expenditure on agricultural aid and education, far too little.

6

The Pond

From *The World We Live In*, 1944

*"There are few writers with Louis Bromfield's gift of story-telling,"
begins the promotional copy on the dust jacket of* The World We Live
In. *"His is a master hand whether it writes of the Cote d'Azur at its
height or of the Ohio farmlands near his present home. Now for the
first time in five years he has gathered together a volume of his
stories -- stories that are supremely diverting, penetrating in
character, deft in plot and varied in background.*

*"Six of the nine stories ... move around the subject of this war...
This is a rich volume that will satisfy every taste. It is evidence of
the breadth of Bromfield's imagination and of his scope as a fiction
writer. When his last book of short stories was published one critic
said of the author, 'as a teller of tales he has the golden, God-given
facility which can hold a reader mesmerized.'"*

It was a still night with the stars very brilliant overhead. You could
see them shining through the fronds of the tall slender betel palms
like diamonds set in filigree against the dark velvet of the tropical
sky. The two boys, one stripped to the waist, the other clad only in
a pair of bathing trunks, sat leaning against the trunks of two of the
palm trees. One of them was fair. He looked a little like a Swede,
young, tall, good-looking and fresh with rather large features. The
other boy was small and dark, tough and wiry. The tall blond boy
was the one who wore the bathing trunks.

In the tents under the coconut palms behind them someone was
playing a banjo. In the stillness of the night the only other sound
came from the lazy beating of the surf on the beach a little way off.
The air was hot but here on the knoll beneath the betel palms there
was a breeze which kept off the mosquitoes.

Sometimes the two boys talked and sometimes they merely sat
there, relaxed and silent. They were both fighter pilots on rest and

the stillness of the night was like a sedative. Every now and then the boy in the bathing trunks would go down to the edge of the Pacific, throw himself headlong into the warm water and swim lazily for a while and then in a circle return to the white beach.

They both knew what it was like to be close to death but they were young and much of their talk was very young. And now in the stillness of the night they had time to think lazily and they were homesick.

"Funny," said the dark boy, "I never dreamed when I was growing up that some day I'd be way out here in the middle of the Pacific Ocean. I used to go down on Saturdays to Long Beach and go swimming and kind of wonder how far it was to the other side but that's about as far as it went."

"What were you going to do when you grew up?" asked the blond boy.

The other boy laughed, "I never thought anything about it. I was just going to work in my father's garage when I grew up and some day inherit it ... and that was about all."

"It must have been swell to have the ocean so near when you were a kid."

"I never thought anything about it. It was just always there, about half an hour from the house. Sometimes when it was foggy in winter we wished we lived a little farther away."

Then they fell silent again and presently without saying anything the tall blond boy rose and went down to throw himself into the water and swim for a time. The other boy lay supporting his head on one arm, vaguely conscious of the beauty of the spectacle. The water was full of phosphorescence and when his companion threw himself into it, it was as if he had thrown himself into fire. The splash was like flame, every drop of water sparkling and glowing like a jewel. And then as the blond boy swam lazily he seemed illumined by light. At each thrust of his arm the water sparkled and shone and at last as he came close to the beach, stood up and walked out of the water, his whole body was outlined in phosphorescence. He was lean with lithe muscles and strong arms and broad shoulders.

The dark boy thought suddenly, "That's the way a fellow must look arriving at the Gates of Heaven." And then quickly, half-ashamed, and half-frightened he put the thought out of his mind. It was a crazy thought. It was one of those thoughts which was taboo. It might bring Tom bad luck. It was funny what this island country and the life did to you, making you think crazy things you'd never think of back in Long Beach.

His companion rejoined him, sitting again to lean against the trunk of the betel palm. He shook the phosphorescent water from his fingers, took a cigarette from the package on the ground beside him and lighted it, leaning back lazily and tilting his blond head to inhale and savor the goodness of the cigarette.

The dark boy, whose name was Jimmy, said, "You never get enough of that water, do you?"

"No," said Tom. "You see, I was born and brought up in Dakota. I never saw the ocean until a year ago."

"Funny," said Jimmy, "about the kids from the Middle West. Porky was tellin' me the other night that about three-fourths of the guys in the Navy come out of the Middle West — kids that never saw the ocean in their lives until they joined up."

Tom stirred and looked out toward the beach where the water rolled up slowly, flickering, iridescent and glowing in the darkness.

"It's a funny thing," he said, "if I ever crash I want to crash in the water and not on land. When I'm over land I'm always kind of uneasy and queer, but when I get out over the ocean everything's okay and I feel fine."

The banjo went on tinkling in some distant tent and after a little while Tom continued, "All the water I ever saw until I was fifteen years old was a pond on the farm. It wasn't much of a pond — just a couple of acres and sometimes in hot weather it very nearly dried up ... wasn't much more than a mud puddle." He laughed suddenly, "But it was the only water for miles around. The country's kind of flat up there, no trees to speak of ... it just stretches away as far as you can see. It's kind of lonely. A pond like that made a lot of difference. When I was a little kid it was like a whole ocean to me. I used to wade in it and sail boats on it. When I began to learn geography I used to pretend it was the Atlantic — one side was America and one side Europe. I used to pretend the boats were ocean liners. When I got a little older I saw an advertisement in a Chicago newspaper saying to send for information about trips to Europe. I wrote and sent for it and they sent me back a lot of pictures of ocean liners — inside and out. They were wonderful and after that I built little boats that looked like ocean liners."

He was talking suddenly as if he were alone and talking to himself.

"In spring and fall the wild ducks and geese used to stop there sometimes. It was way off their course and I don't know why they came except that when the first ones came my mother used to take wheat and corn out to them. She always had to slip out and do it at night because my father didn't want to see good feed wasted on wild birds. She'd take it to the far end of the pond where it was hidden by the cat-o'-nine-tails and the hazel bushes. The birds would eat it up early in the morning and my father never found out. And so they got to stopping at the pond on the way north and south."

The dark boy yawned and said, "Yeah, it's funny the things you think about when you get homesick. I always think about my old man and the garage."

The blond boy lighted another cigarette. "I think about my mother and my wife ... and the pond."

"I ain't married. I never had a real girl friend. I used to run around a lot but I didn't go steady."

They were talking suddenly like old experienced men.

The sound of the banjo died away with the final whirring vibration of a string, and there was only the velvety black silence and the sound of insects and the lazy lapping of the surf.

"What's your wife like?" asked Jimmy in a sleepy voice. You could tell he wasn't really very interested. He was half-asleep.

"She's not very big and kind of shy. I've known her ever since I was a kid. Her folks have a big farm about ten miles from us. It's a nice place but it hasn't got a pond. When she was a kid, she was always beggin' to come over to our place to see the pond."

Jimmy didn't say anything and after a long time Tom said, "My wife's going to have a baby."

"When?"

"Any time now."

"It must make you kind of nervous."

Tom laughed, "It seems kind of funny ... havin' a kid of my own. It don't seem true."

Again the silence intervened and Jimmy said, "I suppose you want a boy."

Tom laughed again, "I don't really care much. I'd kind of like a boy to begin with. I'd like to think of him growin' up there and playin' around the pond like I did when I was a kid."

Jimmy stood up, yawned and stretched and said, "I'm goin' to turn in."

"Okay. I'm goin' to have another swim."

Sleepily Jimmy asked, "Don't you ever get enough of that ocean?"

Tom only laughed and Jimmy walking off toward the tents said, "Don't let the sharks get you."

But Tom was already running down the slope to the sea. He called out, "I'm not scared of sharks or anything in this whole damned ocean."

Jimmy turned to watch Tom's entry into the water in a ring of light. He stood there watching, a little bewildered again by the beauty of the sight. He found himself thinking, "It's like a sea god returning to the sea." And then he turned away and went slowly back to camp thinking, "I must be going nuts — thinking screwy things like that. It's these damned Pacific islands. I'd better get back to the garage in Long Beach before I really go nuts."

Three times Tom made the lazy circle in the warm phosphorescent water and when he came out he stood there on the white beach looking across the channel toward the dark mass of the island opposite. There was no moon but in the brilliance of the night, there was enough starlight to silhouette the rims of the palm fronds. As he stood with his feet planted in the warm sand he was aware of a faint sense of ecstasy, as if he were no longer himself, an individual, a man standing there on the white beach but only an atom, an infinitesimal particle belonging to this whole universe of palm trees and white sand and space and stars and phosphorescent water, an atom forever immortal and indestructible because he was part of something far greater than himself.

And then quickly the sensation passed and he was himself again — a man, strong and young, who might even now be the father of a baby who would live and grow and become a part of this same universe and go on long after he himself was dead. The fact of death was always there, quite near at hand, but now it seems to have no great significance, being lost in this greater thing. He felt a sudden desire to weep, not out of any personal sorrow, but out of a sadness that was vast and incomprehensible — the sadness of the whole human race.

A great coconut crab crawled across his foot, rousing him with a start. He did not attempt to kill it or even to touch it. He only stood there watching it waddle ridiculously up the bank toward the knoll where he and Jimmy had been sitting. There was something clumsy and comical and important in its queer gait, something out of a world which had existed before there was any man on earth. He found himself smiling in the darkness.

Then slowly he shook himself and walked up the knoll and back to the tents. They were silent now and dark for all the other boys were asleep.

He did not fall asleep at once for he could not shake off the excitement of the moment on the white beach and he was tormented by homesickness. Lying there in the darkness, beneath the mosquito netting, he kept seeing again the pond and his mother and Sally. But he saw the two women always in relation to the pond. They were standing beside it feeding the ducks which swam there or Sally was cutting the wild iris that grew on the edge of the pond, or they were watching the wild ducks which came to join and feed with their tame cousins. And sometimes he saw Sally and himself as children playing on the shallow, muddy edges of the pond, pushing out their small boats, building little harbors and ports where the tiny boats might tie up. It was a whole ocean -- that muddy little pond — a whole universe over which he and Sally were God and Goddess. And he thought how much the pond had been a part of his life and Sally's, how they had grown up there beside it taking each other quite for granted until one day his body told him what love was and how different it was from friendship. Vaguely the pond seemed to have a part in that too. It was beside the pond he had first touched Sally's hand in a new way. It was beside the pond he had first kissed her, knowing that they belonged to each other as simply as the birds on the pond belonged to each other. It was beside the pond that he had said, "I'm going to air cadet school. Maybe we'd better be married before I go away."

He could not say what made him say it just that way, why he'd asked her to marry him when he was going away almost at once to leave her alone. Something more powerful than himself, something more powerful even than his conscious love for her. It was something that had to do with that strange sensation he had experienced a little while before on the beach, a sense of being only an infinitesimal part of something vast and splendorous which had to be carried on. There had been a kind of fierce urgency about it, and a sense of time running short. Perhaps that was the reason so many young people were getting married all over America, why so many young people were having babies when in ordinary times they didn't get married and if they did, they didn't have babies right away.

And he thought about a lot of other things too, among them the conversation he had had with Jimmy as they sat there against the betel palms on the edge of the sea. He didn't think about what they had said but what they had not said, pondering what it was that shut men off from each other so that they could not reveal what lay deepest in their hearts. What had happened to him just now there on the edge of the phosphorescent water, for example — that he would never be able to tell anyone, and never would he be able to tell anyone really how he felt about the pond, how much he loved it, how much it was a part of himself, how much it had to do with his life, as if he himself had been born out of its very depths.

While he and Jimmy talked there in the darkness the communication had been through halting, inadequate words. Jimmy was a tough little guy, but for all that or because of it, much shyer than himself. Jimmy had talked about Long Beach and the garage and his father but he hadn't really said anything at all. The things that were important were the things they had not said, but felt there in the darkness — that it was good to be young, that it was wonderful to fly, that being in love was wonderful even for a Don Juan like Jimmy, that both of them were thinking it would be wonderful to have their girls there with them, there in the warm starlit darkness — he, his own Sally, Jimmy just any pretty warm-blooded girl.

And he wondered whether men who weren't fighting ever had these feelings without being able to communicate them. Perhaps back home in the daily round of civilian life there wasn't time to think or feel things like these, or perhaps all feelings and emotions were blunted by the daily round of monotonous living. Maybe it all had something to do with flying, with fighting, with being near death. He knew that he was too young to know how it would have been to marry in the monotonous times of peace, to have a wife you loved who was going to have a baby, your baby, in the next room instead of far away from you on the other side of the world.

Maybe it was good — all this he was going through now. Maybe he was lucky to be young and healthy and to be a flier. Maybe if you got through a thing like this you'd know things which other men didn't know — the stay-at-homes who weren't so lucky. What had happened in the last six months he knew suddenly and without doubt would make all the rest of his life richer and bigger.

Sleep wouldn't come and he went on thinking about the things he and Jimmy hadn't said to each other. Jimmy hadn't mentioned his mother at all. Maybe she'd died when he was a kid or maybe, worse than that, she left his father to run off with another man. Of course he hadn't spoken of his own father because there wasn't much he could tell Jimmy. He wouldn't say that his father was a hard man who squeezed every penny — a man who didn't seem to have much human feeling. He'd never understood about the pond or why his wife and his son loved it so deeply. He'd always talked about draining it and using the land to grow crops. No, there wasn't much he could say about his own father.

And presently the humming of the insects made him drowsy. He turned and quickly went to sleep.

T he pond had always been there, little more than a depression in the endlessly flat prairie, stretching away to the horizon — a depression where the water from the surrounding flatness collected. Before the appearance of the white man the buffalo had come there by the thousand to find water. Indians pitched their tepees beside it during the hunting season, and when the first covered wagons began the long trek across the continent they stopped there to camp and water their horses and cattle. None of them stayed there for they were bound further west, none of them until Abner Wade claimed four sections of land and built a sod house for himself and his family. It was good grazing land with deep soil that would raise wheat, acres and acres of wheat stretching away as far as one could see.

But it wasn't the richness of the land so much as the pond that led Abner to settle there. It was the only piece of water for two days travel in any direction and around it grew a little grove of big cottonwood trees. And all around the edge of the pond there was a little thicket of wild shrubs broken only by the ancient buffalo trails. It was like an oasis in the vast flat desert of buffalo grass.

Abner left the farm to his son who in turn left it to a daughter. The daughter married a Swede, a newcomer into the country, and the Swede was killed a little while afterward, leaving a son who became Tom Peterson's father. The sod house beside the pond became in time a two-room wooden house and at last the farm house where Tom was born and grew up and met Sally and married her. The good land still held out and raised good crops of wheat two years out of three. Tom's father was a good man with cattle and with wheat. He drilled wells and had no more need for the pond.

His wife, Tom's mother, didn't come from the wide, flat prairie country. Axel Peterson, Tom's father, found her at the Iowa State Fair when he went to buy cattle from her father. He was a good-looking, strong, straight-backed fellow of twenty-eight with cold blue eyes and a hard jaw and Annie Wallace, daughter of one of the best cattle breeders in the state, fell in love with him. A half dozen times he went south to court her and at last she married him and went to live in the house by the pond in the bleak, rich wheat country. The first year she bore him a daughter and a year later she had a son they named Thomas after her father and then the doctor told her she could never have any more children. When the little girl was four years old she died of diphtheria. And by that time Annie Wallace no longer loved her husband. By that time she discovered that she came fourth in his heart. His land, his cattle, his bank account all came before her. She knew by then that she had married a peasant very different from the stock she had come from with its comfortable way of life among the streams and rolling, wooded green hills of Iowa.

It was, she knew, a tragedy, but she was a strong woman and made the best of it. When she looked across the table at her husband she understood what had happened to him. The jaw had grown harder, the lips thinner. He was meager and wiry and the long hours he worked in the fields and barns had given him the wrinkled, weather-beaten look of a man ten years older. Being a strong woman, she understood that she was a disappointment to him. He had wanted a peasant for a wife, a big-buttocked woman who would bear him many sons and daughters and, drawn by her pretty face, he had married a woman who came of people whose women had never worked in the fields, a woman who bore him two children and then went barren. She knew what he would do with a Hereford cow who went barren after two calves: he would fatten her up and send her off to the market. Because he was a good Lutheran and a religious man he could not do that with his wife.

And so she tried to fill her life with church work and sewing and a garden, but it was a bleak life. Really all she had in it was the boy Tom and the pond. Tom was a tough little fellow, always tall for his age like his father. He looked like his father's Swedish ancestors but without the hardness in the jaw and mouth and eyes. He had a good hand with cattle and he worked hard in the hours out of school. Very early he had the feeling that he must somehow make up to his father for the brothers he would never have.

But it was the pond that made life endurable for Annie Wallace. She didn't belong in this bleak, flat, treeless country. At home there had been groves of trees and springs and streams and hills. In hill country one lived always with mystery and romance, for over each hill there was a new and unknown world. In this prairie country there was nothing, nothing as far as one could see, nothing to break the horrible monotony but the pond. Sometimes Annie thought but for the pond she would go mad. Beside the streams and lakes of her Iowa hill country, the muddy little pond wasn't much, really nothing at all, but in the interminable unbroken flatness it was a miracle. On moonlit nights its surface turned to silver with the cottonwoods surrounding it black against the vast dome of the sky. In June it was rimmed by the blue and yellow of wild iris. Thrushes and quail hid in the shrubs that bordered it, and in the spring and fall the wild birds came — the ducks, the geese, the herons and once a pair of wild swan.

When Tom was sixteen he went to Des Moines to school. She paid for his education out of her own money as well as for the services of an extra hired hand to replace him, since that was the only way his father would permit him to go. The father asked, "What education does a boy need beyond how to run a farm and know how to raise cattle, especially when he's going to have this farm some day?"

She knew that whatever it cost her she must save her son from being forced into the mold of his father.

When Tom went away to school, the pond became the center of Annie Wallace's whole existence. Sometimes she would sit in the grass, dreaming, very still, half-hidden in the bushes watching the wild birds for hours at a time. And then when she thought of her husband, she was filled with a sudden rush of pity that he was so hard and so narrow, that he knew and understood so little of the richness of life, that he never saw the beauty that lay in the sheen of a mallard's wing, in the lettuce green of the cottonwood leaves in spring or the warmth that came of a calf's nose nuzzling your hand. He had made all of his land and the animals that lived upon it no more than a factory.

When Tom was seventeen her husband first began to talk about draining the pond. It was, he said, good land going to waste. The cattle were watered from wells on the range, they didn't need it any longer.

When she heard him say it the first time she thought wildly, "If he drains the pond, I'll go away and never come back. I couldn't live without the pond."

But she pretended indifference for she knew that by now his resentment of her had turned at times into a cold hatred because she was so useless. She no longer went near the pond when he was in the house or the barn for fear that simply out of contempt for her and her feelings, he would drain it and stifle all the life that centered in it. She pretended always that she had lost interest in the pond. But secretly, when he did not know it, she still fed the birds and sometimes on hot nights she would leave the house and spend half the night there lying in the grass listening to the croaking of the frogs and the sounds made by the night birds.

The pond was somehow tied up with Tom and Sally. They had played there as children and slowly fallen in love by its side. Sally was a good girl. Annie knew that she couldn't have had a better daughter-in-law, nor one whom she could have known better. When Tom finally went away looking very straight and handsome in his flier's uniform, both she and Sally turned to the pond because it made his absence seem less painful. So long as the pond was there a part of Tom still remained. After Sally found out that she was having a baby they sat together beside it in the long still northern evenings. It meant almost as much to Sally as to herself. She knew that Sally came from her mother's home as much to see the pond as to see her mother-in-law.

And then a month before Sally's baby was expected the two of them went on a visit back to Annie Peterson's home down among the hills and streams and woods of Iowa. It was August and the wheat harvest was over and all that flat dusty country lay hot with an aching heat. It was hot in Iowa but the country was green and the woods and streams made everything different and more bearable. It was the first time Sally had ever seen that lovely, rolling, wooded country and it was like Paradise to her.

They stayed there for three weeks — longer than they had planned because Sally loved the Iowa country so much. They would have stayed and let Sally have the baby there save that her mother wanted so much to have the baby born at home. Annie Peterson didn't protest. Sally's mother deserved that much satisfaction. Back in the flat country she didn't even have a pond.

They had a letter from Tom every week or two, telling them not very much. He didn't write about what it was like to fly, or how he felt about shooting down Japs. He couldn't tell them where he was. But he did write about the islands and the sea, and a little about the life on a flat-top. He wrote mostly about the sea — what it was like close at hand when the great moving ship left a long trail of fire behind it in the dark waters, about the flying fishes that darted like arrows of silver through the green foam, how from high in the air it was blue and purple and green and around the coral reefs translucent like jade. And almost always he wrote about the pond. Sometimes it seemed ridiculous to them that with all that water around and under him, he should think of that poor little muddy pond there in the flat plains of Dakota.

And so when Annie Peterson thought they couldn't risk waiting any longer, they left Iowa for the Dakota farm. The long trip was hot and wearing and when they arrived at last at the little depot ten miles from the farm, there wasn't any pleasure in returning home. The country stretched away flat and brown as far as the eye could see, trembling a little drunkenly in the heat. Even the Ford which Sally's mother drove to the station was brown with the prairie dust. They climbed in and as Annie Peterson settled herself in the rear seat she thought, "Anyway, there'll be the pond. It'll be cool there tonight. I'll go out and sit by it and listen to the frogs and the birds."

Sally's mother drove slowly and carefully while Sally talked about her visit and how pretty it was down in Iowa. Sally's mother was a tired woman, from the outside world, beaten down by work and the monotony of life in the flat country. Looking at the back of her thin neck under the dusty black hat, Annie Peterson thought, "When Tom comes back, he'll have to take Sally away out of this country. It's too hard and lonely a life for any woman." Then she thought, "If they go I won't have anything left but the pond." But she was a strong woman. She was prepared to face that. In any case she was middle-aged now, getting old. She mustn't stand in the way of young people. Whatever was life in her was passing on through Tom into the baby that was being born soon. It was like a cycle, like the cycle of the life of the pond. There was order and rhythm in it.

The old car rattled slowly along through the dust, past the Heinrich place, past the Downings, past the Lausches. In a moment against the horizon she would be able to see the tall cottonwoods that grew beside the pond. They passed the Gertner place and turned at right angles along the section road. In a second now the feathery cottonwoods would come into view against the gray sky.

The second passed while the old Ford moved slowly along and Sally told her mother about the streams and hills. Then another second and another, but no trees appeared against the horizon. Annie Peterson leaned forward and then actually rubbed her eyes. She thought, "It must be that I need glasses. I've been afraid of that."

She looked again but still there were no trees. She started forward to interrupt Sally and ask her to look and then suddenly she checked herself, terrified, because she already knew what had happened.

Quietly she covered her face with her hands. The tears ran silently down the dry Dakota dust that coated her cheeks. Her face burned with shame for the moment Sally would stop talking and look for the trees which she had loved since she was a little girl, the trees she had begged to be taken to see as a child.

In a little while they turned in at the Petersons to drop off Annie Peterson.

The odd thing was that neither Sally nor her mother said anything about it. They acted as if the ancient trees had not been cut down, as if they did not see the scars in the brown soil where they had once stood nor the ugly gashes in the sunburnt grass where the caterpillar tractors had moved about their ruthless task. They never spoke of the baked mud where the lovely water of the pond had once been.

Annie Peterson got down and pulled her suitcase out of the car after her. The suitcase seemed filled with lead. Sally leaned down and kissed her. "If anything happens," she said, "I'll send Mama over to get you."

Still she did not say anything but her eyes were brimming with tears. Annie Peterson stumbled into the house. That night there was no sound of croaking frogs or night birds. In all the hot interminable flatness there was only an oppressive silence.

T om found it good to be back on the ship again. After a time the lazy life in the islands had become tiresome and the men had grown bored with each other. Back on the carrier, there was nothing but the sky overhead and the sea all around, that sea that was blue and purple and emerald and jade colored. On the carrier the wind blew all day and all night, smelling clean of salt and spray.

The carrier turned north among the reefs and atolls. With her went a whole fleet of ships, big and small, cruisers, destroyers, tenders. They moved northward, spread out on the blue sea, looking from high in the air like the fleets of little boats which Tom had once sailed on the pond. After two days a big bomber came out of the clouds from the south and dropped bags of mail on the big deck of the flat-top. A little while later Tom and Jimmy and the other boys stood waiting for letters from home.

There were two for Tom, one from his mother and one from Sally. The one from Sally he read first. It was a long letter, filled with the account of her trip to Iowa with his mother. She wrote of the trees and hills and green pastures. Toward the end she said that she was feeling well and that the doctor said there shouldn't be any trouble about the baby. There wasn't anything to worry about — absolutely nothing at all. As soon as it was born she would send him a radio. She missed him. She loved him. She wished he could be there to see the baby as soon as it was born. She said his mother was writing by the same mail. She enclosed a picture of herself and Annie Peterson standing in front of the big red brick house under the maple trees of Iowa where his mother had been born and had lived as a girl.

The letter from his mother wasn't very long and there was a kind of deadness about it, as if somehow each word had caused her a great effort. It was a tired letter; and slowly as he read it, he felt depression creeping over him. And then at the very end he found the reason. She wrote simply, "Your father drained the pond while I was in Iowa." And then, after her name she had added, "You must not worry about the pond. It makes less difference than I thought it would."

But he didn't believe the lie. He knew why she had written a tired letter. The last thing she had to hang on to was gone from her life. There was Sally and there would be the baby, and perhaps the baby would help take the place of the pond. Suddenly sitting there with the sea wind in his face he found himself praying. "Please Lord, don't let anything go wrong with the baby. They need it so badly — more than I need it. Please, Lord, let everything be all right." And then he thought, "The kid won't have any pond. He won't have any trees or birds or water or mud to play with. He won't have anything but that God-forsaken flat country!"

He felt a sudden wave of hatred for his father and then it seemed to go away, swept clear by the fresh salt air of the sea. It was growing dark and behind the flat-top the sea was becoming alive again with light. The crest of each wave sparkled with light.

Then suddenly Jimmy was standing there behind him. He said, "What's the matter? Not bad news, I hope?"

"No," said Tom, "nothing. I'm just kind of homesick."

"It's wonderful to get letters," said Jimmy, "if they only didn't make you think about home."

Tom thrust the letters into the pocket of his shirt and stood up.

Jimmy said, "Looks like we'd get some action tomorrow."

"How do you know?"

Jimmy grinned, "We didn't come all the way up here just for an airing."

It turned out that Jimmy was right. They got their briefing a little after noon the next day. Their job would be to protect the bombers in an assault on an island that lay a little way off, still too far for the range of the land-based fighters. Tom was glad of the prospect for action. The news about the pond had left him alternately depressed and furious. Late that night he had written an angry letter to his father and then tore it up, believing it would do no good and only perhaps make things worse for his mother. Instead he wrote a letter to his mother saying that when the war was over and he returned, he would take her and Sally and the baby back to Iowa, to the country she loved. That he knew would be the best thing he could promise her; that would give her hope. It would make it a little easier to go on living on that bare, treeless, plain.

That night he dreamed of the pond.

It was three o'clock when the attack began. The empty deck was filled suddenly with men hurrying here and there, with the roar of motors tuning up as the great ship turned round and headed into the wind. And then one by one the planes took off.

In Tom, standing there, waiting for his fighter to move up into line, the old excitement came burning back into his veins. He was one of those who were made for flying. Something happened to him, something queer and unearthly. From the moment the plane started into motion, he became a man no longer earthbound who entered upon another level of existence. It was the take-off and the landing which he loved best — that moment when returning out of vast heights, out of the clouds you once more came back to the ship. It was like being a god descending among men. Flying for him wasn't just a matter of gasoline and engines and steady nerves and quick reactions. He had the nerves and the reactions to make him a good flier but it was more than that. A first-rate flier became one with his plane so that nothing separated them until one or the other was wounded or failed.

It was different with Jimmy. He felt a plane the way he ran an earthbound automobile, skillfully at high speed, but in his heart and mind the machine was something he drove, always apart from it. When he climbed aboard it was like jumping into the old coked-up jalopy which he used to drive in races along the city block back in Long Beach.

Just now he was standing near Tom, his legs spread a little to balance himself against the gentle rocking of the big flat-top in the long ground swell of the Pacific. He was watching the curious expression on Tom's face and suddenly he shouted above the wind and the roaring of the motors. "What are you lookin' at?"

The rapt expression disappeared and Tom grinned. "Nothing," he shouted back, "just thinking."

Then Jimmy thought, "It must be the hick in him. Everything is always new and wonderful." Then he moved forward to his ship.

At the same moment across the deck came running a boy called Skippy. He was one of the radio operators. He'd worked in W.T.A.M. in Cleveland before the war. He carried a bit of paper in his hand and came running straight for Tom who didn't see him. Skippy had to come quite close and shout in his ear.

He handed Tom the paper and shouted, "She came through all right, Pappy! Thought you'd like to know!"

Then it was Tom's turn up and as he ran he read what was typed on the bit of paper. It was brief enough. It read: "Fine boy. Everybody okay. Love Sally."

He thrust the bit of paper into his pocket, climbed aboard and opened her up. She gained speed, reached the edge and leapt off into the air above the brilliant blue water, banking a little and climbing to reach her place in the formation.

Below on the deck Skippy the radio operator stood shielding his eyes against the sun as Tom's ship climbed toward it and disappeared into the brilliance of its light. Then he turned and said to the sailor standing next to him, "It was against the rules ... givin' him that message but Hell, goin' off like that and maybe never comin' back, I thought he'd like to know about the kid."

Higher and higher the plane climbed toward the sun until Tom found his place in the formation. Then he turned and over his shoulder watched the last few planes leaving the deck. It was a pretty sight — like the barn swallows coming out at dusk to dart over the pond, hunting insects. The big ship slowly churning the dark green water into a pale jade color grew smaller and smaller and more remote.

Then he heard a voice speaking to him: "This is Jimmy ... Jimmy. Not bad news, was it?"

He answered back, "No. Good news! It's a boy — everybody's fine."

Then he heard Jimmy relaying the news exuberantly to the others, and then the Commander's voice, "Congratulations, Peterson ... and now let's muffle all the gossip."

But Tom, high above the sea, alone in his plane, pulled out the bit of paper and read the message again. He couldn't quite believe it. He felt warm all over and then thought, "What's there to be proud about? You're not the only father in the world." And then suddenly he experienced a curious feeling of awe and fright. He was responsible for another life in the world ... he and Sally together. It kind of scared you.

High up now, all the air about him was filled with clouds, those great white, lazily drifting clouds that hung over the blue South Pacific night and day. Suddenly one by one the ships in the formation would plunge into the mist and be lost for a time as if they had gone out of this world into a white, still misty, eternity. And then suddenly, one by one, they would emerge again into the brilliant light of the sun.

Tom's heart and body were singing.

The target showed up after a little over an hour. It was a little cluster of islands grouped haphazardly about a bigger green island with a small bay on one side and the white streak of a runway made of broken coral rock. In the little bay there was a big ship and what looked like a destroyer and a lot of barges.

The orders began to come in out of the air. He was aware suddenly that the clouds about them seemed bigger and there were more of them. Then out of a cloud on the left appeared three Zeros. They darted at the bombers but two of the boys ahead, breaking formation, went after them and drove them off. Then suddenly Tom's turn came and he let her drop straight down, leveling off at just the angle to catch a Zero full in the middle with a burst of fire. The burst seemed to break the back of the Jap plane. It exploded in flames and then plummeted downward, falling in two smoking bits of debris.

After that it became a general dog-fight, the fighters darting and dodging like hawks while the bombers did their work. Now and then he had a sudden glimpse at a freakish angle of what was going on, like pictures in a kaleidoscope — the big ship burning, bombs falling on the long white runway going up in great flowers of flame and smoke, bombs falling among the barges and on the crescent of the white beach. And in the midst of all the fighting there was a lot of flak. Sometimes it came quite close and again it was far away.

And Tom, a part of the plane itself, kept wheeling and turning and diving and climbing. He was laughing with excitement and thinking now and then, "Tommy. Your pappy is up here in the clouds having a grand time." There was no sense of time. It was as if everything was happening at once. There were more planes and more flak than they had expected.

Then suddenly he was again on the tail of a Zero in the long darting swoop of a bank. It brought him in low over the island. The Zero swooped into a cloud and Tom followed. It was a big cloud and in it he lost the Zero. It seemed impossible to get out of it, out of the swirling, drifting veils of mist. The few minutes seemed like hours and then suddenly he was in the sunlight again directly over the island and there was a violent explosion close beside him which turned the plane over on its side and then another which came all at once with the shattering of the instrument panel in front of him. The plane started to slip and he pulled her back and then he realized that something was blinding him and wiping the back of his hand across his left eye he discovered that blood was running into his eyes. He knew too that the radio had gone dead and that something was wrong with the left wing of the plane. It wouldn't respond.

He thought, "It can't be very bad if I don't feel anything." And then, "Hell, I'd better get out of here. I'm in no shape to fight anything." He looked back over his shoulder and high above coming toward him there was another Zero. It was the Jap's turn now.

He acted quickly. Softly he said, "Come on, honey" and turned the ship toward the great cloud. He was nearer to it than the Zero but the Zero was coming at terrific speed. He couldn't turn and fight back now. That thick, white, soft, fleecy cloud was safety, life. The plane responded. He turned sharply. The Zero fired but the angle was wrong. It dropped close beside him, so near that his plane shuddered a little.

Then suddenly he was in the cloud.

It was thicker than the other clouds had been. He drove the plane straight forward, deeper and deeper into the white drifting mist. Crippled, his plane could not possibly hope to fight. There was only one course, to drive straight ahead until he was out of range of attack and then turn and limp back to the others or the carrier. And then he remembered suddenly — the instrument board was smashed and the radio dead. He could not talk to the others. He did not know his direction. He was alone.

After a time he veered a little to the left thinking he would swing round in a wide circle. The cloud thinned for a moment and he came out into the sunlight. Ahead of him only a little way loomed another great cloud painted rose by the light of the setting sun. He thought, "I am lost and the sun is going down." Down below there was nothing but water, dark now, almost lead-colored.

There was only one thing to do — drop down out of the cloud and hope to find one of his own squadron or a ship or an island. Quietly in a long slow dive he dropped out of the immense cloud into the gathering darkness.

Down below there was nothing but the sea as far as he could see — not a ship, not a plane, not a piece of land. He did not even know where he was. Only the sun, slipping down to the edge of the horizon, showed him where the west lay.

"We came out of the sun," he thought. "If I fly back into it I will be going in the right direction."

The blood no longer ran into his eyes. He was alone in the universe above the darkening sea. Ahead of him the red sun slipped lower and lower, quickly, as it does in the tropics. He thought quite calmly, "I must get back. I've got to get back somehow on account of the kid."

Below him the water grew first red and then purple and as the sun slipped below the horizon it was suddenly black and the stars came out overhead.

For a moment he had a strange sensation of being already dead — as if he and his plane had become no more than a spirit speeding toward the sun. Quickly he experienced again that strange feeling he had known for a moment on the beach, of being only a part of the universe, no more than a grain of the powdered coral beneath his feet.

Then he was aware that the motor was sputtering and thought, "The gas line must have been hit. The gas must have been leaking. She's running out of gas." And then quite calmly, "This is it! This is where I go over the line."

He wasn't afraid. He felt very calm and still and his head ached a little. The plane was dropping lower and lower, pitching forward a little. He thought, "Now I'll never take Ma and Sally and the baby away to Iowa." And he thought suddenly of the pond, seeing it very clearly as he had seen it as a boy with the tall cottonwoods breaking the dreariness of the flat plains, the water ruffled a little by the hot breeze of summer, glittering in the Dakota sun. And then he remembered that it was no longer there — that his father had drained it. He thought desperately, "The boy must have a pond! The boy and Ma must have it back again!"

Then the world crashed about him in utter blackness as his head struck the metal of the shattered instrument board.

In the dark sea beneath the stars there was an uprushing of water as if it sought to embrace the stricken plane and its pilot. Like flame the leaping water glittered and flared with phosphorescence, scattering tiny jewels over the surface of the sea. Then all was still again with only the stars overhead. And far off on the horizon a lonely new moon.

The baby was born a week after Annie Peterson and Sally returned from Iowa. Its coming made the disappearance of the pond a little less awful for Annie. In the days of waiting she never looked out of the windows on the side of the house where the pond had been, and in the hot nights when she could not sleep, there was no longer any place for her to go to listen to the rustle of leaves and the croaking of frogs and the sounds made by the night birds. Outside there was only stillness like the stillness of a dead, empty world.

For three days before the baby was born, Annie went every day to the house of Sally's mother, staying late so that when she came home it was too dark to see the place where the pond had been. In the hot sun, the mud had dried quickly and Peterson was already breaking it up to plant winter wheat.

The baby came early on a Thursday morning and the first thing Annie did was to drive into town to send a radio to Tom. The telegraph office hadn't even opened by the time she got there and she had to wait outside for nearly half an hour.

Impatiently she asked Olaf Jensen, the operator, how long it would take for the radio to reach Tom and he said he didn't know. It depended on where Tom was. Sometimes it took only a day or two and sometimes a week. They'd have to find out where Tom was.

Then Annie went to the drugstore and got a roll of films and when Sally felt well enough to sit up Annie took three pictures of the baby naked save for a diaper. He was a fat baby with a little blond fuzz on the top of his head and Sally said he looked like Tom and had Tom's blue eyes, and Annie, although she knew you couldn't tell what a baby looked like at that age or what color his eyes were going to be, agreed with her because she knew that was what Sally wanted. Each day they speculated a good deal as to when the radio message would reach Tom and what he would say in his reply.

The thing happened five days after the baby was born. It was a hot night and Annie Peterson wakened at the still hour of the morning when tired, old people die, conscious of the faint light from the new moon shining through the window across her bed. For a long time she lay there trying to go back to sleep, but her mind kept her awake, darting here and there to thoughts about Tom, far away in the South Pacific, to Sally and the baby and the baby's future and now and then to memories of the vanished pond. And presently when she grew drowsy again it seemed to her that she heard the sound of lapping water among reeds as she had heard it so many times before the pond had vanished.

Rousing herself she put the notion forcibly out of her head but she still kept hearing the sound despite everything. After a time she thought, "Maybe it's just something I dreamed. Maybe he didn't drain the pond. Maybe it was only a nightmare." But when she thought back, she connected it up with many things and how she had always come home from Sally's mother's house after dark so she wouldn't see the bare dry place where the pond had been. She knew, sadly, that it wasn't a dream but she still kept hearing the lapping of the water although it was a still night without the sign of a breeze.

When the experience became no longer bearable, she rose and in her nightdress walked the length of the house and looked out of the window on the other side where the pond had been.

And there in the moonlight was the pond like a burnished sheet of silver, just as it had been before save that the cottonwoods were gone and the bushes and the reeds. Slowly as if in a trance, Annie Peterson walked down the stairs, opened the door and barefooted crossed the burnt grass down to the edge of the pond. She was crying now and still she could not believe it. She did not believe it until she had walked into the water and stood there, still weeping hysterically, wet with cool water half-way to the waist. She thought, "How glad Tom will be! I must send him a radiogram." He would be almost as happy as he'd be about the baby.

The news of the miracle spread quickly over the county. The words "Peterson's pond is back" went from mouth to mouth and by nine o'clock people were driving from all over the countryside to look at it. The miracle was even greater than Annie Peterson had guessed, for this time the pond was a live pond. Somewhere in the bottom a spring had come to life. It wasn't any longer just a seepage hole. Living water had filled all the depression and was running over, making its own channel across Peterson's wheat ground into the ditch that bordered the long straight highway. There was running water in the county where before there had never been any water but Peterson's muddy pond surrounded by cottonwood trees.

Among the onlookers the speculations grew. Annie Peterson was among them telling over and over again of how she had wakened in the middle of the night to go out and find the pond. And Sally was there, who should still have been in bed, for Annie had hurried over at daylight to fetch her.

The county engineer said there must have been underground water there all the time and that Peterson's blasting of the cottonwood stumps had loosened the shale underneath so that the water worked its way upward. But most people thought that a fishy explanation which was the only one the county engineer could think up. A lot of people said, "Tom'll be glad to hear about this. He always liked that pond."

The whole crowd was filled with the kind of mystical awe and excitement which touches dry-country people at the sight of running water, for water is a source of life and ties all living things together. Only one man among them all was disgruntled and that was Peterson himself. The new spring had wasted all his good land and all the money he had spent clearing and draining the pond. He wouldn't try it again. It wasn't any good fighting a spring.

A week later came Tom's letter saying that when he returned he would take his mother and Sally and the baby away from that dry, flat country now that there wasn't any more pond. Reading it, Annie Peterson paused and looked up at Sally, saying, "He must know about the pond coming back by now. He must have got my radiogram by now. He's sure to know about it."

The baby was doing fine and Sally had come over to spend a week with her mother-in-law. They spent a lot of time making plans about the pond. You couldn't get back the cottonwoods. It had taken God a hundred years to make them. But you could plant other trees and shrubs and iris to replace the wild iris Peterson had killed so ruthlessly. They sent for nursery catalogues and marked the trees and shrubs they would buy in the spring to plant around the water. This time they'd plant a little grove where thirsty people from all the dry flat country around could come for picnics by the edge of the pond. They wanted it well started before Tom came back. Peterson couldn't stop them now. He could never drain the pond for God had taken a hand in the matter.

Henry Orr was the postman for their part of the county. He was an old man with a huge mustache and he was very slow in delivering the mail because he was a gossip as well as a postman and stopped to talk at every house along the way. There wasn't anything Henry didn't know about the county — when a cow died or a girl got into trouble or how Grandma Beattie's rheumatism was. He read postcards and had a power of divination concerning the contents of letters he never quite dared to open. And so he was the first to know that Tom Peterson was dead. He knew it as soon as he saw the envelope, and all along his route he hinted darkly that there was bad news for Annie and Sally Peterson.

It was noon by the time old Henry arrived at the Peterson Place and found Annie and Sally Peterson outside by the edge of the pond planting something, with the baby in the carriage by their side.

At sight of them old Henry lost his courage. As they called out, "Good morning" to him, he carefully rearranged the packet of mail. There was a letter from Iowa and two nursery catalogues and some advertising from a mail-order house. Carefully old Henry placed the awful envelope in the middle and retied the bundle, knotting it so that it would take them a long time to undo the string. That would give him time to get away, so he wouldn't have to see their faces.

Annie Peterson was coming toward him now and he got briskly down and went to meet her.

"A mighty fine morning," he said. "It's sure fine to have the pond back again. Always makes me feel good to see it."

Then he gave Annie Peterson the packet of mail and turned toward his battered car, hurrying but trying not to run. Once in the car he drove off as if the devil were after him.

By the edge of the pond the two women sat down again on the grass and Annie picked out the knots old Henry had tied so tightly. By the time she had it open, Henry's old car was far out of sight in a cloud of dust.

Almost at once Annie saw the envelope and almost at once she knew. She wanted to make the envelope vanish out of sight into thin air for Sally's sake, but Sally was watching, hoping there would be a letter from Tom. And Sally knew too.

Slowly, as if the slowness made it easier and more casual, she tore open the envelope and read what she knew she would read.

Neither she nor Sally said anything nor looked at each other. They simply sat there looking at the pond where the little waves of clear spring water danced and glittered and sparkled in the autumn sunlight.

And then Annie, as if unbelieving, looked at the bitter sheet of paper again, and presently a strange look of wonder came into her face. Her eyes seemed suddenly to shine and slowly she turned to Sally looking at her for the first time.

"Sally," she said in a quiet voice filled with awe, "it happened on September 16th ... that was the night of the new moon — the same night the pond came back."

7

Up Ferguson Way

From *The World We Live In*, 1944

"The Ferguson Place" began in 1817 as 640 acres of virgin Ohio land deeded to John Ferguson, a Scottish immigrant, by James Monroe, fifth president of the United States. It was, Louis Bromfield said, the worst -- "and the most beautiful" -- of the three farms that he joined together to form Malabar Farm. "It is a spot one turns to instinctively when all the world seems collapsing over one's head. You turn to it when fear and depression assail you. In the lofty wilderness and solitude of the Ferguson place one goes back to the beginning of time," Bromfield said in Pleasant Valley.

But this is not the story of "the Ferguson Place" and how the lonely, hilltop farm "was murdered by carelessness and bad farming and greed and ignorance" before it became part of Malabar.

This is the story of going "Up Ferguson Way," which, Bromfield explains, means "going out of this world for a time" to someplace romantic, strange and even mystical. It is a place where all children but only a select few adults can actually talk to and understand the animals of the forest and farm, be at one with creation and taste immortality.

T wice before in my life I have written stories about Zenobia, once more than twenty years ago and again a few years later. Both times I was forced to give her a different name from her own for she lived to a prodigious age and was still alive. Once I called her Zenobia White and once Zenobia Van Essen and both times I invented certain details to disguise her as much as possible — something of course which could not be done because there was never anyone I knew or heard of who was quite like her. Both times I invented the end of her life and both times I was wrong.

The first time, being a young writer and still romantic, I gave her a dramatic death. The second time a commonplace one. The whole point of what I am going to tell you is that while they found a body in Zenobia's cottage and buried it, she never really died at all.

The longer I live the more I am inclined to believe in forces which we do not understand, which compel our destinies along other courses from those we have carefully planned. I can't help believing too that these same forces entangle our lives with those of others, although they may be strangers or persons only encountered casually two or three times in all our lives. Something like that happened with Zenobia's life and mine. I never knew her very well for she was already an old woman when I was born and I saw her only casually in my youth, but in a life spent largely wandering about the earth in meeting thousands of people of every race, nationality and creed I never met one who left upon me so profound an impression. She compelled me to write of her at least twice and still, even after they buried her, she compels me to write of her again. And I have the impression that the story of our vague but strong relationship is not yet finished. I am aware of her presence every time I go "up Ferguson way." You see her real name was neither White nor Van Essen but Ferguson — Zenobia Ferguson, a rich, pretty name.

The first time I saw her I could not have been more than seven or eight years old. My father, a Democrat and somewhat of a politician in his small way, used at election time to drive out over the country visiting farm and village people, seeking the assurance of their votes, either for himself or for some fellow Democrat. He rode in an old-fashioned buggy, driving a team, and very often he would take me with him for company. For a small boy it was always an exciting adventure. We visited very nearly every farm in every township, driving up remote narrow lanes that led from the rich valley farms into the hills.

My father was a pleasant man. Nearly everybody loved him and called him Tom and when noon came or darkness fell we were always invited to sit down for noonday dinner or to spend the night. Going about with him I came to know every farmer and every lane in the whole county, a beautiful county I never forgot in all the years I spent away from it. Irresistibly I found myself comparing other landscapes to it and never for myself did I find a more satisfying one.

It was a country of rich, flat valleys between wild wooded hills with springs and streams everywhere. You could leave a rich valley and driving up a narrow wooded lane leave civilization behind you and climb into a wilderness of tangled ferns and trees, wild grapes and dogwood. Sometimes after climbing for a time through forest you would come upon a kind of small rolling plateau where there was a lonely hill farm with the house built beside a spring. It was the kind of country where over each hill a new and romantic world appears, different from the country you had left behind. That kind of country makes romantic people. Flat country makes dull, prosaic and material ones. Zenobia lived all her life in one of those lonely farmhouses. If she had lived in flat country her story would have been different. People would never have referred to her lonely farm as "up Ferguson way" as if there were something high and strange and mystical about it.

She was a kind of vague relation of my father's and mine because her grandfather and my father's great-grandfather were brothers. Her ancestor had married an Indian woman of the Delaware tribe who on the frontier at that period was known as a Princess because she was the daughter of a Chief. Despite the remoteness of the relationship she called my father "Cousin Tom" and because it pleased her he called her "Cousin Zenobia."

On the first day I ever saw her the weather was bright and the air clean and brilliant with that peculiar brilliance which comes to our country in the month of October. My father and I had risen while the frost was still on the fields of the valley and all morning we had followed the valley road stopping to talk with farmers, sometimes taking a hand at husking corn or ringing pigs or driving cattle while we talked. A little before noon we reached Ed Berry's place and he invited us to stay to dinner but my father said, "No, thanks just the same, Ed. I want to drop in on Zenobia and get down into the other valley before noon."

At the mention of Zenobia, Ed's face relaxed into that peculiar special smile which came over the faces of people when they spoke her name or thought of her. It was a smile in which humor and affection and pity and patronage were all blended, the kind of a smile people have for a beguiling child. Yet it was more than that — an indescribable smile, reserved for Zenobia alone by the people of the county.

Ed said, "So you're going up Ferguson way?" And there was something in his voice that even as a child I recognized as special and different. It was as if he had said, "So you're going out of this world for a time?"

Then he added, "Give Zenobia my best. Tell her we'll be up to get her corn out before Thanksgiving."

It was then the middle of October with Thanksgiving more than a month away. It was odd that Ed didn't count on seeing her in the meanwhile when he lived only a couple of miles away.

We said good-bye and my father spoke to the horses and turned from Ed's lane to the old township road which led from the valley through the forest "up Ferguson way."

Even at that time the road really led nowhere except to Zenobia's place. It was an awful road, full of holes with ridges of red sandstone cropping out of the dark soil here and there. A little way from Ed's farm the road led into the forest up and up winding its way through the thickly growing trees. It was in the days before caterpillar tractors existed and the country was so wild and rough that even if one cut the trees, there was no practical way of getting them out and so much of the forest was virgin, the same forest which had existed there since glacial times. The oaks and beeches and maples rose straight up like Greek columns to a height of a hundred feet or more and underneath them grew a jungle of dogwood and iron wood and wild grapes and ferns and snakeroot. Along the sides of the steep rough road springs gushed out of the sandstone among clusters of maidenhair fern. There was a peculiar almost tropical luxuriance about the forest bordering the road that led "up Ferguson way" and there still is today.

For nearly half-an-hour the horses struggled up through the tunnel of trees and vines and then we came suddenly into the open in a high pasture with a broken gate. The blue grass was still green with the autumn rains and all along the fence rows the sassafras and sumach were flaunting their brilliant autumn foliage against the bright blue October sky. The road had become little more than a trail.

We drove on and presently we came out upon the bald top of a very high hill. It was as if we had reached the top of the world. Above us there was nothing but the clear October sky and below lay valley after valley, big and small, all bordered and intersected by forests of beech and oak and maple which had turned red and gold and purple. Far below in the checkerboard of the valley lay golden squares of shocked corn bordered by other squares green with the brilliant emerald green of winter rye and wheat. In the distance the whole faded imperceptibly into the blue autumn mist of infinity.

My father pulled up the horses and said, "Take a good look, son. You'll never see anything more beautiful than that." It was a bold statement for a man who had seen so little of the world, but nearly forty years later his son who by that time had seen most of the world, knew that he had been right.

We sat there for a long time and presently my father slapped the horses with the reins and without a word drove on. Even then I guessed that he had come all the way up over the awful rough road as much to see the view as he had to call on Zenobia Ferguson. We started downhill again along the wild road and as we rounded a clump of flaming sumach we came full upon a pair of woodchucks and an extraordinary thing happened. They did not scamper off in their heavy, alarmed fashion. They merely sat up on their hind legs like two plump little old people and stared at us. One of them chattered a little as if scolding us. But although we passed not ten feet away from them they did not stir but only turned their heads to follow us out of sight.

I said to my father, "Why don't they run away?" But the only answer I got was, "I don't know. Maybe they don't see people up here very often and aren't afraid of them."

Then the road curved and we came in sight of a cottage set against the hillside below the crest of the high bald hill. It was small and, never having been painted, was the earthy silver gray shade of wood weathered for many years. It seemed to grow out of the hillside and the vines which climbed over the little porch heightened the illusion. Enclosing the little garden was a rather bedraggled picket fence overgrown with vines and before the door stood the inevitable pair of tall Norway spruce that stand before every old farmhouse in our part of the country. At the sound of our approach a white yearling colt ran over to the fence to whinny at sight of the team, and three big dogs, one a very old hound dog and two others that were just farm dogs came running and barking. Then as we pulled up to the hitching rail a strange figure opened the door and came down the path toward us.

At first I thought it was a man for it wore a man's clothes — blue denim pants and a man's checked shirt open at the throat. The figure was slim like a man's and very erect, but the face was too feminine for a man's face and the black hair drawn into a knot at the back of the head killed the illusion.

My father said, "Hello, Cousin Zenobia. We've come to pay you a visit." And she said, "You're surely welcome, Cousin Tom. Hitch the horses and come in." Then as I climbed down from the high buggy she laid her hand on my head and said, "Is this your boy?" And my father answered, "Yes, this is the middle one."

"I don't recall ever having seen him before," said Zenobia. Then she held my head between her hands and looked at me for a long time, and at last she said, releasing me, "Yes. He'll do. He has the right kind of eye." To my father she said, "You know, you can tell people and animals by their eyes, Tom."

I hadn't the faintest idea what she meant. I only knew that I had had my first and only experience with hypnotism. Long after she turned away from me, even though I was looking up into brilliant October sunlight I saw nothing but the eyes of Zenobia Ferguson. They were black Indian eyes, pupilless and opaque and in them there was a fierce intensity, not that of madness, as I understood later on, but the intensity of someone who sees beyond present things into a world beyond.

I know now that I was puzzled too by her sexlessness — that she seemed a very handsome, fierce creature who was not quite like any man or any woman I had ever seen. She was at least sixty at the time, yet she had the figure of a boy and her hair was still quite black. I suppose this, like her eyes, was a heritage from the remote Delaware chieftain's daughter.

The dogs gathered round us sniffing and wagging their tails and the white colt came away from the fence and rubbed its muzzle against my head. I was small and a big colt that behaved like a dog must have startled me for Zenobia said, "Don't worry. He won't do you any harm. He's just playing." Then she gave him a push and said, "Run along, Willie."

Willie ran away and Zenobia said, "Sure, you're staying for dinner, Cousin Tom."

My father protested but it did no good. Zenobia said, "You come in, Tom, and talk to me while I get up something. The boy can play around outside."

They went inside the cottage and I wandered off into the jungle of a garden which surrounded the house. Looking back now that garden seemed to one small boy as romantic, as full of adventure as any jungle in Sumatra. In October few flowers remained save wild asters but the whole place was a ragged mass of iris and old-fashioned rose bushes, grapevines and fruit trees. I helped myself to great bunches of purple grapes and ate them as I wandered about the bushes. The three dogs followed me and Willie the colt, and presently I lost all uneasiness of them. They became suddenly old friends and when the white colt nibbled at my hair I only laughed, with that curious satisfaction which a boy knows in his relationship to a pet raccoon or puppy.

Among the ragged lilac bushes I came upon an old spring house where the water gushed out of red sandstone outcrop into a great stone trough. It was cold, clear water and for a long time I held the grapes beneath the stream for they tasted better when they were chilled. Behind the spring house stood the old log house built there beside the spring by Zenobia's grandfather in Indian times. It was a tiny cabin not more than fifteen by twenty feet in size made of hand-hewn logs with mud plastered between them. I went inside and saw that the old house was now the home of the white colt Willie and the dogs. Behind the cabin I came suddenly on a Jersey cow with a new-born calf that was like a young doe. At the sight of me the cow showed no alarm but only stared at me out of her great sloe-eyes while she licked the calf. I went up to the calf and rubbed its brown nose and still the cow showed no uneasiness.

These were the things which I saw with my eyes but while I wandered about something else was happening to me; something which I did not fully understand then save as a sense of childish ecstasy. I think it began when we emerged from the rough road tunneled through the woods to that high plateau under the brilliant October sky. I know now that it was like coming out of one world into another in which the senses were heightened and sharpened. I seemed to belong here very near the two woodchucks who regarded us so humorously without fear, near suddenly to the old dogs and Willie the colt.

In that jungle of old lilacs and rose bushes the birds came very close. A robin sat on a lilac bough not three feet from me and watched while I ate the grapes. A squirrel sat without fear on the eaves of the old log house and chattered and made faces at me. And the sight of all these things made the heart of that small boy sing, I think because all these living things seemed so near and so without strangeness or fear. It was as if this little world existing high against the blue October sky were a small paradise, a little world that was what all the great world should be.

I was playing on the edge of the little duck pond below the spring house, rapturously happy, when I heard Zenobia's voice calling me. It was a deep pleasant voice with a curious bell quality.

Ed Berry said he could sometimes hear her calling home the Jersey cow from down below in the valley more than two miles away. It wasn't that her voice was loud but it had a clear quality which, when the wind was right and the evening clear, could be heard a long way off. All the neighbors down in the valley knew Zenobia's voice. It belonged in that wild, pretty, tangled spot.

T here were no screens on the doors or windows and although there were, at that time of the year, only a few sleepy flies to annoy us, Zenobia kept a small branch of lilac in her hand which she waved over the table from time to time. Then I noticed her hands for the first time — big and work-hardened but long and beautiful in shape. She wore a lot of rings on them — old-fashioned cameos and amethysts in heavy gold settings. I think she had put them on in honor of the occasion just as she had put on in place of the man's clothes a complicated and elaborate dress of some purple stuff.

It changed the whole character of her appearance for it made her into a great lady — I think really the first great lady I had ever seen. The rather bold Indian features seemed softened and no longer savage but noble and splendid. She was decidedly not a pretty woman; that was too mild and milk-soppy a word. She was decidedly handsome. And she had something which I did not understand then, being a small boy, although I was aware of it. As I grew older I came to know what it was, something which a woman does not acquire. She must be born with it. It has a great deal to do with her figure and a great deal with her spirit. Here on this lonely farm against the sky was a woman who had both distinction and what the French call chic.

The dinner was good. There was squash and beans and cabbage and cheese and milk and jam made of wild grapes and honey and homemade bread and butter cold and fresh out of the icy water of the old spring house. Only one thing puzzled me. There wasn't any meat and when Zenobia went into the kitchen to bring in the frosted pawpaws she had for a dessert, I said to my father, "Why isn't there any meat?"

He looked at me quickly and said, "You mustn't speak about that. Zenobia never kills anything."

She came quickly into the room and that day I heard no more of the story. I did not hear it until long afterward, perhaps because

122

my father thought I was too young.

When lunch was over, Zenobia said briskly, "The boy ought to have his nap, Cousin Tom, and I'd not be surprised if you'd like one too."

We had eaten a great deal and my father was sleepy. I said, "I don't want to take a nap. I want to go out and play." What I really wanted was to re-enter the enchanted world where there were no annoying grown-ups and all the animals and birds were companions. I had never before been any place like that strange wild thicket of old-fashioned flowers and shrubs.

They didn't argue with me. My father said he'd like a nap and disappeared into the parlor to lie down on the sofa. Zenobia began clearing away the dishes and I went back to the pond below the spring house.

I began digging in the mud while the ducks swam in close to watch me, turning their heads on one side in duck fashion to satisfy their curiosity. They chattered a great deal among themselves. The cow came down to the pond to drink, the new calf teetering on its long legs, moving forward in jerky sudden movements. I stopped digging to watch and suddenly the calf became my brother, a small creature for whom I felt a sudden intense love, quite different from the sort of love I felt for any person, even my own parents or my brothers or sisters. It was as if we were both a part of something which other people did not understand, a whole world apart in which there were sounds which no human could understand. I knew suddenly what the ducks were quacking about and understood the look in the great brown eyes of the Jersey cow. The squirrel came down to the edge of the pond and did a curious thing. He dipped both his tiny paws into the water and then put them into his mouth and cleaned them with his tiny pink tongue.

And while I was watching him I felt that someone or something was watching me. The sensation became so intense that I turned and so discovered Zenobia standing near the spring house among the willows, in the old-fashioned purple dress. She was smiling at me and suddenly I had for her the same feeling of fathomless under-standing I had experienced for the ducks, the cow and the squirrels. For a long time we stared at each other and then she said, "That one over there — the squirrel. That's John. He's an impudent bad character but very comical."

Then softly she said, "John ... John! Come here, you rascal!"

123

The squirrel sat up, cocked his head, and then came round the end of the pond, passed very close to me and scampered up the purple dress to Zenobia's shoulder where he sat up again, chattering, his tail curled up over his back.

She looked down at me and said, "You see what they're like. We can talk to each other." She turned her head a little way and said, "How about it, John? Can't we?" The squirrel made a chattering noise and Zenobia said, "He's asking who you are and what you're doing here." Then to the squirrel she said, "It's all right. He knows what we know. He may forget it some day but in the end, it will come back to him. He's one of those that is teched like us." The squirrel turned toward me exactly as if he understood what she was saying. He remained quite still for a time as if studying me, and then suddenly he began to chatter again and scampered down the purple dress across the path and up on to the roof of the old cabin, swearing angrily.

Then I saw what had happened. My father had wakened and was now coming toward us out of the tangle of bushes. Zenobia said softly, "It's no good now. He's spoiled it."

We bade Zenobia good-bye, hitched up the horses and drove off, leaving her standing at the gate in the purple dress with all the rings on her fingers. We drove up the rise of the bald hill and down the other side through the dark tunnel through the forest out into the world again. On Ed Berry's place we passed two hunters, their bags heavy with slain rabbits.

My father said, "They won't go up to Zenobia's place."

"Why?" I asked.

He chuckled. "Because she'd get out her own shotgun and drive 'em off. They all know about her. Once she did kill a man. They all know about it."

We drove for a time in silence and then I asked, "Dad. What does 'teched' mean?"

He looked at me quizzically, "It usually means somebody's a little crazy. Why did you want to know?"

"Because Cousin Zenobia told the squirrel it was all right, I was 'teched' like her."

My father chuckled, "Sometimes I think maybe she's right."

I punched him on the arm and he added, "I wouldn't let it worry you. Most people think Zenobia is 'teched' but I think she's a mighty smart woman." And then he sighed. Why, I did not know then. I only suspected there was something he envied about Zenobia.

I don't know when exactly I heard the beginnings of Zenobia's story. Very likely I never heard it all in one piece, but in fragments, absorbing it and fitting it together in my own growing mind as children absorb folk-tales and the stories of their countryside. Zenobia was very definitely a part of the county, a part of its life and its history. As I grew older I used to see her sometimes on the streets of the town, for she left the Ferguson place about once a month to make the ten-mile trip as best she could, hitch-hiking her way on wagons and in buggies to buy spices and coffee and things she could not raise with her own hands on that high bald hill. Sometimes she bought a ribbon or two and when the first five and ten cent store came to the town, Zenobia was in heaven. She bought all the cheap jewelry she could afford out of the meager income left from her peach orchard and grapes and apples after the taxes were paid.

No one in the town took any special notice of her but upon strangers the sight of her, wandering along Main street in her bizarre clothes with a basket filled with spices and trinkets over one arm, was startling. For these monthly trips into town she dressed with the greatest care and always she wore the same dress and hat and lace mitts.

The dress, I think, must have been one she made for her marriage. The material was yellow taffeta and the design included many ruffles and pleats. It had a train and the faint suggestion of a bustle. On her head she wore a big black picture hat covered with whatever flowers were in bloom at the moment in the woods and fence rows of her high pastures. When winter came she adorned the hat with heads of wheat and the immortelles which grew in her garden. All these she sewed on fresh each time she made the expedition to town. The effect, you might think, was bizarre and sloppy but this was not so. If you saw her in the early morning before the flowers had wilted, the effect had the same indefinable chic which touched her whole appearance. Sometimes she used bunches of brilliant blue bachelor's-buttons, sometimes two or three large sun flowers, occasionally a cluster or two of scarlet geraniums. She would have made a great milliner. I think in New York or Paris she would have made a fortune.

On her fingers she wore innumerable cheap rings and over

these she always wore black lace mitts. The yellow taffeta dress had a train which she rarely troubled to pick up and as the years passed, the dust and moisture created a band of brown at the bottom of the slowly decaying material which made up the skirt. You would think that she had a mad appearance but neither was this true. The upright dignity of her carriage, the strength of the hawk-nosed face, the intelligence of the opaque black eyes gave her both distinction and presence.

To the townspeople who knew her story there was nothing wild or strange about her. And when strangers who had been startled by her appearance, heard her story, she lost her strangeness for them.

Zenobia was born in the cottage where I first saw her just after her parents had moved out of the old log house which later became the barn. When she was four years old her mother died and from then on she lived with her father in that cottage on the high hill close to the sky with its wide view of three counties. In those days the farm was even more remote than at the time I first knew it. In winter it became isolated altogether by snow and mud which made the first crude roads impassable. And so she did not go to school. Her father taught her everything she knew and that was a good deal for her father, although an eccentric man, had an education far beyond that of the neighboring farmers, and he passed it on to her along with all the old books I saw in the cottage. It was a lonely life and she grew up nearer to the birds and wild things than to the people who lived in the valley below.

And then one day when cholera swept through all the county, her father ate a fresh peach on a visit to the county seat and returned home and died before Zenobia had time to go down to the valley for a doctor. She was seventeen when he died, a tall, straight, self-reliant girl with blue black hair and black eyes. The neighbors helped her bury her father and then proposed that she come down to the valley and teach school, for she had a better education than any of them. They proposed that she live with them in turn. They were kindly people and would have welcomed her and all of them, none too well educated, wanted their children to have the benefit of Zenobia's knowledge.

But Zenobia would not leave the farm high on the hill against the sky. Perhaps it was the magnificence of the view of her own nearness to nature and all wild things which held her there. No one ever knew, for she never told them. She only said that she "had to look after Pa's farm." No amount of money or entreaty had any effect.

"It's my land now," she said stubbornly. "I can't leave it after Pa worked so hard to get it cleared." It is possible that even then there was in her Indian blood and in her upbringing something which made her wild and shy of towns and places where people gathered.

But the old men who knew her as a girl and talked about her and as they grew older told her story over and over again, said there was never anything queer about her as a young girl. She was very handsome, they said, and smart as the crack of a whip. And she could dance wildly and well for after she fell in love with Aaron she sometimes came down from the farm to the Square Dances held in the valley. The old men all said that they would have married Zenobia gladly and that they envied Aaron his luck: "A handsomer or a smarter woman there never was in all the county!"

When her father died, the neighbors volunteered to help her with the farm, working for nothing or for a share of the wheat and corn because they all felt friendly toward her and had a curious awe for "education." That is how Aaron came to meet Zenobia.

He was the son of the miller who had the big mill on Honey Creek. The old men who knew him said Aaron was the strongest man in the county. He stood six feet four and was broad and muscular and when he first went up to the farm on the hill against the sky to help with the harvest, he was a year older than Zenobia. He had blond hair and blue eyes and a straight nose. The old daguerreotype which they found after Zenobia was dead shows him sitting up very straight with hands on both knees staring straight into the picture-taking machine. But for all the woodenness of the pose there is in the faded gold-framed picture a twinkle in the eye and a cockiness in the carriage of the head. It is clear that he must have been, as the old men put it, "quite a fellow with the girls." The old men said he liked to joke and had a laugh you could hear half a mile away. His heartiness, his cockiness, were probably just what a wild, shy girl like Zenobia needed and was looking for. Anyway they said that she changed mightily after she fell in love with Aaron and that she came down from the hill farm to go to dances and parties and for a year or more was the belle of the county.

I don't know how they met — perhaps when he came in to the dinner she had cooked for the harvest hands or perhaps they met in the old spring house when he came there for a drink of the cold water that poured into the great trough of pink sandstone. Anyway it happened a very long time ago, well on toward a hundred years. And Zenobia is not really dead yet, or Aaron either for even today young people born after she had been dead have heard their story and know their names.

It was one of those passionate love affairs watched by the whole world around them. Never, the old men said, had two young people ever been more in love. They said that Aaron would sometimes sit out a square dance just for the pleasure of watching Zenobia as she danced with a special wild grace that none of the other girls displayed. The Indian in her gave her not only a gypsy look but a gypsy wildness.

And when the dance or sociable was over Aaron and Zenobia would go back together on horseback up that long tunnel through the woods until they came out on the high bald hill. Sometimes there was glistening snow on the ground and sometimes the night was soft yet brilliant with stars and the air scented with the perfume of wild flowers or the musty smell of the wild grapes which hung down over the road.

Sometimes, the old men said, it was whispered that Aaron did not return to the valley the same night. But the odd thing was that in so respectable a world as the valley the whispers caused so little disapproval and resentment. I think it must have been because even those people understood that there was something special about Zenobia. It was as if she belonged to another world with her strange wild, lonely life. I do not know — perhaps no one ever knew — whether Zenobia and Aaron were lovers but it seems unlikely that they were not. He was a handsome, wild young man and she lived alone without restraint high on her lonely hill.

As one of the old men called Mr. Charles said to my father, "I hope they were lovers. They should have been. It was wrong and bitter cruel if they were not."

They would have married as they planned to do but for the fact that Aaron had a plan. He meant to go out to the West for he wanted to get ahead in the world and he wanted to be established before they married, and so one day he left filled with the idea that he would find a gold mine there and then come back and marry Zenobia and take her with him back to the West.

When he went away Zenobia returned to her old solitary way

of living. She never went down into the valley to the dances and sociables, but remained on the hill girded by forest.

While Aaron was away dark things began to happen in the county which have since become legendary. There appeared from nowhere a band of highwaymen and robbers. In those days farms were far apart. There were no telephones and horses were the only means of transportation. The robbers were three in number, one tall and two short men. They dressed in dark clothes and never were seen save in the darkness and with their faces covered. They would appear on a lonely road through the woods or on a covered bridge to stop a family or perhaps a lone traveler and rob them. After a little while it became evident that they were not a band of outsiders for they remained there in the county and it was clear that they knew who were the rich and the poor. They knew, too, many other things like the Christian names of their victims.

After a time the terror grew so great that no one ventured out on the road at night and then it was that the highwaymen took to descending on lonely farmhouses to break their way in and rob and terrorize the inmates. The sheriff organized special posses to patrol the roads and made up search parties but the efforts of the posses came to nothing and after a time it became clear that someone was informing the highwaymen of the activities of the posse in advance, for they never appeared or robbed anyone on the nights the sheriff and his men went out on patrol.

Of all these activities Zenobia Ferguson on her lonely farm took no notice. People tried to persuade her to leave the place and come down into the valley but she only said that she had no money anyway and the farm was so remote that it was safe. Anyway she meant to stay there until Aaron came back. It may have been that she was not afraid or more likely that between her and that piece of land high against the sky with all the wild things that dwelt there with her, there was some special bond which other people did not understand. In any case she stayed stubbornly in the cottage, coming down only once or twice a month dressed in her finest clothes to buy what she needed in the village.

What she did not know or ignored was the legend that she was rich, that she had money hidden away which her father had left her. To many people it was the only answer to all the books — people who had libraries must be rich — and to the fineness of Zenobia's clothes. They didn't understand her liking for jewelry and ribbons nor the fact that even in a calico frock, she appeared better dressed and more stylish than the banker's wife in her furs and broadcloths. Simple people said, "Zenobia Ferguson has a pot of gold hidden away somewhere."

And so one night when the sheriff and his posse were not out on the roads, the highwaymen came up the tunnel through the forest up to the high farm. It was a still bright night like the nights Zenobia and Aaron had ridden up the same primitive path. Neither Zenobia nor her father had ever had a lock on the doors of the cottage and when the highwaymen entered they found Zenobia asleep. They woke her and, standing about her with handkerchiefs over their faces, told her they wanted the gold she had hidden away. Zenobia, truthfully perhaps, told them she had no money. They found her cheap jewelry — mostly cameos and garnets and a few amethysts set in silver. But that didn't satisfy them and presently they bound her and burned matches against the soles of her feet to force her to tell them where her money was hidden.

It did no good. She did not cry out and afterward in court she said there was only a few dollars in the house. She would have told them where it was, she said, but she hated cruelty and was determined not to give them even the satisfaction of those few dollars. She did not scream. She would not speak to the robbers at all and when the daylight came they went away, baffled.

A week passed before Zenobia's scorched feet were healed enough for her to hobble down into the valley to tell of the highwaymen's visit. The old man said that she always walked differently after that terrifying night. They said that was one reason why, even to the day of her death, she carried herself very straight, with a peculiar air of fierce pride.

Even after the robbery she would not leave the Ferguson place. She did have locks put on the door and she bought herself a pistol and a shotgun and a dog. Later at the trial she said, "I didn't buy the guns to protect myself but my place. I didn't want strange people wandering about all over it. It was my place and I loved it and all the animals on it. I wasn't harming anyone and no one had any right to come up there raisin' hell."

It was a crude explanation, perhaps because she hadn't the words to explain more clearly what she meant, but more likely because she did not believe people would understand how she felt even if she explained. I think it was the first time people began to understand about Zenobia — that she was different and a little "teched," that it was different "up Ferguson way" in that world against the sky. Among the Pennsylvania Dutch settlers people began to whisper that Zenobia Ferguson was a "hex."

In the meanwhile out in the West Aaron had, he wrote, found a "pardner" and was prospecting. Each week now she came down from the hill to get his letter at the post office. It wouldn't be long now, he wrote, until he'd be coming back to fetch her.

She kept all these letters. Mrs. Berry (Ed Berry's daughter-in-law) found them when they went up to bury Zenobia more than three quarters of a century later. I have them now along with Zenobia's journal. They are extraordinary letters, not too well spelled and not always grammatical, but filled with passion and tenderness and a strange, direct poetry and mysticism. In the robust, good-looking young Aaron there must have been a streak of that "fey" quality which Zenobia had all her life. In one letter he wrote, "It's fun out here. You can go all day and never see a house or a man. It ain't crowded like it's getting to be back in the valley. Out here you and I can have the world to ourselves with nothing around us but the trees and the wild flowers, the birds and the beasts. I am coming back soon. I will write you when I am coming. I want you to be there waiting for me when I come up out of the woods. I want it to be evening with the sun going down behind the hill, and we'll walk up and up to the top of the hill overlooking the three counties and then..."

Sometimes he quoted passages from the Bible but they were always the wild pagan, passionate parts. I remember that among them he quoted often enough the Song of Songs, as if he felt his own ardor and words were not enough. He wrote, "How beautiful are thy feet with shoes, O Prince's daughter! The joints of thy thighs are like jewels, the work of the hands of a cunning workman.

"Thy navel is like a round goblet which warmeth not liquor; thy belly is like an heap of wheat set about with lilies.

"Thy two breasts are like two young roes that are twins.

"Thy neck is a tower of ivory, thine eyes like the fishponds in Heshbon, by the gate of Bath-rabbin; thy nose is as the tower of Lebanon which looketh down toward Damascus.

"Thine head upon thee is like Carmel, and the hair of thine head like purple; the king is held in the galleries.

"How fair and how pleasant are thou, oh love, for delights!"

They were a strange pair to be bred among the staid, straight-laced people of the valley. Out of the ashes of Aaron's old faded letters there still arises after nearly a hundred years a kind of wild and glorious passion. I think that all along until the end Zenobia knew proudly that God had somehow set her aside, that there was richness in the strange lonely life which the other women in the county never knew.

At last Aaron wrote that he and his pardner had found a good thing and that he would be coming home soon. In the cottage Zenobia began to pack up the books of her father's library, not without sadness, for only Aaron and his love could ever have made her leave the Ferguson place.

In the county the three highwaymen were still at large. Their depredations had spread now into adjoining counties. They worked on horseback and struck now here, now there, at places far apart. The people of three or four counties began to talk of calling out the militia to guard the bridges and the lonely stretches of road.

And then one night a little after midnight Zenobia was wakened by the barking of her dog and in the darkness she heard the sound of footsteps going about the house from one door to another. As she described it at the trial, she was not frightened. She was only angry again at the invasion of her world. She got out of bed and picking up the clumsy old pistol she pointed it at the door calling out, "If you don't go away, I'll fire." For a moment she waited and then she heard the sound of a man's low laugh, and pulled the trigger.

For a long time after she had fired, she waited listening. The laugh was not repeated and there were no more sounds of any kind outside the cottage and at last she went back to bed. But she did not sleep. At the trial she said she lay awake for the rest of the night, not through fright, but because she was haunted by the sound of the laugh. It kept coming back to her, as if it were the laugh of someone she knew. She kept hearing the laugh, interrupted by the sound of the pistol's explosion, checked before she could really recognize it. Then as the sun came up she dressed and unlocked the door and looked out. There on the doorstep, lying dead face down, was Aaron.

It was late on the same evening before Zenobia appeared at the home of Ed Berry's grandmother. What she did during the long hours of that day alone with Aaron's body, no one ever knew or will ever know now. Ed Berry's grandmother said that Zenobia's face suddenly appeared in the doorway. The lamps were already lighted but even their rosy glow did not change the chalky whiteness of Zenobia's wild young face. The black eyes had a curious hard staring look in them.

Ed Berry's grandmother said, "Come in and sit down, Zenobia. What is it? What's gone wrong?"

Zenobia, without speaking, sat down and stared in front of her. For a long time she was silent, so still that Ed's grandmother thought she had gone mad.

Then very quietly she said, "Aaron is dead. I killed him. I didn't mean to."

Ed's grandmother brought her a glass of blackberry wine which Zenobia drank meekly. Then with the same tense quietness she told her story. She understood it now. Aaron had come home without telling her, to surprise her. She said, "I know what he meant to do. He meant to come into the house quietly and waken me, as he used to do sometimes before he went away, but while he was away after the robbers came I put a lock on the door. He didn't know about that and he went all the way round the house trying to find a way in. That was when I heard him and took up the gun. And when I called out, he laughed thinking I would know who it was ... and I didn't ... I didn't ... not till afterward when everything was still and I kept hearing the laugh in the stillness and I thought 'It sounded like Aaron but it couldn't be.' That's what kept me awake till morning. I told myself, 'If it was Aaron he would call out!'"

Then she covered her face with her hands but no sound came out of her. There were no wracking sobs. She kept that same awful stillness about her. Presently she said, "Will you send one of the boys for the sheriff and a preacher and come and help me with Aaron?"

Ed's grandmother said that for the first time on that evening she saw the mad, fixed look in Zenobia's black eyes. It never again left them until the day she died.

The sheriff came and the preacher and after they had gone away a strange thing happened. Zenobia said to Ed's grandmother, "The sheriff is the leader of the robbers. He has the same eyes and the same voice and the same way of breathing. I saw his eyes above the handkerchief when they were torturing me. That man is the leader."

But no one paid much attention to her, thinking that Aaron's death had driven her crazy. But the odd thing was that Zenobia was right. A month later a woman came to the police in the county seat and betrayed the sheriff. She was the wife of one of the other highwaymen and when her husband left her for another woman, she told the whole story. Only then did it become clear why the robbers never operated on the nights the sheriff led the posse. It was one of those stories which became legends in a frontier country. And in a way it was the sheriff-robber who had really killed Aaron for if the band had not come to Zenobia's cottage to torture her, there would have been no lock on the door and no pistol and Aaron could have walked in as he had planned to do.

They buried Aaron in the old orchard there on the hill because that was what Zenobia wanted and afterwards they held a kind of trial of Zenobia. It was never more than that, for no one really believed that she had murdered Aaron with intent. She would have no lawyer to defend her but simply told her own story, very quietly, and in all the court there was not one person, even the prosecuting attorney, who did not believe her. She walked out of the court and went back, riding in Ed Berry's buggy, to the Ferguson place high above the woods close to the sky with its view of three counties, and there she lived until she died.

But from then on she no longer lived in this world at all but in a world of fancy, nearer to the trees and the water, the rain and the snow and the birds and beasts than to anyone on this earth.

She was over sixty when I first saw her on the day my father took me through the green tunnel in the woods "up Ferguson way." After that I saw her many times, sometimes on the street in the town moving along with her strange air of dignity and chic in the yellow taffeta gown, the black picture hat and the black lace mitts. Twice I saw her at the cottage "up Ferguson way" when my father covered the county electioneering, but never did I quite recapture that strange sensation of moving out of this world into another in which trees and streams had meaning and where animals were not animals, inarticulate and shy, but companions whose language one understood. Perhaps it was because as I grew older I slipped out of that childish simplicity in which I could pass so easily through the wall that separated Zenobia's strange world on that high lonely hill from the world of dull reason and what we call perhaps oddly and wrong "reality." I think Zenobia knew this for she did not appear again in the ragged, jungly garden in her fine purple dress to accept me into her world because I was "teched."

From the day Aaron died, Zenobia never killed anything, not even a fly, and she would allow no one in her world on top of the hill to kill or harm any living thing. Hunters in the county knew that she might kill a man. They remembered Aaron. And when she appeared armed with a shotgun, they did not argue with her. Once in the early morning while it was still dark she very nearly frightened to death two boys whose hound dogs had treed a raccoon on her land. She came crashing out of the underbrush in her man's clothes with a shotgun under her arm and at sight of her wild black hair and wild eyes they dropped their lantern, left the hound dogs and ran. After a little time no hunter ever went near the Ferguson place. And Zenobia and her animals were left in peace.

I saw her for the last time when I was about seventeen years old. I left the county then and did not return for twenty-five years. During all that time I went through two wars and saw most of the countries of the earth but I never wholly forgot Zenobia. I thought of her at the strangest places and times. At least three or four times I dreamed of her, seeing her always as she stood in the purple dress, with the squirrel on her shoulder by the spring pond. There was no reason for this save for that bond between us which she had recognized when she said to the squirrel that I too was "teched."

I have never been a hunter. I have never shot a rabbit or a quail or any small living thing. Although I have killed lions and tigers, panthers and leopards, I never did so with any pleasure but only out of politeness to my host. It took will-power to force myself to kill the first leopard I ever saw, spitting and snarling at me in the tall elephant grass beneath the howdah. And I felt sick the first time I shot a great tiger, for it was like destroying beauty and magnificence itself. Once I infuriated a fellow hunter when he was about to kill a superb *Gaur* in the bamboo and teakwood jungles of Mysore by crying out, "You can't kill anything as splendid as that!"

I am even an indifferent fisherman when it comes to keeping the fish. Although I love the sport my impulse is always to throw back the fish. I suppose that is what Zenobia meant by saying I was "teched." In any case, I know that on the night I killed the tiger in far-off India I dreamed of Zenobia standing by the spring in the purple dress.

When I came back to the county it was to buy land and settle there for the rest of my life. Zenobia was dead by then but the strange thing was that the only desirable piece of land was Ed Berry's farm and by then the farm beyond the woods and against the sky had become a part of Ed Berry's place. It had to be sold together and so I came into possession of the Ferguson place and many strange things which went with it.

The place, Ed Berry's widow said, hadn't changed much except that Zenobia's cottage had burned down.

"It wasn't much of a loss and it wasn't fit for anything by the time Zenobia died. She got poorer and poorer and couldn't pay the taxes but nobody made any fuss about it. The auditor — it didn't matter whether he was a Democrat or a Republican — just let it ride along. She finally got pretty old and feeble but she wouldn't leave the place. We tried to get her to go to the County Poor Farm but she said she couldn't. She was pretty spry though and could take care of herself right up to the day she died. Some of us neighbors used to bake things and make pots of baked beans and things to take them up to her once a week. She had an old cow and she managed to get along. She always seemed happy but when she got to be very old it seemed like she didn't belong to this world at all. She wasn't much interested in what we had to say but she'd talk to the birds and animals just like they were people. I was the one that found her dead — I went up with some baked things and some fresh meat and found the door open — you know she never locked the door again after that thing happened about Aaron — and there she was lying on the bed dead; she was all dressed up in a purple dress with all her jewelry and gimcracks on and her hair neatly done just like she knew she was going to die and prepared for it. Maybe that was something she learned from the birds and animals. It was a funny thing ... the room was filled with birds of all kinds. They flew out the door when I came in.

"No," the widow continued, "the place ain't much changed except the house is gone. Some tramps must have stopped there for the night and set fire to it. It looks kind of ragged and the old orchard don't amount to much any more. We just use the whole place to pasture cattle. A car can't get up the road any more — it's so worn out. You got to go on foot or on horseback."

"Where did you bury her?" I asked.

"Right there on the place in the orchard beside Aaron. It was kind of against the rules but nobody made any objection. The county had got used to her. I guess most people were kind of proud of her. It was Ed's idea to bury her up there. He said she wouldn't rest quiet anywhere else." She sighed. "Ed always had good ideas like that."

It was a bright morning in early May when I went "up Ferguson way" again for the first time in more than twenty-five years. I went on Tex, a big Kentucky mare, because, as Ed's widow said, it wasn't possible any more to get through the lane in a car or even a horse and buggy.

The woods on either side of the lane was little changed save that the wild grape vines grew in a thick tangle almost closing up the road here and there. The white blossoms of the blood-root were nearly gone, but the banks on either side of the lane were bright with hepaticas and yellow violets and spotted yellow Canadian lilies and trillium. Among them the ferns thrust up their first tender green fronds and now and again in the openings of the tangled grape vines I caught glimpses of splashes of white made by the dogwood beneath the tender green and pink of the new foliage on the oaks and maples and beech trees. The clouds of white blossoms seemed to give off light and the whole woods was alive with the sound of wild birds. The rich growth gave the whole forest that air of tropical luxuriance which marks the woods of glacial Ohio.

I thought, "Maybe there is something special about this place. Maybe because of Zenobia things grew more luxuriantly here." And then I put aside the idea as nonsense.

At the top of the lane I came suddenly out of the woods again on to that high open hill against the bright warm sky of early May and as I climbed up, the view of the three counties lay spread out before me once again, only this time the colors were not the bold reds and yellows and purples of October but soft shades of green with the ponds and lakes and deep stretches of Honey Creek reflecting the blue of the sky above.

I reached the top of the hill where the Berry cattle were still grazing and then down below me in the protected hollow by the big spring I saw what remained of the Ferguson place.

The house was gone and only a hollow, grown over with honeysuckle, remained where the cellar had been, but the old log house where Zenobia had kept the cow and the dogs and the white horse was still standing. The tangled garden had spread out, seeding itself across the slope. The two ancient Norway spruces still stood by the gate of the broken fence.

One side of their trunks had been scarred by the heat of the fire that consumed the cottage but the trunks were healed again. Up one of them climbed a trumpet vine.

I tied the mare to the old hitching post and went through the gate. All the earth was yellow with daffodils and above them bloomed the huge old purple and white lilacs. The biggest Japonica I have ever seen seemed like a bush of flame. The spring house was still there, completely hidden beneath the overgrowth of vines and shrubbery, and outside it the little spring pond. One whole bank was covered by the little cool ice-green old-fashioned flowers of the Star of Bethlehem.

I drank out of my hands of the cold water gushing out of the rock and lay down on the bank near the pond, experiencing a strange feeling of happiness and peace. It was not only good to be alive, it was good to be alive in this particular spot on the surface of the earth. And slowly I began to feel again that sensation I had known as a small boy, of coming up out of the valley into another strange world that somehow existed on a different plane from all other human life. I did not fall asleep yet the sensation was that of being suspended between sleep and consciousness when everything becomes amazingly clear and one's senses are awake to things which at other times go unseen and un-recorded. I was very near again to the trees and the flowers, to the rocks, to the water that gushed from it. It was almost as if I could understand what the birds were saying as they chirped and sang in the ruins of the old garden.

Then suddenly I felt that I was being watched by someone or something, exactly as I had felt on that October day as a small boy when Zenobia appeared suddenly among the bushes beside the spring house in the purple dress. I turned and found myself saying "Zenobia." It was the strangest sensation I have ever experienced, of reaching into another world, of being almost at the brink of understanding. At the same moment I heard Tex, the mare, neighing exactly as a horse calls to another horse. She did it twice and then three times. I thought, having somehow lost myself in time and space, "She has seen Zenobia's old white horse." And then, expecting fully to see Zenobia in the purple dress, I turned a little further. But in the spot where she had stood with the squirrel on her shoulder, saying, "He's teched like us" there was only a red fox sitting perfectly quietly, his big bushy tail curled about his feet. For a moment we both stayed there, very still, watching each other. Then after a little time he yawned, stood up and with a final look over his shoulder at me, he trotted off through the daffodils under the shrubbery. The mare called again twice and then everything was still but for the noisy chirping of the birds.

I don't know how long I stayed there, perfectly happy and still as if I had become a part of infinity, but when I wakened the sun was already down behind the top of the hill. I had no consciousness of having dreamed yet I was aware that something had happened to me; some experience which I could not quite recapture, some experience that was rich and satisfying.

I thought, "I must get home for supper." And after a final drink at the spring I turned past the hole that had once been the cellar and came upon the great flat rock which had been Zenobia's doorstep. It was charred and chipped by the fire that had destroyed the cottage but that made no difference to me. I saw the cottage again as it had been with the little porch covered with trumpet vine and suddenly I thought, "Here is where she must have found Aaron, lying face down dead as the sun came up." And for the first time I knew the full horror and tragedy of what happened there. Until then it had only been part of a story. Now, suddenly, I knew it, almost as if I had been Zenobia, opening the door to look out into the garden.

Tex had broken loose while I slept and was up near the top of the hill feeding on the fresh new blue grass. I caught her without difficulty and we set off down the ruined lane through the woods back again into the world. As we entered the green tunnel she neighed twice again and turned her head to look behind us. I too turned, believing that I would see Zenobia's old white horse trotting up to follow us. But there was nothing there in the green-hued twilight.

I went away to the East and two months passed before I again went "up Ferguson way." This time I went on foot accompanied by Rex, Prince and Regina. They are big Boxer dogs and when I am at home they go everywhere I go and sleep at night in the same room with me. They do not go away from the house unless I go with them. They are as much my friends and companions as any living person, and so it never occurred to me that I should never take them "up Ferguson way" because that was a wild world in which they did not belong.

It was midsummer and the woods were full of damp heat, of ferns, of lush growth and dancing deer-flies. The climb up the long ruined lane left me breathless and dripping but at the top where one came out into Zenobia's high world, there was a breeze and the air was fresh although the whole panorama of the three counties lay blurred and dancing in a haze of midsummer heat. Again I had that same sensation of entering another world.

We followed the lane over the crest of the hill and as it descended the other side, I saw ahead of me on the edge of the winding lane a woodchuck, descendant no doubt of the pair I had seen years before at the same spot while Zenobia was still alive. He sat up very straight watching me and the dogs. He did not scamper away as I came nearer and then I thought, "Let the dogs give him a run. It'll be fun for them and they'll never catch him." He sat up there on the edge of the lane not twenty-five feet from the safety of his burrow. They couldn't possibly catch him before he ducked out of sight.

Boxers are not hunting dogs. They are essentially watch dogs. Their noses are not good and their eyesight is scarcely better. They hear everything even at a great distance but they did not hear the woodchuck. They were running about, their blunt noses to the ground, scarcely a dozen yards from him.

Suddenly I said, "Look!" and the three of them raised their heads and saw the woodchuck. From three sides they ran for him but still his way of escape was open. He was safe.

But a strange thing happened — something I have never seen before or since. He did not run. He only sat there, upright, chattering a little, full of trust, as if he had no fear of anything. In a second the three dogs had him and in a second it was all over and suddenly I was sick.

I had done an awful thing. I had betrayed Zenobia and the squirrel. I had violated all that world of which I had been permitted to be a part ... a world into which I could enter because I was "teched." Even today, three years afterward, I feel shame and disgust over what I did without thought on a shallow impulse. The sight of the comic woodchuck sitting there full of trust and without fear will always be with me. I had done a dreadful thing.

I did not even go on to the garden and the spring house although the heat and climb had given me a terrific thirst. Instead I turned back, leaving the dead and mangled woodchuck for the buzzards, called the dogs and set off again down the hill.

But I never again took the dogs when I went "up Ferguson way."

The next morning George, the postman, brought me a heavy package. It came from Abilene, Washington, from Ed Berry's daughter-in-law. Inside it was a letter from her. It said simply that she was sending me some old letters and a journal which she had found in the cottage after Zenobia died. Now that I owned the place and was vaguely Zenobia's only relative she thought that I should have them.

The letters were Aaron's love letters written while he was in the West, the ink on them long since yellow and faded on the rotting paper. As I have told you, they were passionate letters, pagan and wild, strange letters to have been written by a young fellow born and raised in the straight-laced atmosphere of the valley. It was clear that he and Zenobia knew a strange satisfaction and glory that was very near to the woods and birds and streams and remote from the everyday lives of the valley people. In these letters there was the feeling of Pan, of Dionysus, of Diana of Ephesus.

Of the Journal, Ed Berry's daughter-in-law wrote, "I can't make out what is in it. A lot of it sounds like nonsense and none of it makes much sense. I thought that, being a literary man, you might understand it."

The Journal took a little reading and a great deal of understanding, but after a while it became clear. The names Zenobia used were not the names of people but of animals. The conversations were not conversations with people but with the birds and the beasts of the fields and the forests. There were even recorded conversations which must have taken place with spirits — the spirits of trees, of stones, of waterfalls. There on the high lonely hill in the midst of the forest, Zenobia had lived in a world peopled by friends which none of the others of us could ever know or understand, unless you were, like Zenobia and the squirrel, a little "teched."

There is only one more incident to tell. I have a daughter, now eleven years old, who has grown up largely in the valley. She is tall and like Zenobia, very straight. But unlike Zenobia she has blonde hair and very clear blue eyes. She has a horse and caracul sheep and rabbits and pigeons and she knows all there is to know about animals and farming and the earth, for she has a feeling for these things and without that feeling, no one can ever understand about animals or how things grow. A friend once said, "She is a disconcerting child. When she looks at you out of those clear blue eyes you know that she knows things you don't know and never will know." It is what Zenobia undoubtedly would have recognized as a "teched" look.

She has a friend called Mary, unlike her as possible. Mary is small, and plump, and merry, and gossippy, but they understand each other and a lot of things some of us older people do not understand. When they were eight, they took to going off for the day, sometimes taking sandwiches with them. Where they went was a secret. Sometimes they begged sandwiches from the kitchen and stayed away all day. There were many places to go — the woods, the creek, the wild tangled swamp called in the family "The Jungle." There were caves and waterfalls. Neither of them had any fear of wild things, even of snakes.

One evening they did not return until after dark. I went out to find them and after searching for an hour, returned home to find that they were already in the kitchen having a late supper.

I said, "Where were you?"

Sally wouldn't say anything but her friend Mary said, "We stayed to see the raccoons come out. They don't come out until after dark."

"Did you see them?"

I saw Sally give Mary a black fierce look to enforce silence but Mary was already talking, "Yes, we saw a mother raccoon and a whole family. They came to the spring and the mother raccoon washed everything she gave the babies to eat before she gave it to them."

"If it was dark how did you see them?"

"We saw them all right," said Sally stubbornly.

"Weren't you scared coming home after dark?" I asked.

And with scorn, Sally asked, "What is there to be scared of?"

A little later when I was alone with my daughter, I said firmly, "I must know where you go. You must say where you're going. It's a big place and I must know where I should go to look for you."

"We didn't go any place."

"That's a silly answer. I must know or I'll have to forbid you to go out alone."

The clear blue eyes were filled suddenly with anger and resentment, "We can't do anything around here without everybody butting in."

"Why can't you tell me where you go?"

"Because it's a secret."

"Why is it a secret?"

"Because it is ... Because if you knew, you'd spoil it for us."

I knew it was no use going any further. There was behind the blue eyes a determination which was more than a childish whim. I don't know why it never occurred to me what lay behind it. I should have known.

After that Sally was forbidden to go off for the day unless I knew where she was going. For three days she stayed around the house, miserable, sullen and resentful, and on the fourth day she came to me and said, "I'll tell you where I go if you'll promise not to tell anybody else."

"I can keep a secret. I promise. Where do you go?"

She looked away from me and was silent for a moment. Then she said, "Up Ferguson way."

I didn't answer for a moment because the phrase seemed so startling. I hadn't heard it since I was a boy. She could never have heard it, for by now all the old people who had ever talked about "up Ferguson way" were dead ... all, I thought, but Zenobia. She went on living. I said, "Why do you call it that? Where did you hear it called that?"

"I never heard anybody call it that. We just made it up. It was a secret." She looked at me strangely for a long time. Then she said, "Do you call it that too?"

"Yes. That's what they used to call it when I was a child."

Then she dismissed me, "Can I go now? Mary and I haven't been there for a long time."

I wanted to ask her what she found there and why the place so fascinated her but I knew I wouldn't get any answer. I had never told anyone what I had found there. Why should she? She'd think as I had always thought that to talk about it, to tell anyone would spoil everything. I had so nearly spoiled it the time I thoughtlessly took the dogs with me.

I did not ask her. I only said, "Yes, I like it up there too."

She glanced at me quickly out of the clear blue eyes and as our glances met I knew that she too was "teched" like Zenobia and Aaron, the squirrel and me. And I knew that she suddenly understood about me. She said, "I'm glad you put up those 'no hunting' signs." And in the blue eyes there was a sudden glint such as I had once seen in Zenobia's eyes and I knew that she, like Zenobia, would run any hunter off the Ferguson place with a shotgun. I knew too that Zenobia wasn't really dead at all, that she was still there and Aaron with her perhaps now, in the trees and in the spring, in the animals and in the waterfall, of the earth itself far more than she would ever be in the grave in the orchard where she lay beside Aaron. She was still alive in my consciousness and in the eyes of my daughter with that kind of immortality which she understood perhaps better than any of us. For me she is always there on that high hill against the sky when the rain falls there, or the wind blows, or the evenings are breathless and still high up above the three counties. It is the kind of immortality I should like to know, to find my place forever in God's scheme of life and sky and sea and earth.

Sometimes I hear again Zenobia's voice saying to the squirrel, "He knows what we know. He may forget it some day but in the end it will come back to him." It may be that we have to lose that knowledge and understanding which children have and then perhaps it comes back to us through living experience and wisdom. Maybe that is what Zenobia meant.

8

The Return

**From *The Heritage — A daughter's memories
of Louis Bromfield*, 1962 by Ellen Bromfield Geld**

*"Then I pushed open the door and walked into the smell of cattle and
horses and hay and silage and I knew that I had come home and that
never again would I be long separated from that smell because it
meant security and stability and because in the end, after years of
excitement and wandering and adventure, it had reclaimed me. It
was in the blood and could not be denied. But all of that story I told
long ago in The Farm."* -- L.B.

How often it has been said that all the things we love when we are
children are kept in our memories much larger and finer than life
until we see them again when we are older and, supposedly, wiser.
On that day, after a second look at their disheartening
unremarkability, we are supposed to bid farewell to all our last
childish illusions.

If this is the case, then my father's good fortune was all the
greater. For he had known the Ohio country as a boy who had fished
in its streams and roamed its forests with a child's unflagging hope
for adventure and it had all remained very grand in his memory. Yet,
when he returned with a hesitant and suspicious heart, he found it all
more richly and excitingly beautiful than he had dared imagine it to
be during his absence. He had not been deceived. Instead, he had
found his youth there, waiting and intact. And something more as
well, for he was able to greet it and look upon it with the perception
and vision of an older man.

He named his place Malabar Farm after the Malabar Coast of
India because that name bore many beautiful connotations he wanted
always to keep in mind and because it was with his earnings from the
Indian books that he was able to buy the land. It was not what a

banker or a real-estate agent or even a cold, purely practical farmer (something very difficult to be) would have considered a sound investment. Its soil had been worn thin by years of bad, unimaginative farming. Deep gullies slashed its hills and remained like open wounds kept festering by wind and rain and never allowed to heal. Its pastures were slowly giving way to cocklebur, Scotch thistle, poverty grass and creeping blackberry brambles: the final stage of land which has been abused by foolish, thoughtless men who have no business calling themselves farmers, keepers of the precious land.

But from the low, broad valley across which a little stream, called Switzer's Creek, cut its shallow, wood-shaded swath, the green Ohio hills — the first foothills of the Blue Ridge Mountains — rose wondrously on every side. Here the hills were covered by aged forests of oak, maple, elm, sycamore and ash, left mercifully and wisely by the Scotch and English and German farmers who had walked in over the mountains a hundred years ago; who had understood and left to their children an understanding and love of trees. Elsewhere, they rose beyond the gnarled, wind-tormented trees of an old orchard to end sharply in cliffs of pink and yellow sandstone over which the wild grape and trumpet vines extended their coarse, woody ropes and dark greenery as if to conceal remnants of some near-forgotten, savage past.

There was a maple-sugar bush, which when my father saw it again for the first time in many years was gray and leafless and laden with snow. But seeing it thus, with its old shed where the boiling vats lay rusting under the snow, turned over for the last time by hands that knew well the incomparable fragrance they produced, he must have thought of how it all would be in spring when the sap coursed toward pale leaves and smoke rose again from the battered chimney.

Above the sugar bush, and the taller trees which stood over the maples like strong, protecting brothers, was a high, windy and deeply grassed land which, in spite of many attempts, had never quite been tamed by the hands of man. From the top of its great, tree-bald dome, one gained an illusory view of the Ohio country, in which houses, roads and all signs of modern civilization were eclipsed in the vast sweep of forests and lakes and gray-blue distances. Looking over it all, one was brought back to the chilling and reviving sensation of man's solitude in the beginning of things.

Altogether, this was the kind of farm which Pa would have bought and struggled gallantly and hopelessly to restore. It had suffered many a dull-witted, thoughtless owner, but it had always been meant for a big-hearted, imaginative man who was something of a dreamer and could see in every bend and hollow and proud hill the answer to some special yearning.

My father was just forty when he returned to Ohio and, but for increased knowledge gained over the years, perhaps the best way to express the difference in him is to say that he hadn't changed so very much, but simply ripened. For although we may improve our manners, increase our savoir-faire, become more tolerant in some ways and less in others, it is doubtful if any of us ever really succeed in overcoming the basic traits, good or bad, that make us. If at some time we actually come to pretend or even to believe that we have overcome them, we simply deceive others, and worse still ourselves.

As it was, the Boss never made much attempt, if any, at basic change, and so at forty he was more of a stubborn, willful, mood-ridden, raging tyrant than ever. Even though he deplored his own weaknesses, he defied others to consider or criticize them.

This nervous state of being resulted in scenes at which the innocent bystander was dared to show signs of surprise, shock or any other form of disapproval. "If you don't like it, you know what you can do," his eyes warned as he called us "idiots, gland types, psychopaths, gold brickers," and accused us of everything from outright deceit to calculated homicide and subversion by persecution. Under fire we screamed right back so that the dreadful noise must have been truly terrifying to that "innocent bystander," who might as likely as not have been an amiable Fuller Brush man, snatched up on an impulse and invited in for lunch.

But no less astounding was the manner in which two or three minutes after the most dreadful row, we were all laughing and talking gaily again as if all our days passed in Louisa May Alcott-like cheerful and unbroken composure. The results of this strange behavior were twofold. For one thing, in later years with our own families we never bothered much, either, with controlling our tempers. For another, hanging on to our sense of humor, we were always able to forgive the Boss any outrage as long as it was ridiculous enough to give us a good laugh later on.

I will gladly admit that there were other reasons as well for his earning our forgiveness. For even when he raged, there was a certain lionlike fascination about him of which he, too, must have been fully aware. The thought of this amused and softened us. For it made us aware more than ever of the fact that our father was in every way intensely human. As well as the tyrant, he could be, in the space of a day, delightful and amusing, sage and assuring, uninhibitedly generous and incredibly tender at the most unexpected moments.

The Fuller Brush man must have sensed this as well. Else why, with all his illusions about the great man shattered, should he have come back again and again? (We were not, after all, very good customers for his brushes).

These were my father's traits, little changed since the day he'd had a violent row with Ma and gone off to join the French Army. Physically he was tall and angular still, and leathery from countless days spent in wind, rain and sun from Johore and Sumatra to the cold, brooding winter countries of Scandinavia. At the corners of his eyes, the crow's-feet, made from laughter and looking into the sun, mingled with other lines of weariness and dissipation, which gave him the look of a man who had lived a great deal, both by day and by night. He had fished and swum and walked along country roads and, at the end of the day, relished perhaps more than his share of good food and drink and satisfying talk. He had hungered for and devoured music and literature, observed the thoughts and behavior of all kinds of people, both brilliant and dull. He had tasted nearly everything worth tasting in life, and the impressions of all were stamped in his humorous, canny blue eyes, while the dissatisfied hunger for more showed in his outthrust, perpetually determined jaw.

When he came home again, America struck him in the same way that she strikes most Americans who have lived for a long time amidst the changelessness and solidity of the old world. He found his country to be almost frighteningly dynamic, its people rootless and nearly hysterically obsessed with success and change. The more it seemed to him that Americans were unstable, constantly in motion and striving for "the good life" through dependence on one another (generally termed co-operation), the more his entire being yearned for the stability and independence of the old life he had left behind somewhere in the Ohio country and which he was determined to re-discover. Because of this anxious determination, sometimes in the beginning at Malabar Farm he would sit in the evening on the porch with one friend or another whom he had not seen in many years and there would begin a conversation something like this:

"You must hardly recognize the America you left behind," the friend would say with obvious pride and enthusiasm, "so much has happened, everyone is so prosperous and well fed. It looks as though the American dream has paid off. It would be hard to find anyone today who can't seek and achieve 'the good life.'"

My father would nod in agreement, but already there would be a quizzical look in his eyes.

"No, I suppose there are only a few left behind — mostly poor white trash, driven out of the dust bowl," and he would stare threateningly at his friend. "Don't for a minute overlook them.

"Still, I'll tell you something. I find this American dream business pretty damned frightening at times."

"Now just what do you mean by that?" the friend would counter, already anticipating the superior sour-grapes attitude of one who had long been an expatriate. "Isn't that what you howled so about in your first books and articles, putting an end to the exploitation of the many to enrich the few, so to speak?"

"Of course I did," the Boss would snap back. "I lived in the midst of it as a boy. I used to make the rounds as a reporter right in the town of Mansfield. I saw plenty of squalid flats, six people to a bed and sleeping in shifts at that. You don't need to give me a moral lecture on the worth of collective bargaining. That isn't what worries me. It's the instability that comes with great industrial cities, the mess it puts people's lives into, the way a man loses his roots and ties."

"Oh, come now, you're talking about security?" The friend would be ready with a fool-proof formula for modern security, but he was never allowed, unless he was Frank Lausche or someone else equally impossible to intimidate, to give voice to it. For my father would lean forward, piercing his friend's self-confidence with an accusing stare. "You're damn right, that's it. Good God, if you think for a moment that iceboxes and a new car every year on the installment plan, or even old age benefits are security, you're out of your mind! That's just the trouble," he would go on, by now thoroughly excited by his subject. "We're all too dependent on one another nowadays; even the farmer who instead of raising his own food grows cotton right up to the door. All we need is a crisis for the farmer to have to find some way to eat his goddamn cotton because nobody'll be able to buy it and he's lost his credit at the canned-goods store."

"If you're thinking of a depression," the friend would lean back in his chair with the confident air of one who has lived close to the scene, "that could never happen again. The government's got to keep things running smoothly these days or..."

"Christ!" The bellow of a wild bull would cause the alarmed friend's drink to fly up and splatter over an already well-marinated porch floor. "It makes my hair stand on end to hear that crap about government control. It's just because of that that we're all such self-satisfied goddamn lazy fools!"

As suddenly as he exploded, he would become quiet again, and, looking out over the lower pastures which the last of the day now covered with a soft, golden light, he would say, "I came away from Europe because it was being destroyed by dishonesty and rottenness and greed and there was nothing I could do about it. I came home to find the security I've often dreamed about, which seemed to me perhaps existed only in America. But I haven't found it. I think it has been destroyed by people like you, who think that subsidies and old age pensions can be put in its place. If I'm ever to have that security," he would add quietly, "I can see that I'll have to make it myself; a world of my own that's solid, complete and apart. That, by the way, is what I'm going to do, right here on this farm, or kill myself trying."

The defiance and certainty in his voice, as he uttered this ultimatum, were such that the friend would either bow his head in pity at the writer's romantic naïveté, or regard him with a new sense of wonder that could never again be quite destroyed.

In either case, there was nothing on earth that friend could have said that would have made my father pause for a moment in his determination to make Malabar Farm all that he had often dreamed it would be.

9

The Farm
and the Plan

From *The Heritage*

W e came to Malabar Farm in early spring, which is an important condition in the matter of fixing a farm in the heart. We saw the winter whiteness that covered the hills and burdened the limbs of trees dissolve, under the cold misery of March rains, into thick, sucking mud which dragged off our boots a hundred times between the house and the barn. The mud and rain, chill and sorry, converged upon Switzer's Creek, swelling it to the proportions of a roaring river. It lapped at the groaning iron frame of the bridge, grating its underside with bits of driftwood and trunks of fallen trees which, once the rains had ceased, would lodge to form deep pools where trout streaked temptingly silver in the summer sunlight.

Then, as the sun appeared, its light glancing off the plows in the field and warming the plowman's chilled and sodden bones, we became aware, suddenly, of the smell of an Ohio spring. It was a combination of thawing manure in a clogged barnyard (a smell that is not unsweet), of earth opening and grass breaking through and, as one bent searchingly toward the ground, the miraculous scent of violets to convince one that the earth dared not freeze again. The warmth that had touched the earth, entered the roots of trees and made the sap stir and rise until it reached the outermost twigs and there produced the first childlike greenness, telling us that it was time, at last, to begin our farming.

It was a rudimentary job the first year, of getting as much into the ground as possible with the material at hand: a John Deere tractor, plow and disk and a pair of handsome gray Percheron mares. Farming is like that, especially in the beginning. While you dream and long for it, spring comes without warning and you are caught between rains, running helter-skelter, doing the best you can.

But all of us were taken with a wild enthusiasm for the farm, even Nanny with her inherent English love of roses and good vegetables in the damp earth, and George, who acted as kibitzer, making great fun of our labors and photographing Nanny in compromising positions as she bent over her seed beds. Together we managed, along with the planting of corn and wheat and potatoes, to root willows in the banks of Switzer's creek to bind the earth against next spring's torrents and to plant roses and lilacs about the big, ugly house into which we had moved, in the hope that its crudeness would soon be softened by their growth.

The ewes, bought with the farm, were ancient and dropped many orphans that had to be fed cow's milk from Coca-Cola bottles and raised with the goats which already more than sufficiently occupied our porch swing.

The goats were incredibly destructive: eating the bark from young saplings, making holes in the roof of the Ford station wagon, so that it was necessary, when it rained, to drive under the shelter of an umbrella. They even devoured manuscripts, and when their destructiveness became too chaotic, my father would regard us all with a look of stern resignation and murmur, "I'm afraid we'll just have to take them up to the Ferguson Place."

Our corresponding shouts of delight were not born of childish insensibility to the banishment of our pets, but of the well-founded belief that there was not a fence on that high, lonely outpost of the farm that could contain the little beasts anyway, and that their removal to the Ferguson Place was simply a poor excuse during a busy season for a walk in the woods.

With the dogs, sheep and goats at our heels, we made a strangely Zenobia White, Annie Spragg-like procession as we headed in early afternoon toward the woods, where the sunlight pierced the shelter of the trees and touched the earth below with warm patches of light. We ran crazily from one patch to another, our feet rustling through the winter's old leaves, spreading them apart to find masses of yellow and purple violets and white trillium clustered like fallen stars among the roots of great trees.

The road we followed was impassable to cars. Sheltered by the trees, its earth was always damp and cold, even in the drought of August, and in many places it was worn away to a bare shelf of sandstone and shale over which spring water trickled from somewhere deep in the earth. Walking along this road in the shade of the tall trees, one had the sensation of having come unexpectedly upon a part of a great, enclosed world which had avoided, or perhaps even defied, progress. It seemed almost as if the noise and clatter and brassiness of the modern age were prohibited here and, knowing this, one felt extremely grateful. At the top of that road, we passed through a sagging gate and came upon the great dome of wind-swept grass that was the Ferguson Place, high above the Ohio country.

There was an orchard of peach trees, the fruit of which was small and touched with the concentrated sweetness of fruit gone wild with time. And near by, a pair of tall spruce trees creaked and groaned in the wind over the front steps — all that was left — of a house that had been razed to the ground long ago. No one knew how the house was burned but it stood as another proof that civilization had been tried on the Ferguson Place and, like an illness, cast off.

It was as impossible to drag heavy machinery up that weather-beaten road as it was to drive a car, and so my father made the Ferguson Place into an immense pasture for the herds of beef cattle. With time, as they roamed over the land, the cattle trampled out much of the thorn and berry bush and seeded white and red clover with their manure so that the earth flourished and grazing became lush and plentiful.

The cattle grew fat and dropped healthy calves and thrived in their lonely life above the trees. And whenever we human beings climbed the hill to look them over or find a little peace of our own on the Ferguson Place, they all came running to greet us as if they had had their fill of solitude and would like to "get shed" of it for a long while.

Sometimes we'd come in the evening to collect fallen branches and trees which had died of age or been broken by wind or lightning. As the light faded from the sky, we would build an immense bonfire and settle down to eat steak and roast corn, drink boiled coffee, sing songs and tell stories as the fire roared upward and sent its sparks toward the star-lit hood of the sky. Then the cattle would gather all around us in a circle and stare entranced, their white and roan and black faces oddly illuminated in the dancing light of the fire.

That was as near as the Ferguson Place ever came to being "civilized" in the present sense of the word, and that was quite near enough. No swarms of cars full of curiosity seekers, no one who would have sought that hidden place simply out of a desire not to miss anything ever got to the top of the hill. For only those who loved a long walk in the wood for no other reason than to smell the forest smell, know its lights and shades and coolnesses and the solitude beyond, could go there any time they chose -- on foot. Only they, at any rate, would have understood it.

For all of us at Malabar it was a private place where one could sort out one's own troubles or, if we were filled with some special joy, shout it to the wind up there, with only the grasses and trees and wild creatures startled in a fence row to share our abandon. All of us respected the sanctity of its seclusion and no one ever accompanied anyone else up that steep, forested trail without first being invited.

Undoubtedly, the world's tormented souls would be in far better shape if every man had a Ferguson Place to go to or, at least, if every man understood the full value of such private beauty and solitude.

Certainly this was so in the case of my father. The only emotions he ever really cared to show were those of rage and amusement. The rest he kept for the Ferguson Place. He could not have become neurotic, for he was too strong, too healthily explosive, but it would have been infinitely more difficult for him to live and to think things out had it not been for that lovely, untamable land above the trees.

On those goat-exiling days, we were noisy and exuberant and full of adventure. We covered most of the Ferguson Place, climbing to its crest and then down to the other side to sit on the houseless steps for a time, smelling the fragrance of old spruce needles and young lilac flowers and speculating on the memories of the log cabin which had been the Fergusons' dwelling before the house had been built, and which was sinking now under the weight of storms and wild honeysuckle back to the rich earth from which it had arisen. In fifty years — soon in time, distant in a lifetime — there would be nothing left but the lilac and the spruce if only (and that was our silent hope) progress could continue indefinitely to be defied.

When we had rested a little, we returned home by devious trails. My father had by then forgotten our existence and wandered off on his own, leaving us to find our way as best we could.

More often than not, his head full of new ideas aroused by his walk through the woods, he would not turn home without first stopping at the house of Max Drake, which stood sheltered by an immense aged elm tree on the other side of Switzer's Creek.

Max was the farm manager, a darkly handsome young man, who had the strong, square hands, good humor and soft, unruffled speech that one finds among those who have been raised in the country with a great love and understanding of all that is country living.

Among those who were, as he put it, "too old and 'sot' in their ways, or ... too young and too eager, too innocent of the hard work that is inevitably a part of farming," the Boss had been looking for Max for a long time. When at last he found him, he wrote of him: "He was himself the son of a good farmer .... He was interested in anchoring the soil and salvaging what remained of our good land. And he was interested also in the whole intangible side of a farmer's life which had to do with farm institutes and square-dancing and fun."

These, evidently, were what my father considered the necessary prerequisites of a good farm manager, and he was right. In finding Max he made an excellent choice, probably the best in his lifetime. For not only was Max all these things; he was intelligent and curious and had a mind and will of his own.

I think Max became, as most people did, deeply attached to the Boss from the start. Certainly he had enough vision to respect and admire in my father an even wider vision which could perceive magnificent horizons and encourage others to see them and (though he often failed himself) gain them. Yet Max was never overimpressed. He was aware as well that such an imagination was likely to lift a man like my father to such heights that he might never again regain the not quite so bright reality from which he had risen, to see things as they were. Thus, while Max's wife, Marion, a handsome, auburn-haired young woman with a shy, hospitable country manner, served them beer and sandwiches, Max sat down with an enthusiastic but occasionally dubious look on his face as together he and my father went over the plan of the farm.

Thomas Wolfe is right, of course. You can't go home again.

For in the space of a lifetime people and places and situations change so drastically that the "old life" loses its place in the whirling confusion of new inventions and growing populations, new conceptions of living and the politics to fit them. Yet that was what my father tried to do in the beginning at Malabar Farm. In many ways, he failed, for it was no longer possible in this day of interdependence to return fully to the old life in which a man's world is entirely his own. That era, except for a few remote regions of the world, is finished. My father had declared so himself over twenty years ago, in *The Farm*. But of course in pushing constantly into the future we need not break all ties with the past; and even though in many ways it was a failure, the first plan of Malabar Farm served as a basis for another kind of richness to come, to be recognized and shared by a great many people, giving them a new vision and lease on life.

The plan was roughly that of a co-operative farm, on which each family would earn a good salary, have a house rent free and all the necessities except those staples that could not be grown on the farm. In order to provide these necessities, it was to be a general farm, with beef and dairy cattle, hogs, and chickens, a large common vegetable garden and fruits in season: grapes, currants, gooseberries, peaches, plums and tart apples, and, of course, the maple-sugar bush restored to working order to sweeten our country meals. My father was to finance the whole thing until a profit was made, and then, after taking the first 5 per cent for himself, the profit was to be divided among the families who lived and worked on the farm.

Sometimes, perhaps because even then — though I understood little of what they talked about — the atmosphere of beer and pickles, cigarette smoke and farmers talking about the land somehow fascinated me, my father used to take me along on the return through the wood, from the Ferguson Place to the Drakes' house. Then I would sit back in one of Max and Marion's comfortably shabby armchairs and listen as they went over the plan.

When the Boss discussed contour plowing, the planting of legumes to restore and enrich the soil, or allowing the forest which had been grazed down by sheep and cattle to grow back thick and lush once more, Max would lean forward, at times almost falling out of his chair with an eagerness and enthusiasm he could not contain. But then the conversation would turn to the subject of feeding ourselves almost entirely from the farm and suddenly Max would lean back again almost as a passenger seated in a car next to a reckless driver automatically leans back and puts his foot out to brake the disaster he knows it is not within his power to avoid.

"Somehow, I just can't believe in it," he would say in his soft, unargumentative voice, "not with the cost of machinery and labor what it is today. Why, more than half those things you can buy cheaper than you can raise them yourself."

This comment, placed so calmly, as an unalterable fact, before my father, caused the usual noisy reaction. "Good Christ, that's just what I've been trying to get across ever since I got back to this country," and then he would begin all over again about the sad plight of the farmer who grew cotton up to the door and ate canned vegetables in midsummer.

Still, when the speech was over, Max would retaliate in his quiet way, wondrously unperturbed, it seemed, by the uproar. "I see your point; see it very well. But I guess we have to live with it, Mr. B., or go broke trying to match a factory hand's wages. That's why my dad sold his hogs and chickens and stayed with just the dairy. Things got too complicated. Couldn't even find a good hand and couldn't do it all himself. Get into too many things here and we'll have the same kettle of fish. Nobody wants to work on the farm any more."

But the Boss was never one to agree he had lost an argument — especially one in which his heart was so set on the rightness of what he had said; and seeing that his adversary was not going to "scare easy" he would try a new tactic. Regarding his farm manager with a fatherly look of pity, he would begin again.

"I really can't blame you, I suppose, for these damned half-baked ideas. Where'd you go? Ohio State? Not that it makes any difference. But just listen to me for a minute, and remember, I am twice your age and I've seen quite a lot — a hell of a lot more in fact than any of your autocratic college professors quoting from revised editions of that goddamn bible, *Morrison's Feeds and Feeding*, year after year. What they know about economics you can put in a U.S.D.A. pamphlet and chuck it into the wastebasket.

"Now listen to me. You never saw the kind of farm I'm talking about because they did away with it here before your time. But it still exists in places like France and Belgium, a progressive, thrifty island of security, not of the kind that buys an icebox every year. That's phony. But of the kind where a man can dig himself in, in times of disaster, live well, feed himself and his family and even his friends. Do you see what I mean?"

Max, seeing the trend of conversation moving in a direction beyond his reach, would grow quizzical.

"I'm afraid I don't know much about France and Belgium, sir. But if you'll excuse my saying so, it seems to me that I've heard from you yourself that Europe's growing old and kind of stagnant.

Our country is young and dynamic — do you think you can fairly compare the two?"

"Stagnant!" Remembering with a sudden upsetting clarity a dissertation he'd brought forth the night before about Europe's creeping senility, the Boss would seem to feel a certain sense of stagnation himself. But as rapidly as he had fallen into Max's well-set trap, he pulled himself out by rejecting the argument from the contradictory point of view and beginning afresh on the ills of progress in America.

"You're right. We're a rich country. I won't deny it, the richest country in the world, and we got that way by taking what the farmers started for us and building a great industrial economy on top of it. But now, for the love of Christ, our 'standard of living' is pushed down our throats morning, noon and night. We feel as though we must work, live, buy and buy more to maintain it. The fear of losing it has made us into a lot of gullible nincompoops."

He would glower for a moment at Max and then seemingly soften again with pity. "You can't know, Max, how can any young American who has to fight against this incredible swamp of propaganda know that there are other things besides a standard of living, such as roots, and land passed on from generation to generation. You've heard of the wines of Alsace and Burgundy? How do they do it from century to century?

"No, wait a minute, they're not toiling slaves as you picture them, but small prosperous farmers who send their sons to universities and to know the world."

Max would remain silent for a moment after Boss had spoken, caught at last in the shrewdly descriptive web. He'd never thought of it that way before, of having the standard of living forced down his throat, but perhaps it was true. He'd had an answer for every one of those arguments about "cotton up to the door," but now indeed where were they? Undoubtedly, it would have helped a great deal if he could have gone off on an extensive tour of the vineyards of Burgundy before giving his response. But his one feeble pawn, the recollection of what the Boss had said the night before about Europe's growing stagnant, had gotten lost somewhere in a rich, tantalizing glow of often irrelevant but strangely convincing words. To find the thread it would have been necessary to think all night. So, laughingly,

Max would, without surrendering, put an end to the argument by saying, "All right, sir, you've got me by the tail. I disagree about this business of general farming and self-sufficiency. I don't think it will work. But I guess the only way is to give it a try."

This said, the two would turn toward the plan again, in their faces youth and eager, sleepless excitement, not unlike that of a revolutionary's, defiant against the world. And soon they would be engrossed in the more pressing details of remodeling broken-down barns, restoring eroded fields and bramble-strewn, grass-bare hills and earning themselves a bit of money.

As they talked, the moon rose to edge the thin spring clouds with silver, and in my armchair I fell asleep unnoticed and forgotten, often until the small hours of dawn.

Max Drake Remembers Bromfield

To help celebrate the 100th anniversary of Louis Bromfield's birth, the Ohio Ecological Food & Farm Association held a special commemorative workshop at its 1996 annual conference at Muskingum College in New Concord, Ohio. The speakers included Gerry Payne, a volunteer guide at the park who lived on Malabar as a child while his father worked on the farm in the '40s; Louis Andres, manager of Malabar Farm State Park; George DeVault, and Max Drake of Reading, Mich. Drake was personally hired by Louis Bromfield as the first manager of Malabar Farm. Bromfield's two-page vision of his ideal farmer — the job description and yardstick he used to measure scores of would-be managers — begins on page 186 of this book in the chapter "A Good Farmer."

"Looking for all these qualities among a hundred or more strangers was not an easy job," Bromfield explained in Pleasant Valley, *"but I found them at last in a young fellow called Max Drake. He was himself the son of a good farmer. He had a brilliant record in the state agricultural college. He was interested in anchoring the soil and salvaging what remained of our good land. And he was interested also in the whole intangible side of a farmer's life which had to do with farm institutes and square-dancing and fun."*

Here, in his own words, is how Max Drake remembers Louis Bromfield:

I was 32 when I went there and I'm not that age anymore. I grew up in northwestern Ohio, which is pretty much flat land in comparison to what we found at Malabar Farm. I went to Ohio State University and spent four years there. There weren't any jobs available in '33, so I stayed on. I was making 22 cents an hour milking cows six hours a day — by hand. The bank holiday came. The university owed me money. I owed them money. Then they said, "Well, go to graduate school, anyway. We won't charge you anything."

Next I got a job down on the Ohio River managing a dairy farm. They had gone through three fortunes already and they expected me to make it pay. I left there six months later and became a county agent in Medina, Ohio. After five years I decided I wanted to get my hands into something. I mean education is fine, but it wasn't really for me. So I read that Louie was looking for somebody and I interviewed in Oberlin and then again in Mansfield. He tried to get me drunk that day at lunch. He was on his third martini and he got me into two of them. I think he enjoyed seeing how folks would react when they got more under their belt than they should have. That's the way he knew what they were really like.

I was at Malabar about six months before Louie came down. We had two little kids at that time and we lived in what was called the Ceely Rose Home. They had remodeled it so it was nice and livable with the big elm tree and the spring, but he didn't tell us that she had killed both parents until after he was sure we were going to be staying a while there. I don't think he wanted us to know that might be a haunted house. It was close to six months before Louie and his family got moved into the Beck House, which was being remodeled so that it would be livable. And that is now the youth hostel. So when the Big House was finished, they moved out of there and we moved in.

Long story, but one of the first things I did when I went down there was kind of take inventory of what we had. I lived with the Herrings, who had owned the property and showed it to Louie. Real nice people. She was a good cook. But Clem was as worn out as the soil and the equipment. Had a couple of old horses and nothing but some old horse-drawn equipment that had long since seen its best days and when I finished putting together what we had it wasn't very much. We were going to have to start right from scratch and get some tractors and equipment in here. And that was fine with Louie. What we found on the farm, honest to goodness, were several gullies that you could lose a horse in, bury it and nobody would ever know it was there. The soil on that farm was very loose, sandy alluvial soil and really would wash away and did. So one of the first things I said to Louie was, "I don't know how to farm this land. I've got to get somebody to help." Friend of mine, we went to school together, Herschel Hecker, was over at Mt. Gilead and he was in charge of the Soil Conservation District.

Louie and George Hawkins left for India to finalize the book *The Rains Came* or the movie, I don't know which. That was the first summer of '39 and they were gone about six weeks. Well, I got Herschel over and he drew out a plan. I told Louie what I was going to do. I didn't tell him I was going to go whole hog and finish it. But, anyway, Herschel worked out this program. They had folks over and did the surveying and laid out diversion ditches and changed the fences and put in contour strips. When we got finished I said, "It's going to take quite a bundle to do that." "No," he said, "the CCC is ready and I got enough of 'em we can bring 'em in anytime you want to. I said, "Well, I'm supposed to be in charge, so bring 'em in!" About three months later we had everything changed around and you wouldn't know the farm. Louie got home, he didn't know it, either. And he kind of blew his stack. I thought I was going to lose my job right then and there. But he soon saw what it would do. Diversion ditches right where the gullies were would drain that water off on a slope so that it wouldn't gully.

I spent four years with him. And we didn't agree on everything. One of the first things he said was that we had to use *all* of the land, like they did in France. And I said, "Well you can't get closer to the fence rows. The tractor won't plow any closer than that." And he said, "We gotta do it!" I said, "Well, I'll get you a shovel. I'm not gonna do it." That was our first disagreement. But, he didn't do it, either.

Louie had a feeling that that farm should be totally self-sufficient. I mean produce everything under the sun except tea and coffee. It was to be his dream farm, his place in the world. And I couldn't quite buy all of that. And as we developed the plan, he decided he would take care of the gardens and that sort of thing and I'd just simply look after the farm.

Louie had come home to a dream. The first introduction I had to Louie was *The Farm*. It was recommended reading when I was in school. I got through a couple of chapters and found it so dull I didn't finish it, so I didn't have a very good introduction to Louie. But that's beside the point.

Louie was a — I wish there was some way to tell you how much he really loved the land and particularly Malabar Farm land. I can't commence to tell you. Because it was a dream that he came home to and after being in France for years before Hitler chased him out and burned all of his books and they decided it was time to get out of there, so he came home to this Pleasant Valley that was where he really grew up as a boy. And so he was coming home. There is no way that I can quite feel about Malabar and about that land the way he did. But I hope I had some influence on what happened. No man in America has popularized soil conservation in any degree to what Louie Bromfield did.

Louie was not an organic farmer. We added fertilizer where we needed it and most of those soils were worn out and needed it. We attempted to do some mulching with vetch in with oats. It was some experience. We only did it once. We did buy a one-row drill and I drilled with one horse down the corn rows to put in rye so we'd have a cover crop. We tried some things without equipment to do it, is what I'm trying to say. We felt we knew what we needed and we tried different things to achieve it. Today, Louie would be one of the greatest exponents of no-till farming that ever lived. As I say, we sort of tried it ourselves, but we didn't have the equipment or know-how.

When I decided to leave, George Hawkins — you gotta know George, bald headed, short — but George was Louie's right hand and left hand. George stopped me on the tractor one day and said, "I made arrangements. You can't leave, in the first place. You're the only person on this whole damn earth who can talk about the thing that Louie loves the most, and that's this damn farm." George didn't like the farm. And he said everything that Louie wrote about the farm was trash. So you folks that are publishing, keep on doing it because I don't think it was trash.

But anyway, he said, "Made arrangements. You're to go with us tonight. We're gonna go into Chicago. He's gonna stay there, we'll go to a club and then you and Louie are going on to Des Moines." Louie was to talk at the Iowa State Chamber of Commerce farmers night. We get in there in the wee hours of the morning and we go out to Henry Wallace's farm. Had to cross the Des Moines River. Terrible rains. Flood stage comin' down and you could see the river was really boiling. We get out to the farm and he was raising hogs on concrete slats. Louie said, "It'll never work. Hog has to wallow in mud. It'll never work!" We go back across the river again and stop at "Ding" (Jay) Darling's. Great cartoonist, well-known at that time for agriculture and conservation. I had happened to meet him when I was at school, just by accident, so I was really impressed when I was in his shop and saw what he was doing.

At the banquet that night I could see that Louie was set, primed because he had that group of people. Now, mind you, here were some top-flight best farmers in Iowa, the best research, I mean everybody who knew anything about agriculture was there that night. There were somewhere between five and six hundred of 'em. And he had them eating out of his hand. In his talk, not only were the banks going down that river, the outhouses were going down the river, the farms were going down the river and he laid it on. "Now," he says, "what you've got to do is what we have done at Malabar! We started to do contour farming. The soil has responded. We've got springs that have started flowing that never flowed for years." Well, we cleaned 'em out, that's the reason they flowed. He didn't say that. That was because we were doing strip cropping. And, he said, "Our oats yields were up 50 percent last year. And our corn yields" — Every time he pulled a fact out of the air like that I'd go down in my seat, I was sitting right up beside of him. When it was over, believe me, they all lined up to shake his hand. Nobody wanted to see me. I got off in the corner and was kind of enjoying what was going on and somebody put their arm up over my shoulder and I looked and it was Ding Darling. "Max," he said, "don't worry about it. Somebody's got to scare the bejesus out of 'em." I never worried about it again. I don't care how much he exaggerated, he got his points across. He got people concerned and just was great. I loved the guy.

10

The Big House

From *The Heritage*

"There is a kind of aura about every house I have ever entered, so strong that I believe I could tell you a great deal about the owners after ten minutes spent within the walls — whether the wife was dominant, whether the family was happy or unhappy, and almost exactly the degree of education and culture and knowledge of the person who built and furnished and lived in it." -- L.B.

How true were those words written by my father when applied to his own house on the hill overlooking the lower pastures of Malabar Farm. If the Presbytère was a reflection of his character, the Big House was even more so. For the walls of the Presbytère echoed still with soft footsteps of ancient monks, but although an old Ohio country way of living was blended into the building of the Big House, still the laying of every floorboard and the raising of every wall originated in the heart and head of its owner.

Only a man smitten with an irrepressible love of theatrics and grandeur could have built in the living room of a farmhouse a mirrored wall, spangled at the top with forty-eight gilt stars and a golden American eagle, or installed an old pink marble fireplace from some long-past great house in New Orleans, or covered the grand, sweeping double stairway with deep red plush carpeting.

This accomplished, my father, with a fanatic hatred of the protective fussiness of middle-class housewives, proceeded to trudge up those stairs daily with boots thoroughly muddied from tramping in the fields. Before that enormous gilt-spangled mirror in the living room he laid a carpet with a bright enough design in it to disguise the spots made by countless generations of puddling puppies. And because variety is the essence of life, he adorned that elegant and beautiful marble mantelpiece with a sculpture of his favorite dog, created with mystical dexterity out of clay by his daughter Anne, a handsome bust of Lafayette, a pig's embryo preserved in plastic and a clod of Malabar's most fertile topsoil.

He conceived of a house with many rooms for many different people and made them spacious and cheerful enough to suit everyone's longing for lightheartedness and warmth and a noisily rambunctious and yet inexplicably peaceful existence. The old chairs from the Presbytère, still covered in their faded Brittany cloth, came to rest within the walls lined with books and gay paper patterned in a design of strawberries and cool, green leaves. The guest rooms were large and airy, and the sunlight filtered through clean muslin curtains. The little lavatory beside the front door had a gilt mirror, gold and red velvet curtains out of *Nana* and a photograph of a fat and bonneted garrulous American mother-in-law declaring in large print, just beneath her pouting bosom, "Rest room, hell; I ain't tired. Where's the can?"

One could seek and find laughter any time one wanted in the Big House, or peace, or solitude, or good company. And one's rage or grief was given vent and quickly lost in the atmosphere of a house big enough and diverse enough to allow each of its inhabitants to live as he pleased.

The Big House grew as an immense addition to the simple, kindly, two-story frame house that my father had bought with the part of the farm called the Herring Place and which looked across the lower pasture and Switzer's Creek to the "mail-order house" where we were encamped.

Unlike the "mail-order house," which my father described in *Pleasant Valley* as having been built without knowledge or taste or regard for beauty, but simply to show off the success of its owners, there was nothing pretentious about the house of Clem Herring, from its big roseate-and-yellow sandstone kitchen in the cellar, to the sitting room and parlor for deaths, births and marriages on the first floor.

The twin doors of those rooms opened onto a simple stoop from which Clem and his wife had watched the setting sun fill the valley with a pale bronze light for perhaps fifty summers or more. They had tended their land as best they could, but in the end they had to give it up because of a common tragedy which often occurs to people who love the land. Their children had not inherited their love and there was no one, now that they were old and feeble, to look after things. The farming strain, as it so often does in America, had quickly run out.

The Herring house, like so many in Ohio, gave one, on seeing it, a yearning to live as one might have lived as a child, amidst old, worn and indestructible things, sheltered by the trees and untroubled by the world. And, oddly enough, in spite of its new scope and grandeur, when my father added on the Big House, room by room, level by level, he managed to maintain this sense of quiet and continuity with an old and dignified country past. He did it with wooden porticos and cast-iron pillars in designs of grapes and leaves from old houses along the Ohio River; with here a fanlight from a house in the original Mormon settlement of Kirtland, and there dormer windows copied from an old inn at Zoar. He did it by adding one wing after another, slowly and thoughtfully, as if, indeed, he had in his mind taken on the form of different persons in different generations, beginning simply and expanding the house as the farm had grown and prospered. The final effect was such, when all was completed, that it was difficult to remember, even for those who lived there, which had come first: the old orchard behind, the great white barn below, the broad-leafed catalpa and giant black walnut trees on the lawn, or the house itself, so comfortably shaded, so at ease in its setting that it might have been there for centuries.

There were plenty of places in that house, once we had moved into it, where my father could have gone to read over and answer the countless letters he received every day. He tried them all, one by one. But for some strange reason, in the end, he came to spread his correspondence over the dining room table and work there for most of the morning every day.

The door from the pantry to the dining room never stopped swinging with the passage of children and dogs and people on flying errands. With every fresh entry the papers on the table flew up and scattered in great white drifts while my father glared at the door and struggled hopelessly with coffee cups and ash trays to secure order. And yet, although this must have occurred a hundred times every morning, he doggedly insisted on holding his ground.

The dining room in early morning was especially delightful, for the sun shining through its large bay windows seemed to bring the garden and the farm right into the house. Through the front window, one could look out over the lawn and watch beyond the black walnut tree the boys with the wagons and tractors passing by on the road below in the healthy, busy activity of a farm's green season. Through the back window, one saw the orchard and calf pasture, full of ornery long-legged heifers and bull calves, kicking their heels and sending up sparks of dew in the morning freshness; or a chipmunk frozen on the fence, caught in the act of stealing last year's berries from a bank covered with white multiflora roses.

Within, the sunlight shone on walls of baroque Austrian green which might have been too violent but for the softening effect made by the lovely faded colors of old French prints of fruits and flowers, the white borderings of woodwork and the sparkling crystal chandelier — an immense and intricate work which hung over the center of the table and gave the room, which was otherwise simple and countrified, the air of being always ready for a gala affair.

The buffet which had supported the burden of so many Sunday lunches at the Presbytère sagged cheerfully, like a handsome old woman whose fine features can only be enhanced by the ravages of age, against one bright green wall. The sight of it always managed to renew in my father his satisfaction at having succeeded in rescuing his beloved French furniture from destruction by the Germans.

The furniture stood now, safe forever, in this beautiful house he had created all by himself. And so, sitting in the dining room in early morning, struggling with wind and mail and all, he could look out the great bay window over the farm, glance about him and think to himself, "Everything is here that I have ever really wanted," and, so saying, come very near the truth.

We watched the Big House grow and came in the very beginning to love it with the eager love of children who have scampered over a house's foundations and played hide and seek among its roofless walls as gradually they rose toward the open sky. Then, one day, the big front door, set in its handsome white portico, with the potbellied figure of Ganesha, the Indian God of Plenty, in a niche above, stood ready to be opened.

My father grasped the handle and pushed it open. And, as Nanny stood by clutching her hair and agonizingly shrieking, "Ooh, ooh, ooh, oh, damn the ruddy mutts," seven boxer dogs leapt into the hall and, slobbering and panting, sped on muddy feet from one room to the next before they returned at last to welcome us in.

There it was, finished at last, shining and new, smelling still of fresh-sawed wood, paint and wax, yet already strangely homely with the old things: the Valois chaise longue and rotund Norman bureaus, like old friends turned up unexpectedly to blunt the shock of one's over-new surroundings.

That was on the first day, in the spring of 1940. Before very long, all the rooms were filled with people who had come for a weekend or forever. And by the time autumn came, the polished floors were worn dull in familiar paths, and the chintz-covered sofas were pleasantly faded. Lafayette on the mantel had been accustomed, it seemed, to sharing his laurels with the pig's embryo, the clod of earth and Voltaire, who sat — as in France — among his books on the other side of the room.

From the little balcony off the nursery, Nanny's petunias hung in purple and lavender frills like the indiscriminate flounces of an old lady's petticoat. Wisteria had clambered over the iron pillars of grapes and leaves and invaded the portico, where sparrows had set up housekeeping protected by Ganesha's numerous outstretched arms. And already to everyone it seemed as though the Bromfields had lived in the Big House at Malabar always.

11

The View From Mt. Jeez

From *The Heritage*

My father followed up *Pleasant Valley* with two more books, *Malabar Farm* and *Out of the Earth*, each compiled from a new store of understanding and knowledge that had come to him from the years of continually deeper involvement with life on the farm. In chapters such as "Farming from Three to Twenty Feet Down" and "The World Can Feed Itself If It Wants To," he managed to describe the vast complexity of agriculture, which is at once a science, a business, a gamble and the basis for the survival and happiness of the world.

In other chapters, such as "The Farm Pond," he brought alive, in the quiet consideration of a spring pond from dawn until dusk, the small and fascinating world which exists and is multiplied time and again in every facet of farm life.

With the publication of these books, it didn't take long to discover that there were a great many people who shared my father's misgivings about the unstable, almost too dynamic, rootless rush of American life.

And there were others as concerned as he was about the manner in which, year after year, our soils were being depleted and our resources wasted by poor, unimaginative farming methods which had existed ever since our country's beginning, as if, indeed, there were still virgin soils to be squandered.

In a way it was surprising, in a time of constant pressure of superficial distractions from thought, how many seemed to read *Malabar Farm* with eagerness and an innate longing. Perhaps we forget after all the permanence of values such as my father rediscovered. Man cannot live without satisfying those basic needs to use his hands and his brains and create the roots which bind him to the earth. My father was sure of it. And once they had read his point of view, there were many who, if they did not agree wholeheartedly with him, felt their own ideas akin enough to his to make them want to come and talk it over.

There were, of course, a liberal number of crackpots, who, having read his words, believed they had discovered a Messiah. Their letters provided exquisite dinnertime entertainment when the Boss, leaning back in his chair and decorously adjusting his reading glasses, quoted in reverent tones — "I want nothing more than to touch the hem of your garment"; or with the tremor of desperation in his voice, "What does it matter to me that you have a wife and three children? Nothing seems to matter any more"; or with a voluptuous moan, "Oh, I would I were a vampire bold!" This last went on interminably, in rhymed couplets. If the writer had made true her vows, we would undoubtedly have found the Boss, a marvelous spectacle for the tabloids, wrung dry and flung over a cliff somewhere with a couple of mysterious marks in his jugular vein. But the poor woman evidently hadn't the courage of her convictions and so remained, as her intended victim so often described her and her epistolary colleagues, "better imagined than seen."

As for the rest, the people who read *Pleasant Valley* and came to visit Malabar Farm seemed to be of a normal, hardworking, clearminded sort. They were doctors, fascinated by the relationship of man's health to the soil. They were businessmen who, at my father's age, felt suddenly that they needed something more for their free time than a game of golf and drinks at the club. The greater number of them described their feeling as simply a desire for better understanding of humanity and life itself. They were not sure how this could be achieved, but they felt somehow that it had something to do with living closer to the land.

There were other businessmen, young and vigorous and able, who had found in *Pleasant Valley* a concern matching their own, which had to do with the isolation by great industrial cities of the workingman from the land and the very roots which could provide him with stability at any time regardless of the installment plan.

There were politicians with intense, busy ambitious minds who loved to talk long into the night with a man who believed deeply that no soft comfort or governmental security was worth the price of a man's privilege to choose and direct his own life.

And there were farmers, tough-minded, experience-etched,

hard-to-convince men who took every opportunity to needle the Boss mercilessly with facts and figures. And they were grateful to find someone who wrote of farming in a simple, sympathetic language which any man who had lived on and loved the land could understand immediately. And that is how the Sunday tours began.

The visitors would arrive in the morning, bringing their picnic lunches with them, prepared to spend the day. Out along the driveway would appear a line of vintage Fords, black and quaintly sedate, belonging to one sect of Mennonites, who were freer in their ways than those who insisted still on horse and carriage. They strode about in strange, tight old-fashioned trousers and lifeless gray shirts which, like the Fords, gave a sturdy romanticism to their strong bodies and sun-creased faces ringed by prophetic beards.

Up in the paddock, beyond the waving lines of laundry and a row of young blue Douglas firs, a hundred or more cars, up to their hub caps in bluegrass and sweet white clover, would be parked beside a couple of buses with banners across their sides declaring in bright red letters some such legend as "Jackson, Michigan, visits Louis Bromfield."

There in the early morning the visitors wandered at will, inspecting the beehives in a grove of butternut trees on the hill, looking over the hay loft, a cattle barn and milking parlor, testing the silage with critical experienced hands. When they had satisfied their curiosity as best they could, they sat down to eat their picnic lunches under the trees, respectfully scrupulous as farmers are about litter and paper or trampling of anything delicate and green. And, when they had drunk with a tin cup from the little faucet of cold spring water by the greenhouse, they settled patiently on the lawn to wait for the Boss to appear.

He was indoors having his Sunday dinner amidst the racket of three or four simultaneous conversations, all shouted to be heard above the violent noise of Traviata roaring over the loudspeaker in the next room.

Perhaps Walter Pretzer, the greenhouse genius from Cleveland, a gentle countrified man with a sharp, intelligent mind, was giving a discourse on the effect of liquid fertilizer on hothouse tomatoes.

At the same time, it was likely that Frank Lausche, who was then Governor of Ohio, was torturing the Boss with the obnoxious recollection that twice, during what was often referred to in our household as "the Roosevelt reign of tyranny," he had voted the straight Democratic ticket.

And, cutting across both conversations, George, his entire round little body shaking with disrespectful hilarity, was likely to be regaling a titled lady with a description of her leap from "bare-footed Georgia Crakerdom" into Parisian society.

"Deny this!" With a triumphant cry that made his stiff, Balkan hair stand straight up on end, the Governor would produce some such incriminating evidence as a photo of my father and Mrs. Roosevelt apparently in intimate conversation.

"Hah! You had them stuck together! I know you crooked politicians through and through," my father would shout, leaping to his feet as if making ready for a heated speech of denial. But instead of uttering a further word on the subject and seemingly regarding his action as something unneedful of explanation, he would turn on his heel, leave his luncheon guests at the climax of their various conversations and stride through the front door onto the lawn.

The moment he appeared before the crowd, the man whose eyes in the past hour had been one moment blazing with fury and the next flooded with uncontrollable tears of laughter was completely transformed.

He became another self, one least seen by his closest friends and family: a calm, rational man, with sensible, perfectly-controlled emotions, apparently never upset by anything. It was quite obvious that this man never shouted. It was doubtful if he ever uttered a goddamn in his life. If anything about him was the same now, it was the quick, easy sense of humor and its accompanying natural charm, which even in moments of rage with us made him less frightening than he otherwise might have been.

He cut a romantic and yet gratifyingly authentic figure as he appeared, surrounded as always by his dogs and dressed as always in faded work clothes. Like Pa, if he could have thought the shenanigans of politics worth the trouble, he would have made a good politician, for people liked him immediately and, perhaps more important, he liked them. Often, in later years, when I heard George express doubt as to the worth of his exhausting himself by conducting these tours, which had increased from once on Sunday to twice and often every other day of the week as well, I heard my father give a reply, which from someone else might have sounded like hard-boiled, modern practicality. But coming from the Boss it only gave me a pang of rather poignant weariness. "You must realize one thing," he would say suddenly putting on what he must have thought to be the air of General Motors president at a board meeting, "every one of these people who come to listen to me on Sunday reads my books and buys them for his friends," and he would continue with a dreadful pomposity, "I can't afford to ignore them."

George's immediate reaction was invariably expressed in one all-inclusive word, "Nuts." For perhaps George knew better than anyone else that much as my father liked to envision himself as "capable of anything," shrewd business not excluded, he was nevertheless neither a businessman nor a salesman nor a politician. If he ever sold anything, it was because he believed in it with all his heart and mind. And if he came out to meet those gatherings of people on his lawn on Sunday afternoon, it was because he was grateful for and flattered by their recognition and because he was as interested in what they had come to talk over as they were. On no other basis could as ambitious, egotistical, thoughtful and curious a man as my father have talked so much and with such enthusiasm about one subject nearly every day for over eighteen years.

Sometimes he would sit down among the people on the broad sandstone steps that lead from the bountiful arms of Ganesha down across the lawn to the lower pastures. Sometimes, if the crowd was large, he would come around with the jeep, and leaning against it with a microphone in his hand, talk in a gentle, friendly voice which put everyone at ease.

For one like myself so used to his caged-lion antics within the household and the disrespectful results they gained, the way in which the crowd quieted at his first word never ceased to be amazing. It was as if the sound of the gentle, unassuming voice evoked a kind of loyal response from those around him so that the gossip and even the squalling of babies on the outer edge of the crowd came abruptly to an end.

"This is not a model farm," he would begin. "You have probably already noticed that there are no fancy white fences here, no registered cattle, no varnished stables. Nor is this an experimental station. We don't pretend to call ourselves scientists. We are simply farmers like yourselves, trying to combine a bit of book learning and modern theory with common sense and put the whole to practical use. One of our special prides here is that any operation in practice at Malabar can be carried out by any farmer of normal circumstances anywhere." Then perhaps he would begin to talk about the manner in which our soils and resources were being drained by the "government-supported, lazy, unintelligent squanderings of bad farmers." Of how "poor land makes poor people" describing the listless migrant workers whose ancestors had systematically plundered the rich prairie until there was nothing left by the great dust bowl from which they were forced with their meager selves and meager possessions to take flight.

Or suddenly, it would become apparent that Walter Pretzer's quiet lecture had penetrated beneath the dinner-table racket earlier, as he launched on a well-informed description of the use of liquid fertilizer.

He was seldom accurate in his descriptions. If anything, he was expansive and grossly optimistic and I think any good farmer with sharp ears and a practical eye could have tripped him on a hundred disparities. But, somehow, his audience didn't seem to care about these enthusiastic exaggerations. What seemed to be important was the picture they evoked, the whole vast scene of farm life which suddenly became complete, important and, using one of his favorite expressions, "limitless in possibilities." The common everyday practice that most of those people carried out became suddenly alive and meaningful as he described them in a way that every farmer understood but could never quite describe to himself.

A dozen times during his talk some hard-bitten, weather-beaten old doubting Thomas must have been forced to say to himself, "Well, I never thought of it that way but — yes — it's true." And just when the old troublemaker, determined to discover some soft ground somewhere, prepared himself to snag the Boss with some such confidence-shattering question as "What you got down there on those lower fields that can't be seen from the road?" — my father would look him straight in the eye, grin disarmingly and say, "Perhaps some of you would like to take a quick look around?"

The "quick look around" required two things: undying enthusiasm and a staunch heart, for even in the punishing heat of mid-summer it lasted the entire afternoon.

On one such tour, a poor old lady who had come especially to inspect our bird sanctuaries was sent flying into a swamp by five charging boxers, broke both ankles and had to be bedded down in the Big House for two weeks. Another time an old gentleman fainted from heat stroke and had to be revived with smelling salts on my mother's pink chaise longue.

But even if the flesh was vulnerable, enthusiasm seldom seemed to flag. It enabled garden club ladies, crackpots, Mennonites, grange masters, plain farmers and a good percentage of the population of Jackson, Michigan, to follow my father in a thick, rolling cloud of dust along a bumpy back road which led through every acre of cultivated land at Malabar Farm. Even the old rabble-rousing farmer with the constant look of doubt in his eyes must have been at least partially convinced of the Boss's knowledge of his land as, panting and wheezing, he paused to examine a clump of rich brown earth held out to him by the Boss, or to measure the height of a wheat field by the length of the Boss's own towering frame.

At last, just at dusk, when the sun had given up its furious attack on the human body and had relented in an almost conciliatory way, with a pale yellow light that seemed to flood the entire world with coolness and peace, my father led his still faithful tribe to the top of Malabar Farm's highest hill.

George, who had little if any respect for the Sunday visitors and regarded their admiration of the Boss as irrational and silly as a religious fanatic's faith in the ultimate reward of heaven, named the big hill Mount Jeez, in honor of my father's weekly Sermons on the Mount.

Being a swearing family who never confused our cuss words with our Christian sentiments, we were never much troubled by a title which might have seemed sacrilegious to some. We liked it because we, too, liked to make fun of the Sunday visitors. But even if we hadn't, even if there had been no visitors and no sermons, there was something about the hill which once the name had been given could never quite justify casting it off. It gave a broad view of countless hills and forests which hinted temptingly of the untamed beauty lying beneath the trees and in the half-hidden valleys. Above the forest there was a distant glimpse of the wild, lonely Ferguson Place, forever secluded and reserved for the lonely dreams of men. And just below, bending toward Switzer's Creek and the heart of things, lay the low contoured fields of the farm, in broad, ribbonlike strips of bluegrass, alfalfa, yellow wheat and dark, vigorous corn, with here and there a tall white barn and a farm pond surrounded by feathery willows, fresh and cool and half asleep.

Since the day I left Malabar Farm for good, I have climbed

many a mountain and looked down upon views more grand in many ways than the view from my father's highest hill. And yet, almost every time, looking out over the land from one or another high South American summit, I have felt a strange and, at first, inexplicable disappointment. Then suddenly a vivid memory comes to me of lying still between the grass and the sky of Mt. Jeez, looking down over my father's valley, and I have known where the difference lay. For only in a few places has there ever existed for me such a sense of devastating majesty and at the same time intimacy as in the view from Mt. Jeez.

Always in other vast scenes the sense of intimacy and civilization has somehow been overwhelmed by the huge, beautiful, parasitic wilderness, and the scene has become, rather than inspiring and reassuring, an unsettling reminder of man's continuous rift with nature. In the view of Mt. Jeez there was no such fearful sensation. Instead, one felt the continuing peace of man living in accord with the things about him. It was as if a truce had been made here between man and nature. As everywhere else, nature attacked Malabar with the heartless violence of a summer storm, intending to tear at the earth, washing it down the stream and leaving behind naked roots and the scars of open gullies. But here, man had curved the earth around the hills to hold the rain and water the plants and allow the roots to grow and secure the land. Nature, the aggressor, it seemed, had been impressed by this man's defense and somewhere in the midst of the battle one sensed that the two had become friends.

That was what I felt in my child's heart from the top of Mt. Jeez, and a great many saw what I saw, and, strangers though they were, must have felt something of what I felt. In the evening, they packed up their picnics at last and went away, some convinced, others skeptical still. Yet even the most doubting must have caught a glimpse, if only for a moment, of something far deeper and more satisfying than what life, on the surface, generally seems to provide.

My father had a simple way of putting it: "Of shallowness and dissatisfaction, happiness and a sense of accomplishment you get from life in exact degree the amount you give to it." If the view from Mt. Jeez was proof of such a statement, it was credible enough. For to it he had given the best of everything he possessed.

12

The Heritage

From *The Heritage*

Although there was no sign to tell of it, I think even a stranger arriving for the first time knew the moment he entered Malabar Farm. It happened suddenly, almost as if by enchantment, as you turned the bend in the road that led into the farm, and transported you into a world that was neither French nor American, but a little of both; and something more. It was at once romantic, earthy, garrulous and frenziedly busy, yet peaceful and beautiful as anything made by the hands of an artist who took at random hills, rivers, forests and fields and made of them a conglomeration of what he believed life itself should be.

As the Presbytère had been a reflection of my father as a young man, so was the farm the reflection of that same man grown mature and more thoughtful, more concerned with a setting down of roots and finding a reason for living beyond success. As my father grew, the farm grew with him. As he changed in his mind, the farm changed from something whose creation had been an end in itself. The Big House began to weather and bear the neglected look of something loved but forgotten in the perpetual busyness of the day. The garden on the hillside, so like the one in Senlis with its abundance and variety of carefully, personally tended plants, was taken over by periwinkle, day lilies and narcissus in season: plants that were strong enough to survive the total neglect of hands too busy discovering other things more useful, such as the best way to plant corn and legumes and fatten cattle.

Yet, as this change took place, my father never entirely gave up one life for another; never lost his love of gaiety, good food, beautiful things, or his curiosity about people. All these things gained from experience made Malabar Farm "different" from the day my father first set foot on the land to the day when suddenly, old and ill, he went away from it forever.

So, foolishly, it was still this sensation I sought when, a year after my father's death, I went back toward the farm. I had often dreamed, in the four years of our absence, of returning to Malabar; of walking over the fields and along Switzer's Creek with my father and my children at my side. In the evening, I had thought, we would sit in the big comfortable living room, listening to music, talking and laughing with the new-found ease that had come to us since our status had changed from that of father and daughter to that of friends. But now that we had at last been able to make the long trip, I would have to walk over the fields alone and, at night, return to a house whose emptiness was yet impossible for me to conceive.

On that hot July day, as we turned the bend that led into the farm, I was filled with the same elation I had so often felt coming home as a child. It was an elation I could not shake off after so many years of enchantment. It sprang up as naturally as the anticipation of seeing one you love. And then gradually, of its own accord, it seemed to die.

Beyond the multiflora rose hedge that bordered the road with its great cascades of delicate white flowers I could see the fields as they had been, heavy with beginning grain in the hot July sun. The waters of Switzer's Creek shone beneath my eyes, inviting me on a long, cool walk into the depths of the wood beyond, and in the crook of the hill I saw the Rose house under the benevolent shade of the ancient elm and my heart went out to it. And yet nothing in this scene seemed to welcome me home.

We turned up the road between the tall Babylonica willows and approached the Big House. It stood gray and weathered behind the greenery of hemlock and lilac and the tall walnut. But, though it was mid-July, there were no hurried comings and goings of tractors and wagons, no flurry of dogs rushing at us in joy and high excitement. For an instant, I thought the place to be entirely deserted, and then I saw one of the dogs on the lawn.

It was Rex, a big, beautiful, bounding, senseless pup when we had gone away, who had grown gray-muzzled in the four short years of our absence. He did not rush toward us with his usual exuberance, but simply sat and watched our approach, without curiosity. It was a stance I had often seen the dogs take when they knew somehow — by the size of his suitcase or the tone of guilt in his voice — that my father would be gone a long time and that the countless arrivals and departures during the interim held nothing for them. The dog was waiting and I realized that, in that hot July afternoon, suspended in stillness, the whole farm seemed to be waiting.

This sensation followed me wherever I went as, alone, I walked over the land: an emptiness that dampened every action from walking through fields of hay left to flower past their time, to wandering the wild roads where, in hot midsummer, blackberries hung fat and ripe for the picking along every wild, overgrown fencerow. Once I had gathered pecks of them. But now what would I pick them for? For whom would I make the jam the Boss had so vehemently denounced as "goddamn seed-strewn glue" and had eaten, all the same, until his teeth turned blue? I plucked a few and ate them, but their taste seemed disappointing.

In the end, I climbed to the top of Mt. Jeez to look down upon the view. But, as I reached the top at last and sprawled panting and exhausted in the soft grasses of my childhood, I saw that, rather than escape the sense of waiting, I had come here to my father's highest hill to meet it head on. I saw still below me the fields with their ribbonlike contours, the pond with its fringe of willows, the stream and the lakes that shone distant and peaceful among the forested hills. I looked over it all and I was touched with an odd sense of fragility, as if already that truce between one man and his land had come to an apathetic halt.

As if to emphasize the truth of this, as I looked across the valley toward the forest we had loved and respected for its inviolability from the very beginning, I saw, barely discernible in the distance, a strip of brown which ran from the Ferguson Place, cutting down through the forest to Switzer's Creek. But for the brown of deadness, like a scar amidst the lush green of summer, one would not have noticed the strip at all. But I knew what it was. I knew simply that it marked the beginning of the destruction of the indomitable, timeless world of Mt. Jeez.

Again the explanation was simple, as if reality had borne down with a kind of brutal vindictiveness upon one who, in his own world, had often chosen to ignore it. Quite simply, living as he wished to live, never considering illness, my father had spent himself short. His forfeit in the end had been the sale of his forest to pay for the hospital in which he was to die of cancer. He had lent and given often, but he had never borrowed when he was well. To have done such a thing when he knew there was no possibility of his recovery, even though there were many who would gladly have helped him, would have been unthinkable. And so in the end he had had to commit on his own land what he believed to be one of the greatest sins against life, "the ravaging of a forest."

As I looked at the gash in the forest, I knew, with a certain deep pride, that in order to remain alone, to be himself, he could have done no other thing. Yet how savage the price and why should it have been so? There is no answer, of course, except that those are the chances of life and each man must take them in his own way. And no one would have been more ready to say so than my father.

I didn't stay long at the farm, for there was nothing there to keep me. Inheritance tax, mortgage and an economic situation that was ruining many a farmer more businesslike than my father had made it impossible for us to keep the farm. It had already been sold. I had often hoped that it would fall into the hands of one of those bickering, red-faced farmers who, in their hearts, loved and understood the land as passionately and stubbornly as my father. But beyond this hope, there was nothing I could do.

I took with me when I went away a sense of futility that remained for a long time afterward. For some years it seemed to touch my every action with a sense of irony and hopelessness. And yet it seems my disappointment never really did away with my determination, my desire. In the end, in fact, I discovered that, if anything, my determination had been strengthened and at the same time as I realized this, I came to understand the reason why.

The knowledge came to me one day in one of those moments in the midst of the half-seeing uncertainty of our lives in which, for some reason, a great many things become suddenly clear.

My family and I had been traveling in Brazil, searching as we still did in our every spare moment for land. After days of driving over the deep-rutted red rivers of roads through an almost uninhabited land of open stretches of wild grasses and dense forests that sloped down, after many miles, to the sea, we came to the edge of a high plateau. Before us, a land broken by steep yellow and ferrous sandstone cliffs slanted down to forests of acacia, cedar, giant peroba and the tall, prehistoric Parana pine. Behind us, on the plateau, a rich green, fertile land stretched as far as we could see in open fields and knots of shadowy trees. We had no idea to whom the land belonged and only the fact of its great emptiness could have given us the vague hope that it might be for sale. But as we stood looking out from this high place over the lush, green and beautiful land, Carson turned to me suddenly and said, "Well, what do you think?"

Instinctively, without hesitation, as if the words had been sure in my mind for a long time, only waiting for the right moment, I answered, "Yes, of course, this is the right place."

It was, in truth, as awesome and fearful a statement as the taking of a marriage vow, for I knew simply that we meant by this to bind ourselves to this land for life. I knew that I, who loved to be in the center of things, of good company and talk, who loved the theater and had certainly seen only a small part of the world that I wanted to see, would undoubtedly have to forgo a great many of these things, perhaps forever. Yet I also knew, simply and without doubt, that if we devoted ourselves to this land, even if, in the end, we failed, every moment between would be of a rich and real value that none of us would ever regret. It was at this moment as well that with a sudden clarity I understood the reason for this certainty that abolished all the doubt and pessimism I had felt for such a long time.

The reason had begun when, as a tiny child, I had sat still on the dunes that edged the forests of Ermenonville to listen to the mating calls of deer, had eaten mushrooms by the firelight in the kitchen and danced in a room strewn with saris in an old Presbytère long ago. It had continued to grow as, later on, I had lived and grown in a house full of music and books, good food and all manner of people from harlots to prima donnas to clergymen and red-faced farmers — all of whom were good people with strong hearts, humor and a tolerant understanding of their fellow men. From that house, I had wandered over the fields of spring, searching among the high grasses for the first shivering lambs. In autumn, I had helped with the harvest and known the special pride and independence of the farmer who, more than any other man, because he lives close to the land, lives close to all that is life. And on many a hot summer day I had followed my father down the middle of Switzer's Creek, halting silently to watch the rise of a crane and then splashing noisily in the cold, cleansing waters of a swimming hole deep in the forest. And quite suddenly, as I thought of this, there came into my mind the words my father had written about Pa in *The Farm* long ago.

"What he gave them was destined to stay with them forever. It was the most precious heritage one could receive. He was a man who knew how to live. He knew the things that count."

And so, quite naturally, with little effort on my part but that of sheer enjoyment, I had come to know the things that counted. It was why I had come as a young girl to live in this distant country, which was, in the beginning, so strange to me, but in which I knew I would find a good life and friends and the exciting knowledge of things I had never before seen. It was why, in the end, I had come upon the rich and fertile and precariously promised land which I know would one day be mine.

Here, plainly, was my Heritage. And great was my fortune that it had been handed down to me by a lively teacher, a brilliant, temperamental, deeply human man, for whom, just at the mention of a new idea, life had had a way of beginning all over again in all its vigor and beauty, time after time after time.

|13|
A Good Farmer

For some strange reason, Louis Bromfield never did write a book titled A Good Farmer. *(The closest he came to such a title was a 1927 novel called* A Good Woman.*) It's doubly curious, because this would have been an easy and eminently enjoyable book for Bromfield to write. He even had a good start on it, since the subject of "a good farmer" crops up again and again in many of the 18 books he wrote after* The Farm *in 1933. This chapter is merely a sampling, a taste from half a dozen different Bromfield books of his astute observations, strong opinions and deeply held beliefs surrounding good farmers and good gardeners, which he also includes with all due respect. There are many more such "gems" left for you to discover in reading the complete text of Bromfield's books in their original form. To aid you in that most enjoyable pastime, each quotation is followed by the name of the book and the page number where it originally appears.*

A Good Farmer:
Feels the Earth

The Colonel had always been a "gentleman." He loved his land and would never have lived in any city, but he was never, like Jamie, a part of it. Jamie, in the mere necessity for physical activity, could never, like his father-in-law, have remained apart, surrounded by books and specimens, simply supervising the work. For his temperament it was a necessity that he should take part, helping with the ploughing and threshing, the harvest and the milking. He had to have the feel of the earth on his big freckled hands. The Colonel had been a squire. Jamie was a farmer.

The Farm, 55

Loves the Earth

With James Willingdon it became more and more clear that the Farm was for him simply a refuge from the disillusionments of life.

His love of the Farm was sentimental and romantic. He liked roaming over the fields with the dogs, starting rabbits and the pheasants which he hatched under white Leghorn hens who took their broods into the fencerows and with them returned to the savage state. He liked walking among his cattle in the big pasture and he liked lying under the catalpa tree in the dooryard, watching the woodflies dance. But with the work and the reality it was different. He had no farmer's blood in him, and at fifty it was not easy to change all one's life and acquire new tastes. He had no heart in the work and so whatever task he undertook went against the grain. It gave him no delight to leave a field of corn with each furrow neatly cultivated and every weed buried. There was for him no keen pleasure in the sight of a field of thick dew-wet timothy falling beneath the knives of the mowing machine. He found no real satisfaction in the smell of the earth stirred by the plow. Heaps of manure had not for him the aspect of piled-up treasure; if he did not regard it with indifference, he saw it only as a pile of filth. The sight of corn burnt by an early frost before it was ripened did not fill him suddenly with a sense of pain almost as sharp as at the sight of a friend dead, cut off before he had lived. These things he did not understand. They were simply not him. They are born in one person, and in another lacking. There was nothing to be done about it. If one lacks these reactions, they only seem over-poetic and perhaps idiotic, and one is inclined to mock at them. Yet they are real. They are what makes a true farmer, different from other men. Johnny had them, and his father had not, and because Johnny had them a kind of passion entered into whatever he did, forcing him to go on working after his strength was exhausted. Old Jamie had the feeling. Johnny's father would begin to plow or to cut hay in high spirits, moved perhaps by the beauty of the scene about him and the feel of the morning air and the sun, but after a little while he would grow bored and for the rest of the day the work was only drudgery which left him at sundown tired, baffled, and irritable. It was simply not in him. He was a "gentleman farmer" and not a real one. Like the Colonel, he loved the land, but that was quite different from the feeling of old Jamie and Johnny. Those two loved the earth.

The Farm, 327-328

Lives Close to Nature (Max Drake's job description)

A good farmer in our times has to know more about more things than a man in any other profession. He has to be a biologist, a veterinary, a mechanic, a botanist, a horticulturist, and many other things, and he has to have an open mind, eager and ready to absorb new knowledge and new ideas and new ideals.

A good farmer is always one of the most intelligent and best educated men in our society. We have been inclined in our wild industrial development, to forget that agriculture is the base of our whole economy and that in the economic structure of the nation it is always the cornerstone. It has always been so throughout history and it will continue to be so until there are no more men on this earth. We are apt to forget that the man who owns land and cherishes it and works it well is the source of our stability as a nation, not only in the economic but the social sense as well. Few great leaders ever came out of the city slums or even suburbs. In France, in England, in America, wherever you choose to turn, most of the men who have molded the destinies of the nation have come off the land or from small towns. The great majority of leaders, even in the world of industry and finance have come from there. As a nation, we do not value our farmers enough; indeed I believe that good farmers do not value themselves highly enough. I have known all kinds of people, many of them celebrated in many countries, but for companionship, good conversation, intelligence and the power of stimulating one's mind there are none I would place above the good farmer.

But there are two other qualities, beyond the realm of inquiring mind or the weight of education, without which no man could be a good farmer. These, I believe, are born in him. They are a passionate feeling for the soil he owns and an understanding and sympathy for his animals. I do not believe that these traits can be acquired; they are almost mystical qualities, belonging really only to people who are a little "teched" and very close to Nature itself.

Often enough people discover late in life that they have these qualities, without ever having known it. They did not acquire them suddenly; they were always there. It is only through the accident of a fishing trip or the purchase of a farm, they discovered them. I have any number of friends who spent all their lives as bankers or industrialists or workingmen or insurance salesman, only to discover at middle age that in reality they were farmers all the time, without knowing it. I know of no human experience more remarkable than that of men whose whole existences are changed and enriched by the discovery late in life that they have a close bond with the earth and all living things, and that they have lost vast and intangible riches by not making the discovery when they were younger.

Conversely, there are many men on farms in America who have neither that love of soil nor of animals. They are the bad farmers who have done us such great damage as a nation. They do not belong on farms. They are there, most of them, because they were born there and have not the energy to quit and go to the cities and factories where they properly belong. There are too many of them in America, and they have cost us dear.

For the good farmer, his animals are not simply commodities without personality destined only to be made into pork chops or beef steaks or to produce milk all their lives. To a good farmer, each animal has its own personality. A good farmer cannot himself sleep if his animals are not well fed and watered and bedded down on a cold winter night. Watch any good farmer showing his sheep or cattle or hogs at a county fair or an international stock show and you will understand how much he respects the animals that are linked into that chain of life which explains and justifies the whole of his activity, or watch any Four-H club boy or girl with tears in his eyes when the moment comes for him to part with the fat steer he has raised and brought to a cattle show. He has slept in the straw in the stall beside his steer for days. The steer is a part of the richness of his own existence. He will go cold himself or go without food and water before the steer shall be deprived of these things.

Pleasant Valley, 51-55

Sees, Watches & Learns

A good farmer, a "live" farmer is not one who goes into the field simply to get the job of plowing completed because he must first turn over the soil in order to plant the crops that will bring him a little money. The good, the 'live' farmer is the man who turns now and then to look back at the furrows his plow turns over, to see that the soil crumbles behind him as rich, good soil should crumble. He is the man who sees the humus in his good earth and counts the earthworms, and watches his crops as they grow to see whether they are strong or sickly and what it is that is needed to make his pastures dark and green, his corn tall and strong. He is the man who learns by farming, to whom the very blades of grass and stalks of corn tell stories. He is the man to whom good crops sing a song and poor ones convey a painful reproach. He is the man who knows that out of the soil come the answers to the questions which torment him. He is, I think, the happiest of men for he inhabits a world that is filled with wonder and excitement over which he rules as a small god; it lies with him whether his world shall be rich and prosperous or decaying and poor and wretched. He is the man who knows how deeply Nature can reward the conscientious, intelligent worker and how bitterly she can punish the stupid shiftless ones to the very marrow of their bones.

Pleasant Valley, 146-147

Tries New Ideas

Experimentation is the very essence of the "live" farmer. It is the enemy of stagnation and of evil practices, of the whole school of thought which believes that "if it was good enough for my grandfather it is good enough for me."

Pleasant Valley, 154

Is Eternal

The wisdom of the good farmer is an eternal wisdom and indestructible. As Liberty Hyde Bailey once wrote and as history has testified so many times, "The farmer is the first man and he will be the last man." The good farmer, working with soil and plants and animals, living in peace and co-operation with his neighbors, outwitting the weather or profiting by it but never ignoring it, is far nearer to the eternal truths and laws of our existence, by which we must live and within which we must find our salvation, than the workers of the industrial age, fitting similar nuts onto similar bolts eight hours a day five days a week throughout the whole of his life. When all industry lies in ruins and the industrial worker has died either in riots or against a wall in the war of brother against brother or by starvation, the farmer will still be there, tilling his bit of earth — in China, in Russia, in Germany, in the United States, everywhere.

A Few Brass Tacks, 9

Is No Slave of Technology

Of all the elements of modern society, the good, modern farmer seems to me to have understood more clearly than others the way to use the mechanical-industrial world rather than permitting it to use him. He has used machinery to increase the efficiency of his farming, to eliminate from it the drudgery which once made agriculture a kind of slavery, and to gain for himself more time from his physical work and hardship in order to employ that time for increasing his knowledge, improving his methods and his economic status and security and establishing himself as a good, intelligent and informed citizen. To be sure, there are many elements on his side — the fact that he does not live in a great city, that his work is always changing and full of variety and does not confine him to noisy steel sheds or a dusty office. Most of all he lives in nature, with the soil, with animals, with the weather and these things provide him with those fundamental values of philosophic balance, of respect for natural law and for faith, which are so largely lacking in our modern mechanical life and are disappearing more and more rapidly.

These things perhaps provide him with that wisdom and judgment which permit him to understand how to use the marvels of our mechanical world instead of their using him. The great tragedy is that there are so few good "modern" farmers that their influence upon a disintegrating age is negligible. If I wished to find a well-developed, intelligent, balanced civilized specimen of mankind in our times, I should have to seek him among the good farmers, among the foresters and the engineers engaged in building government dams and canals or in terracing, worn-out eroded land. I should certainly not find him among the industrialists and bankers of our great cities, nor among the labor leaders nor among the desiccated specialists of our universities, nor among the sterile, arrogant, materialistic philosophers of the school of Bertrand Russell. I should have to find him in the narrowing element of those who have not, in their small conceit over a carburetor or their overwhelming conceit over the atomic bomb, lost faith in something greater than all of these things — in short among the men and women who still remain, like the great and civilized men of the Renaissance, a part of nature and of the universe itself, among the people who still remain both humble and possessed of a profound and true sense of human and civilized values.

A Few Brass Tacks, 299-300

Feeds Many

It would be good to remember that at least 60 per cent of our American farmers practice in one form or another a whorish, greedy agriculture. Thirty percent are moderately good farmers and ten per cent bear the burden, out of all proportion to their numbers, of feeding the nation...

The farmer, the good farmer has in a starving world become an increasingly important and vital citizen. No young man with any aptitude for agriculture could undertake a more fascinating and, probably in these times and for years to come, a more profitable career than agriculture or one in which he could do more for the welfare of mankind. The good farmer or livestock man is no longer a 'hick,' as indeed he never was. He must always be an intelligent man of parts, knowing perhaps more about more things than any other citizen. He must know and understand something of markets, the weather, distribution, machinery, economics, history, ecology, disease, bacteriology, and many other things, but most of all he must understand the earth and the laws of God and nature which govern its maintenance and productivity. This last is a vast field and it is a startling fact that, although agriculture is the oldest calling worthy of the name 'profession,' it is only recently that we have begun to understand beyond the realms of superstition the laws which govern its relationship to our economy, our health, and indeed our survival as decent, comfortable, happy citizens. There is much that we still have not discovered or understood. In the field of experiment and research alone there exists a whole unexplored world of great fascination, for in a cubic foot of good productive soil one can find the pattern of the laws which govern the universe — laws before which political ideologies, manipulations of currency, short cuts, and all manner of man-made dodges become singularly silly and puerile.

Malabar Farm, 7-9

Works With Nature

One thing a good farmer quickly learns is that in fighting nature he will always be defeated but that in working with her, he can make remarkable and immensely profitable progress.

Malabar Farm, 83

Cherishes the Land

The good farmer is a man who knows as much as possible, never stops learning, and has the intelligence to apply his knowledge and information to the conditions and the program of his own piece of land. It is the kind of farmer we must have in the nation and in this world; it is the kind of farmer we will have inevitably because the other kind is certain to be liquidated economically, despite bribes, subsidies and price floors and their land will be taken over eventually by those who cherish it and can make it productive and maintain that productivity. In the world and even in this country, where there was once so much good land that we believed it inexhaustible both in fertility and in area, mankind, if he is to survive, cannot permit agricultural land to be owned and managed by the lazy, the indifferent and the ignorant.

As Dr. Hugh Bennett suggested recently in a memorable address at Princeton University, the time may not be so far away when in order to practice agriculture, a farmer will be required to have a certificate exactly as a lawyer or a doctor or an engineer must have today, in order to own or to cultivate the earth. Such a condition has already virtually arrived in England where food is so scarce that the poor and unproductive farmer cannot be tolerated if the people of the nation are to eat and survive. Such a measure will not be the result of any political ideology but of grim necessity.

Malabar Farm, 136

Has Faith

Every good farmer is a mystic at heart and a religious man, but a good farmer's mysticism and faith are founded upon the base of the earth itself, and so very different from what to me is that implausible mysticism of the detached spirit.

Malabar Farm, 262-263

Is Proud

There is in every good farmer a curious, overwhelming, almost malicious pride common to the human race but especially well-developed in the cultivator. It is born of satisfaction in being "smarter" than his neighbor, in having his acres look greener, in getting his crops earlier, in having fields where the hay or the pasture is heavier. And conversely there is in every good farmer a kind of perverse satisfaction in the discovery that his neighbor's fields look poorly. The sight of a poor crop in someone else's field somehow warms the heart of the farmer whose own fields are lush and green.

Often when I have been driving across Ohio with Bob, he will grin, as we pass a miserable pasture or field of yellowish weedy hay and say, "I suppose that makes you feel awfully good." And I'm afraid that sometimes it does. The pride of a good farmer is often his worst sin, but it is also what makes a good farmer and what helped to feed this nation and the rest of the world in the difficult years when lack of machinery and labor made farming a back-breaking, long-houred job. It is that same pride that makes the good farmer resist subsidies and government payments and all the paraphernalia of a "kept" agriculture. In his heart a good farmer wants to show that he cannot be "licked," and that without help from anyone he can grow abundant crops despite every handicap.

That is why a good farmer grows short-tempered and desperate when the weather turns against him. With each day of drought or flooding rain, he becomes more frustrated and savage, because the weather alone he cannot lick altogether either by machines or muscle or long hours in the field....

It is only the poor farmer who wails and looks for scapegoats or excuses for his own failures of energy or intelligence. But that, of course, may be true of the whole human race. It just stands out clearly in the case of the farmer who long ago discovered what many others rarely discover — that in life there are no "breaks" except as one makes them for himself.

Malabar Farm, 327-328

Values Results

Money is poor recompense to a good farmer; he wants his crops and the satisfaction that goes with raising them.

Malabar Farm, 340

Sees The Good

Good farmers are by nature optimistic; otherwise the uncontrollable vagaries of Nature — the floods, the droughts, the plagues of locusts — would long ago have discouraged them and the world would have been left starving.

Malabar Farm, 341

Benefits Wildlife

All good farmers engaged in a good program of land use automatically produce conditions favorable to the potential maximum population of fish and game.

Malabar Farm, 354

Builds Beauty & Peace

There are spiritual and aesthetic values to good farming just as there are brutal economic ones, and all contribute to a good agriculture, good land use, good and healthy citizens and above all, happy ones with minds which are intelligent, alert and adventurous.

Malabar Farm, 359

Saves Work & Money

The odd thing is that it takes no more labor and no more money to farm well than to farm badly — usually it means much less labor — yet a lot of farmers won't change their ways and spend a good part of their time finding excuses why their crops don't look well.

Malabar Farm, 391

Stops, Looks & Listens

The good farmer has always been and always will be a man with great powers of observation and great intellectual curiosity...

If more were explained to him of what goes on in soils, in plants, in livestock and explained in an interesting and stimulating and even controversial fashion, progress toward a better agriculture would be infinitely more sound and rapid. It would inevitably bring about more and greater contributions from the farmer himself to the science of agriculture. It could ignite a thousand sparks in a thousand young men and women who might one days make immensely important contributions to the science. The good farmer is no fool and he need not be treated as a child. He can understand the "mysteries" if given half a chance.

Malabar Farm, 400

Is Intelligent, Eager

I know of no element of our population more intelligent or more eager for information than our average good farmer.

Malabar Farm, 400-401

Takes the Good & Bad

Agriculture to the good farmer is a calling of intricate variety and fascination which he would not exchange for any other regardless of rewards in money.

On reading over this book, I noted that it appears like a many-layered sandwich in which heavy foods were alternated with light

194

ones. This was a pattern which was partly conscious and partly unconscious but it is, I think, somewhat symbolic of the life of a good farmer. There are periods of hard work and worry, alternating with periods of relaxation, delight, and satisfaction, but again they are interwoven and overlapping, and contribute to the fascination which a good farmer finds in his profession.

Malabar Farm, 402

Is Part of the Whole

Because of the weather and the fact that the good farmers live close to the earth, to the trees, to the animals and are aware, whether they choose or not, of the eternal, inexorable, ruthless and beautiful laws of creation and nature, all of them are religious men in one way or another. I do not mean by this that every farmer is a fanatic church-goer or a "shouter." That kind of farmer lives usually on marginal land, too poor even to provide a decent living. Often enough his motivation springs largely from fear and the hope for a future life less bitter and poverty-stricken than this one. Your good farmer on good land is constantly aware, perhaps more than any other element of the population, save the sailors and fishermen, of an immense plan in which compensation, order and precision are all involved. It is a plan and a force with which he must live and he learns by necessity to understand and respect it.

Malabar Farm, 403

Knows Security

In good or average times the income of the average good farmer is far larger than that of 85 percent of the rest of the population. In bad times the difference between the status of the good farmer and most of the rest of the population is the difference between that of a roof, good food, security and that of destitution and public relief.

Malabar Farm, 405

Learns and Grows

The best farmer is the man who knows every foot of his farm, the condition of the plants and of the soil and has the capacity to learn as much from his plants, his soil and his animals as any college of agriculture can teach him; and what he learns from these elements will not have to be unlearned later on because some evangelist jumped at a conclusion or because some specialist asserted as universal law some truth which has a local or regional basis but failed as truth under other conditions of soil or climate or diet in a world in which the variety of all these things is infinite.

The good farmer is the man who learns as much as he can about the vast range of things which the good farmer must know concerning veterinary science, economics, chemistry, botany, animal husbandry, nutrition and countless other fields, all of which are tied into the ancient, complex and varied profession of agriculture, and then knows how to apply this knowledge to his own problems.

Perhaps no stupider human saying has ever been formulated than the one that "anybody can farm." Anyone can go through the motions, but not 10 per cent of our agricultural population today could seriously be called "good farmers." Thirty percent are pretty good, and the remaining 60 per cent do not, through ignorance or laziness or sometimes through the misfortune of living on wretched land fit only for forests, deserve the dignified title of "farmer." Most of them still remain within the range of a completely primitive agriculture confined to plowing, scattering seed and harvesting whatever crops with luck turn up at the end of the season. That they perform these operations with the aid of modern machinery does not make them either good or modern farmers. Tragically, a great many of them actually hate the soil which they work, the very soil which, if tended properly, could make them prosperous and proud and dignified and happy men.

Out of the Earth, 5

Lives to Work

The good independent successful farmer produces both [good and highly nutritious foods]. Better than any man he knows, through his plants and animals and his daily contact and struggles with the weather, that out of the earth we come and to the earth we return...

The men and women of no other profession are as content to die when their time comes as the good farmer and his wife, for, better than the people of any other profession they know by living with earth and sky and in companionship with their fellow animals that we are all only infinitesimal fragments of a vast universe in which the cycle of birth, growth, death and decay and rebirth is the law which has permitted us to live.

What we have done with our individual lives is another question for which we ourselves must accept responsibility. If it has been a good life, full and rich, and especially if it has been lived close to the earth from which we come, there are no terrors and no yearnings for a silly heaven of pink clouds filled with angels twanging harps. Rarely does the good farmer long for any immortality better than the rich fields he has left behind him and the healthy, intelligent children who will carry on his work and his name. If there is an after-life that is pleasant and comfortable, so much the better, but he hopes that it will not be an after-life in which there is no work, for it is by work of hand and brain that he has lived a full, rich life, which leaves him at the end ready to lie down and fall asleep in the quiet knowledge and satisfaction that what he has done will live on and on after him into eternity. The good farmer is one of the ultimate peaks of evolution away from that silly one-celled creature wriggling about in the sea water of a billion years ago. He is the one citizen without whom mankind and civilization cannot exist. As that very great and vigorous old gentleman, Liberty Hyde Bailey, has put it so well, "The first man was a farmer and the last man will be a farmer."

Out of the Earth, 8-9

Is An Artist

A lot of things have changed on the farm today, but the essence of the farm and the open country remain the same. The freedom is unchanged and the sense of security and independence and the good rich food and the beauty that lies for the seeing eye on every side and, above all, that satisfaction, as great as that of Leonardo or Shakespeare or any other creative artist, in having made something great and beautiful out of nothing. The farmer may leave his stamp upon the whole of the landscape seen from his window, and it can be as great and beautiful a creation as Michelangelo's David, for the farmer who takes over a desolate farm, ruined by some evil and ignorant predecessor, and turns it into a Paradise of beauty and abundance is one of the greatest artists.

Of course, I am talking about the good farmer, the real farmer, and not the category of men who remain on the land because circumstance dropped them there and who go on, hating their land, hating their work and their animals because they have never discovered that they do not belong there, that they have no right to carry in trust the greatest of all gifts Nature can bring to man — a piece of good land, with the independence, the security, the

197

excitement and even the splendor that go with it. The good farmer, working with Nature rather than fighting or trying to outwit her, may have what he wants of those treasurers which are the only real ones and the ones by which man lives — his family, his power to create and construct the understanding of his relationship to the universe, and the deep, religious, humble sense of his own insignificance in God's creation.

The good farmer today can have all the good things that his father knew and many that his father never knew, for in the modern world he lives with all the comforts of a luxurious city house plus countless beauties and rewards forever unknown to the city dweller. More than any other member of our society — the farmer has learned how to use machinery to serve him rather than his serving machinery. That is a very great secret indeed and one which the other members of our society need desperately to learn.

Out of the Earth, 299

Knows Real Satisfaction

Certainly one of the happiest men is the good farmer who lives close to the storm and the forest, the drought and the hail, who knows and understands well his kinfolk the beasts and the birds, whose whole life is determined by the realities, whose sense of beauty and poetry is born of the earth, whose satisfactions, whether in love or the production of a broad rich field, are direct and fundamental, vigorous, simple, profound and deeply satisfying. Even the act of begetting his offspring has about it a vigor, a force, a directness in which there is at once the violence of the storm and the gentleness of a young willow against the spring sky...

I know of no intellectual satisfaction greater than that of talking to a good intelligent farmer or livestock breeder who, instinctively perhaps, knows what many less fortunate men endeavor most of their lives in vain to learn from books, or the satisfaction of seeing a whole landscape, a whole small world change from a half-desert into a rich ordered green valley inhabited by happy people, secure and prosperous, who each day create and add a little more to the world in which they live, who each season see their valley grow richer and more beautiful, who are aware alike of the beauty of the deer coming down to the ponds in the evening and the mystery and magnificence of a prize-winning potato or stalk of celery, who recognize alike the beauty of a field with a rich crop in which there are no "poor spots" and the beauty of a fine sow and her litter.

These are, it seems to me, among the people who belong, the fortunate ones who know and have always known whither they were bound, from the first hour of consciousness and memory to the peace of falling asleep for the last time never to waken again, to fall asleep in that tranquility born only of satisfaction and fullness and completion. In a sense they know the whole peace of the eternal creator who has built and left behind him achievements in stone, in thought, in good black earth, in a painting upon a wall or some discovery which has helped forward a little on the long and difficult path his fellow men and those who come after him. It is these individuals who belong and need not trouble themselves about an after life, for at the end there is no terror of what is to follow and no reluctance to fall asleep forever, since it is the direct and the natural thing for them to do...

From My Experience, 8

Understands the Universe

Farming, and especially good and intelligent farming, comes closer to providing a key to adjustment and understanding of the universe than all the algebraic formulas of Albert Einstein.

From My Experience, 12

Is a Hero

I think very few city or town dwellers have ever appreciated the actual heroism of the average good farmer in carrying on and even increasing production of food for ourselves and for our allies during the interminable period of the last war...

From My Experience, 47

Sets an Example

The fact still remains that the good farmer is the fundamental of any good agriculture and that his mere example to his neighbors is more important to agriculture and the nation in general than the huge army of bureaucrats and technicians, despite all the great contributions made by the inspired and devoted members of this important group.

From My Experience, 53

Finds Satisfaction Everywhere

It is true that one can have as much excitement and satisfaction out of a fifty-foot-square plot in a backyard as out of fifty thousand acres. Indeed, if you are a good farmer or gardener, you can find more excitement and satisfaction out of such a small well-managed plot than many a giant wheat farmer can find out of thousands of acres of mediocre wheat production ... certainly vastly more satisfaction than the low-production wheat speculators who go by the name of "suitcase" farmers, the men who have cost the nation so much not only in taxes but in the destruction of land through erosion by wind and water. These "suitcase" farmers seem to me to rank among the contemptibles of our time, somewhere between the Capones and money lenders practicing usury. They belong to a breed with which, fortunately, I have had little contact, and have less and less as time goes on. I am an easygoing and tolerant man, but one has to draw the line somewhere.

From My Experience, 176

Seeks Practical Beauty

All in all, we had achieved what every good farmer seeks to achieve ... the combination of beauty and utility.

From My Experience, 252

Can Always Do Better

Many a good farmer could increase his net profit from 10 per cent upward right on his own land through better production and greater efficiency without asking any raise in price.

From My Experience, 279

Nurtures the Soil

The ultimate aim of every good farmer, of every good agricultural worker and scientist is to create a living soil which will produce not only the food without which man cannot live, but the biggest yield and the finest quality in food. Without such soils, man cannot in the end continue living and eating on any level of decency in a world which continues to increase its population at a truly appalling rate.

From My Experience, 289

200

Reveres Life

This principle [what Albert Schweitzer called "Reverence for Life"] is known to every good farmer, as it is known to every truly good and truly happy person. It is unfortunate that we are sometimes weak enough to sin against it, and each time we sin we suffer a weakening of our dignity. The sin can be committed in countless ways from unkindness to the greedy ravaging of a forest, from the making of a "smart deal" to the wasting of land which belongs not to us but to Life and which we hold only in trust for future generations.

In no other field of activity can the whole principle of the Reverence for Life, which may indeed constitute the very basis of the preservation of our civilization, be so thoroughly, easily and profoundly understood and exercised as in the field of agriculture for ... it is the only profession in which man deals constantly with all the laws of the universe and life. A productive agriculture of high quality is the very foundation of our health, our vigor, even our intelligence, for intelligence expands, grows and functions best in a healthy and vigorous body. But agriculture is also one of the greatest of civilizing influences, especially in those backward and ill-fed and confused nations which have become increasingly the gravest problem of the world and of man himself. Often enough, it is more important in the early stage of sociological and economic development and advance than education in all but the most primitive sense.

Every good farmer practices, even though he may not understand clearly, the principle of Reverence for Life, and in this he is among the most fortunate of men, for he lives close enough to Life to hear the very pulsations of the heart, which are concealed from those whose lives are concentrated upon the unbalanced shabbiness of the completely material.

From My Experience, 348-349

14

It Seems To Me

While Louis Bromfield is remembered in his native United States mostly for his farm writings in the last third of his life, he was much more than a barynard philosopher, the guru of grazing or the messiah of the manure pile. This small-town Ohio boy was, like Ernest Hemingway, a true citizen of the world. He was as fluent in the intricacies of global economics, sociology and world politics as he was in feed formulations, forages and French. A voracious reader of books, magazines and newspapers, Bromfield had an opinion — usually a strong and informed one — on just about everything and everyone of consequence during his lifetime. Readers instinctively knew he was climbing up on his soapbox as soon as they saw the phrase "It seems to me." Many of his predictions were uncannily insightful and unerringly accurate. The quotes in this section come from seven books that Bromfield authored:

1. The Farm *(1933)*
2. Pleasant Valley *(1945)*
3. A Few Brass Tacks *(1946)*
4. Malabar Farm *(1948)*
5. Out of the Earth *(1950)*
6. A New Pattern for A Tired World *(1954)*
7. From My Experience *(1955)*

An eighth book — Flat Top Ranch (1957) — was Bromfield's brainchild. He wrote the first two chapters for that book about his friend Charles Petit, a pioneering "grass farmer" with a 17,000-acre ranch between Waco and Fort Worth, Texas. They were among the last, if not the last things Bromfield wrote before his death on March 18, 1956 in Columbus, Ohio. Flat Top Ranch was later finished by others and published by the University of Oklahoma Press.

Those eight books total some 2,600 pages, so the selected quotes that make up this chapter are just a sampling of what Bromfield thought and felt about a wide variety of topics. Many are repeated here just because they are so good and still so true that they deserve to be repeated. Others -- especially the ones that mention The Colonel, Jamie, Johnny and Greataunt Esther -- are also meant to make you curious enough about Bromfield's stories and characters that you will read some of his books in their entirety.

Absentee Landlords, Tenants & "Suitcase" Farmers

It is simply a truism that unless both owner and tenant are enlightened, both steal as much as they can out of the soil, with the result that the economy of a whole area or the whole of the nation suffers as well as promoting the steady decline in income of both tenant and absentee owner. No other single factor has destroyed more good land in the nation than the absentee-tenant, short-term, year-by-year arrangement.

Out of the Earth, 209

And there are the wheat lands, some owned by farmers who live on their land and some by the speculators known as "suitcase" farmers, who plant and go away to return months later and harvest the money from the buyer and from the taxpayers for the crop. It is from such land and from the worn-out grazing land that the dust storms come, blowing away the soil and carrying it high in the air as far east as the Atlantic. There are millions of acres of such land already abandoned and more acres on the way.

Flat Top Ranch, 5

Age of Irritation

This modern world, this Age of Irritation is not one in which man can take pride. This is so, I think, because man himself has established false values and false gods, often in defiance of his own nature and certainly of natural law. He is in the process of selling his great birthright of aspiration, of achievement, of growth and advance for a mess of pottage composed of selfishness, materialism, indolence, confusion, pride and despair.

A Few Brass Tacks, 11

Agricultural Colleges

It has always seemed to me that our great agricultural educational structure — the greatest and most expensive in the world — had been guilty of two great weaknesses: (1) That it has too often been a closed affair in which professors and research men wrote papers at each other and that much of the material sent out to farmers is so technical and so dull as to be unreadable and at times unendurable. Agriculture is an exciting profession, one of the most exciting on earth but, save in the case of a few men like Liberty Hyde Bailey, Hugh H. Bennett, Aldo Leopold and H.E. Babcock, little of that excitement has ever reached the average practicing farmer or the young men and women about to enter the profession. Of course these men, and others like them, are essentially both great crusaders and great teachers, and are born, not made. (2) That all too often the farmer is told to adopt certain practices because he will get better yields and make more money or even improve his soil, but all too rarely is he told why this is so, or are the processes by which improvements and better yields come about explained to him.

If more were explained to him of what goes on in soils, in plants, in livestock and explained in an interesting and stimulating and even controversial fashion, progress toward a better agriculture would be infinitely more sound and rapid. It would inevitably bring about more and greater contributions from the farmer himself to the science of agriculture. It could ignite a thousand sparks in a thousand young men and women who might one day make immensely important contributions to the science. The good farmer is no fool and he need not be treated as a child. He can understand the "mysteries" if given half a chance.

Again and again I have heard a middle-aged farmer say, "Why didn't somebody tell me that? I would have understood how the thing worked and it would have made all the difference." And you could read in his sun-burned face the disappointment at the interest and satisfaction he had missed by not knowing how a "thing worked."
Malabar Farm, 400

Sometimes, in the case of the farm boy, the shoe is on the other foot ... that college tends to corrupt him or give him ideas that somehow farmwork and the raising of cattle and hogs is beneath him and that if you go to college you must be a specialist of some kind who will tell other farmers what to do. There was a time when the specially trained agricultural graduate had a mission to perform in the field of education and there is still a great need for such education but the field is by now badly oversupplied and the jobs scarce and not too well paid. The agricultural colleges themselves are largely responsible for this peculiar snobbery — that it is better to be a poorly paid bureaucrat or specialist than a sound, property-owning independent farmer — for their tendency is to seize at once upon any bright boy or girl who comes to college with the intention of being a better farmer and to attempt immediately to convert them to some specialized task and to a snobbery toward such fundamental things as the manure spreader and the cow and the pig. One great agricultural college, I discovered, over a period of three years was sending an average of 94 per cent of its graduates away from the farm into some specialized teaching or bureaucratic field.

From My Experience, 53

Agricultural Research

The greatest handicap in all our agricultural research and experiment today is the lack of imagination and of the passion for exploration in the vast areas of knowledge and scientific fact which are as yet virtually untouched...

The overspecialization which is the greatest fault of American education in almost every field is by no means absent from agricultural education. It has tended more and more to separate agricultural research and experiment from the earth itself and to confine it to the test tubes of the chemical laboratory. Broadly and fundamentally speaking, the earth itself is the source of all agricultural knowledge...

Certainly half the sound contributions and advances in agriculture, horticulture and the livestock industry have come not out of the laboratory but from the smart farmer and livestock man who lives with his soils and his animals, observes them and employs his imagination and powers of deduction.

From My Experience, 40-41

Alfalfa

Alfalfa is not a pampered aristocrat but a real pioneer when trash mulch plantings are coupled with lime and a little fertilizer.

Out of the Earth, 63

Alfalfa ... is one of the best and most accurate of soil-testing plants, not only because of its somewhat complex and in some respects almost voracious demands upon soil, but also because of its very deep-rooting habits and the undeniable capacity of its roots for breaking down and making available to its own growth and even that of plants which succeed it, soil mineral particles even though they existed originally in the form of large rocks and coarse gravels.

From My Experience, 201

America & Americans

I think that if Alexander Hamilton had looked ahead he would have had the American dollar stamped with the motto, "Nothing succeeds like success." It lies at the root of the average American's incapacity to understand and appreciate life, of his habit of living always to the limit of his income and often beyond it. It lies, I think, at the root of the American passion for speculation, and for the abysmal helplessness of the American in a financial depression — the American who does not own his own home, although he has his automobile — the American without enough saved to support his family for six months. One has to keep up a false front, and a good many Americans worry themselves into the grave struggling to maintain the bogus facade.

The Farm, 181-182

The average American trusts far more the decisions of a local "town hall" committee than he does any decree by government politicians, even to the President of the U.S., and rightly so.

A New Pattern for a Tired World, 97-98

The fact is that too many Americans take for granted what they have and assume that their welfare, security, prosperity and high living standards, the roads, the communications, the schools, the research, the opportunities, exist elsewhere and everywhere. All of these things simply do not exist everywhere and few of them exist elsewhere in any remotely similar degree.

A New Pattern for a Tired World, 213

Those of us who lived in Europe and Asia between the first two world wars knew and understood pretty well both Nazism and Fascism and we knew too all about Communism in all its manifestations, and knew that there was nothing to choose between the doctrines; one was merely a perversion of an unnatural political and economic philosophy and vice versa. They were both derived from the philosophy of a sick and psychopathic German called Marx...

Fifteen years after I hoped bleakly to escape from all the evils I knew so well at first hand, I have discovered bleakly that there is nothing superior about my own people and that they do not have any special wisdom or vision. We have merely been more fortunate than other peoples. We are generous because we can afford to be generous. We are perhaps open-hearted because we are still a young people, but we still understand very little about the evils of the world or how they can be cured or at least modified. We lack almost entirely the capacity of putting ourselves in the place of other peoples and the knowledge of the average citizen concerning the life and the circumstances of other nations and peoples is primitive, frequently enough even among those who occupy high places in our government.

From My Experience, 2-3

A friend who spent some years working for American oil companies in Arabia told me a curious story about a spring and fountain which supplied the houses of a whole Arabian village. For centuries the women of the town had carried the water from the fountain to their houses, but with the arrival of the bustling Americans who sought to impose the latest comfort and plumbing upon all the rest of the world (whether it desired it or not), the waters of the spring were pumped into a great tank to flow by gravity into each house and the fountain, where Moses and Abraham may have drunk, turned dry and dusty. After a little while great discontent occurred among the women-folk, a discontent which presently reached such proportions that there was an actual threat of rebellion. The women did not want the running water in their houses; they wanted their fountain back for it was at the fountain that they met and talked and gossiped and heard the news; the American plumbing had condemned them to loneliness and boredom. And so in the end, the expensive pumps and tank and plumbing of the progressive Americans were abandoned, the spring ran again through the ancient fountain and the women carried away the water in goatskins or in pots on their heads and everyone was happy again.

From My Experience, 253

Most Americans, if they were faced each day with the monotonous and limited diet of even the average middle-class European family, would consider it a hardship.

From My Experience, 273

In the vigorous, temperate climate of the North ... there can only be the fierce activity, the driving turmoil that affects nearly all Americans, and prevents us at times from really living at all, permitting us merely to go through life in one long and somewhat noisy procession, always animated but at times empty.

From My Experience, 338

Nothing is more dangerous than for a single country to assume that it has world responsibility thrust upon its shoulders and then to behave in a domineering, unpredictable and irresponsible fashion, which is exactly what we have been doing.

A New Pattern for a Tired World, 16

One of the greatest weaknesses of American public opinion and decision and even foreign policy is the common tendency of the man in the street to think, consciously or unconsciously, of all other countries in the physical terms of his own United States. This is a weakness and an error which certainly is not confined to the less prosperous, less educated and less prominent members of society, although it does reflect one of the many defects of our generally loose system of education. The error extends even to individuals on a high level of government in Congress and in the Administration. When many an individual talks or thinks of Russia, as he thinks of Brazil, he sees in his mind's eye, half-unconsciously, a nation of great factories, of roads and railroads which lead anywhere and everywhere, making even the most remote parts of the wilderness accessible. He envisages, unconsciously, a nation where modern hospitals and schools, refrigerators, housing developments exist in every province, every city, every town. Unconsciously, he thinks of the workers as having automobiles, radios and television, as living on mechanized farms in a country where one can drive for miles in the best and most remarkable of automobiles, over excellent roads, past farm after farm on which there are one or two cars, several tractors, television, radio, refrigerators and deep freeze machinery. Lazily and carelessly, he frequently conceives of whole networks of roads and railroads capable of transporting quickly and efficiently commodities, people, troops and ammunition. The general vague picture in his mind is preposterously wrong, but it is useful both to the military, who harp constantly upon "the Russian menace," and, under certain circumstances, to the ardent Communist. The real Russia bears little or no resemblance to such a picture.

The word "unconsciously" I use advisedly, for these people, even up to a man like Truman, who have had little experience either with geography or world economics, or experience in other countries, or the experience of living with other peoples or nations, and frequently not even a moderately good general education, see the rest of the world in terms of the world which immediately surrounds them. Many of them make no effort to see or understand the rest of the world in terms of reality or fact, and many lack the imagination or the powers of abstract thought to conceive of any foreign nation in terms of anything with which they are not themselves familiar in an immediate sense.

If it were possible for every American citizen to understand and know the other nations of the world as well as a few Americans are able to, the American people would be infinitely more cynical and isolationist.

A New Pattern for a Tired World,130-131

American Youth

Life in the United States is too easy for young people... There are families, in moderate or even poverty-stricken circumstances, which fail somehow to provide their children with a sense of responsibility and a pride in achievement, which in turn are the very fundamentals of any career that is successful or of any value to the country or to one's fellow citizens. Too many American parents expect the schoolteacher to provide the fundamental education and the basis of character and achievement for their children. These lacks in fundamental training produce young people, and especially young men, who are singularly immature and frequently even at eighteen or twenty seem more like children than mature men. I would say that as a rule the average European boy of eighteen is as mature, as dependable, as sober, as thorough and as responsible as the average American of twenty-five or thirty.

Again I think there are many factors contributing to this immaturity. They begin in the American home where all too often there is never any really intelligent conversation around the table but talk limited largely to gossip or baseball or golf or how the old man's business is doing; and home is the very beginning of education. Without a base established in the home, the schoolteacher and professor have little ground to work upon. Even the average knowledge and interests of countless college and university graduates of mature age are shockingly deficient; one wonders sometimes how they ever obtained a college degree.

From My Experience, 49-50

At Malabar there exists one of the largest agricultural libraries outside an agricultural college and it contains not only the standard agricultural works but countless books and pamphlets of advanced scientific importance which are frequently unavailable in most libraries. For many years now, virtually every book or pamphlet on agricultural advances from machinery to antibiotics, in many languages, has come to funnel into the library at Malabar. Yet not one American boy in ten has ever made any effort to take advantage of the vast stores of knowledge, and especially advanced knowledge, which is available there.

From My Experience, 51

In the field of machinery, and especially harvesting machinery which is frequently complicated and subject to accident, it is very nearly impossible to entrust any of it but the simplest field tools to the average American boy or transient American worker. Again they will drive round and round a field without looking behind them, without listening for the ominous sounds which tell even an amateur mechanic that something has gone wrong inside the machine which may end disastrously. The first awareness comes to him when an expensive machine tears itself apart.

Behind this perhaps lies a special psychological and material factor that in this country machinery is abundant and low-priced by comparison with machinery in other countries. The average American boy, quite naturally, grows up with the feeling that if you break up a machine, you can quickly replace the parts or the machine itself, or maybe even the insurance company will take the loss.

To the average foreign-born boy, any expensive agricultural machine is a treasure and something almost sacred. It is not something to be wrecked and turned in after a year or two; it is something which he respects and cherishes. He takes care of it; he listens for the faintest sounds which might indicate trouble.

From My Experience, 53-54

Animals (Livestock & Stockmen)

To all the family at Malabar, animals somehow are not animals and are not treated as such. I believe that all animals have a dignity, an integrity and an entity of their own and men get back from them in understanding and loyalty and quality of understanding exactly what they give.

Pleasant Valley, 224

One of the most remarkable things about animals is the variety of their personalities and the fantastic tricks which, untaught, they will develop. To the average town dweller and even to some farmers all cows or hogs or horses appear to be alike and indistinguishable in characteristics and behavior, but nothing could be less true. A good stockman must have, it seems to me, three characteristics: (1) He must know and love his animals and divine the fact that they are sick or off their feed and what is the matter with them. (2) He must have a "feeling" for them so strong that he can virtually divine what they are thinking and what they are up to. (3) And in a broad sense he must treat them as companions.

Malabar Farm, 165

Any man handling livestock must first love and understand the animals he is handling and possess an imagination which makes him of value to the animal and consequently to the farm as a whole. If he has further technical education so much the better, but no amount of college degrees would bring a man into our employment unless first he had an instinctive love and understanding for livestock. Without those qualities, no matter how much education he possessed, he would in the long run be a liability, sometimes in a very damaging way.

Out of the Earth, 87-88

Any animal knows far better than any college professor or commercial feed expert what it needs and in what quantities, provided a sufficient variety of nutritive elements are placed in front of it for free-choice feeding.

Out of the Earth, 90

There are no ill-treated animals at Malabar, for the first consideration of employment in connection with any livestock is that the man must be able to imagine himself a cow, a pig or a chicken and so to know what would make that particular animal or bird happy, healthy and comfortable. And so you get to know animals pretty well and the more you know them the greater respect you have both for them and for God and Nature. The people who think all cows are exactly alike are merely stupid or ignorant; cows can sometimes be as individual as the people of any group and not infrequently a good deal more interesting and sympathetic.

From My Experience, 15

Bureaucrats & Bureaucracy

One of the great evils of bureaucracy is that it tends increasingly

to become self-perpetuating at the expense of the country.
A New Pattern for a Tired World, 1

Initiative is the very last of the characteristics of the professional bureaucrat. In most cases, and particularly at the lower levels, the bureaucrat has chosen to be a bureaucrat because he is without ambition, curiosity, creative energy or even vitality and is looking first of all for the security of a government job, from which it is difficult to expel him no matter what his stupidities, his incompetence, his dishonesty or his laziness. After the security of his routine job, he will have a pension, which again will give him security paid for by other citizens. He lives a drone's life, mechanical, uninspired and colorless, on a treadmill with guards in the form of civil service which prevent him from falling off it. In the end he dies without having contributed much to the world in any sense and without even having found much enjoyment in living. He is immensely expensive and depressing to the economy of any nation, and can, like Brazil's own pirana fish, if allowed to increase indefinitely, succeed in changing quickly enough a living nation into a meat-bare economic skeleton.

It is small wonder that to the French, one of the most bureaucracy-ridden peoples in the world, the word "fonctionnaire" or bureaucrat has become an expression of abuse and a dirty word.
A New Pattern for a Tired World, 112-113

Chemicals

In the cases of many of these poisons now used wholesale — although some of them are so virulent that the operator using them is cautioned to employ a gas mask — we know little or nothing regarding their eventual effect upon the human system. Years of research would be necessary to arrive at a definite answer but such poisons are created, released and used wholesale overnight in vast quantities. The fact is that many a food producer, in all fields, is constantly looking for more and more virulent poisons which will do away more quickly and more effectively and more cheaply with the disease and pests for which his own exploiting operations are frequently largely responsible.
From My Experience, 185

Church & Religion

For me religion and faith have never come through churches

and rarely through men. These things have welled up in me many times in contact with animals and trees and landscape, at moments when I was certain not only of the existence of God but of my own immortality as a part of some gigantic scheme of creation, of an immortality that had nothing to do with plaster saints and tawdry heavens but with something greater and more profound and richer in dignity, the beautiful dignity of the small animals of the field, of a fern growing from a damp crevice in the rock, or a tulip tree rising straight and clean 100 feet toward the sky.

Pleasant Valley, 275-276

It seems to me that real faith and religion begins in people with love and respect for the earth and for animals.

Malabar Farm, 35

A church may be an instrument of great good in a rural community or it may be a dead thing, or it may be merely a force to promote ignorance, bigotry, and evil. Usually it depends upon the pastor or priest who heads it. Too many of our rural churches serve more as social meeting places than as houses in which to worship God. Too many of them have little or no relation to the daily lives of the people in the neighborhood. A rural pastor has in his grasp potentialities for immense good if he chooses to use them.

The religion of the good farmer goes far beyond all of this. He has faith in the Great Plan with which he must live daily, as an infinitesimal part of the whole divine scheme. He knows that he must adjust himself to the immutable laws of that Plan. If he is clever or wise he will learn even to turn these laws to his own advantage. He will understand them and plan so that the rain becomes a blessing rather than a curse. He will learn new ways of combating a drought and even perhaps of turning it into a profit. He is a foolish man who sets himself in ignorance or defiance in opposition to the laws of nature for in the end he will be defeated and crushed.

A good many of the best farmers I have known were not regular churchgoers, usually because the church in their community was a dead or sometimes even an evil thing. When the weather is against them, they will work on the Sabbath, for the sin of waste, as our Lord made clear, is a far worse sin than that of missing a service and never was this truer than in the starving world of today. The faith of a good farmer is far beyond church-going or the conventional fears or superstitions of the ordinary man. It is a direct faith in God himself,

214

in the very universe with which he lives in so close an association. The church can minister to and support that faith or show the way to use it to the advantage of one's fellow man, but even the church is an insignificant thing in relation to the greater faith, no more than a feeble attempt of man to understand and formalize the greater law, to reach up and bring down to earth for the limited understanding of man what is essentially beyond understanding.

Malabar Farm, 403-404

Cities

Outside each small or middle-sized American town there are growing concentric rings of small houses and small holdings which represent the spontaneous intuitive movement of industrial and white-collar workers toward decentralization, economic security and a more decent life.

A Few Brass Tacks, 184

The very pressure, physical and psychological, of noise, of filth, of confusion, of fighting for transportation, common in our great cities can reduce man to the level of a nerveracked, suffering, snarling animal hating his own kind and even his own wife and children.

A Few Brass Tacks, 190

The few vast cities of a nation are not its greatest assets but frequently serious liabilities, creating many economic and social problems, including transportation and traffic, and constantly hovering on the verge of bankruptcy despite steadily increasing taxes.

A New Pattern for a Tired World, 105

City Farmers & Dirt Farmers

The city farmer is not content with farming as his grandfather farmed. He does not consider it good enough. City farmers are looking for new and sound ideas in agriculture. They are making experiments of great value which the average dirt farmer is unwilling to make either because the experiments represent financial risks which they dare not take or because they lack the initiative or the energy to make them. It was only natural that *Plowman's Folly* should find many readers in their ranks.

Pleasant Valley, 166

Not the least of the satisfaction has come from the visitors, the thousands of people, mostly dirt or city farmers or scientists who come on Sundays from late April to well into November. They come ... from two hundred to a thousand each Sunday ... in such numbers that mere curiosity-seekers have long ago been eliminated ...

Most of them are good and serious and successful men — the City Farmers as well as the dirt farmers — most of whom, like ourselves, are making contributions to cattle, swine and poultry breeding and to the New Agriculture. More than half of them are young men and many of them are boys — the group which will have to cherish our soils and feed not only ourselves but a large part of the world from now on until Doom's Day. They are of all stations of life and all degrees of affluence, from the symbolism of the big shiny Cadillac to that of the jalopy containing a young tenant getting a start with a wife beside him and four or five children in the back seat. But they all have one thing in common — an eye which shines at sight of a beautiful heifer or a shiny fat steer or a thick, heavy stand of lush pasture and a willingness to sit on the fence and talk farming and cattle breeding until darkness falls. At Malabar we have learned much from the new friends who come on Sundays.

Malabar Farm, 43

The general, widely diversified, and self-sufficient program is, however, admirably suited to the small-scale enterprise of industrial, white-collar and middle-bracket-income citizens with a few acres in the suburbs or in the country itself. This category of small, largely self-sufficient holdings is increasing constantly in numbers and it provides not only a bulwark of security for the individual but a source of strength for the nation as well. A well-managed small place with vegetables, fruit trees, chickens, perhaps a pig or two and a cow provides not only a source of large saving in the family food budget, but it also is a source of health, recreation, outdoor life, and general contentment for the whole family.

Malabar Farm, 61-62

Colleges & Universities
The tragedy is that again and again we find the highest positions of authority in many of our schools and universities are occupied by men of rigid mind, without imagination or the fundamental vitality which lies behind all true scientific advance and research, men who

are lacking not only in imagination but even in curiosity, who are without discontent and are happy with things as they are since imagination, speculation and curiosity are uncomfortable and even dangerous elements which upset the even tenor of lives in which, by being safe, a salary will go on forever with a pension at the end. This is essentially the mentality of the hack government bureaucrat everywhere and there is far too much of it in our agricultural education today.

But behind the unimaginative, congealed mind there lie other more subtle factors of tradition, of education and experience. The great scientist, the great painter, the great creative artist is always an essentially simple man with the capacity to advance unhindered by conventions or limitations of any kind, straight to the point, because it is the point, the end result, which is his principal and indeed his only concern. He is not especially concerned merely with the tag of an academic degree (although he may on the way acquire great quantities of these). The academic degree does not necessarily make him a great thinker or a great teacher; it means merely that he is able by determination and persistence to acquire and retain beyond the point of examination or the writing of a thesis certain facts and figures... The acquisition of these tags has become increasingly not only the primary requirement but the primary consideration of American education in nearly all fields, with the result that in many of its aspects American education has become hidebound, limited, overspecialized and in its more extreme manifestations a kind of living death.

The great scientist and the great creator, indeed the great man, is not primarily concerned with academic honors or campus politics or a salary to be counted upon which is followed by retirement pensions or by keeping up with the Joneses or any of the things which confine and plague the ordinary limited mind. And, of course, the tragedy of this limited mind is that it is wholly unaware of the difference between fire and dead wood or between achievement and mere academic recognition. His very goal is frequently not the achievement but the academic recognition; and so he is perpetually blinded and limited, while at the same time he is uneasily aware of his error and suspects that far beyond and above this lies something which he does not quite understand and which he will never quite achieve...

Perhaps I am being oversubtle; what I am trying to say is that over the years I have acquired a kind of dread and horror of much that is associated with campus life, with its limitations, its politics, its jealousies, its "life in death" self-satisfaction and the aggressive smugness born of a sense of inferiority. Perhaps this is because I have been singularly fortunate in having been able all my life to lead the independent life of an individualist, but in the end such an advantage may not be so much good fortune as determination and free will and the will not to seek refuge in conformity and safety.

Let me add again at this point that despite a certain savagery in the above paragraph, the writer is really a very amiable fellow, very fond of people and with countless friends in the world of agriculture and agricultural education.

From My Experience, 45-46

Too many young people look upon four years of college or the university as a kind of lengthy holiday during which their parents provide them with a car and plenty of money to spend. All too often those four years of college are merely a prolongation of adolescence, in which the virtues of maturity and responsibility do not develop at all.

From My Experience, 50

Compost

There also arises the question of labor and machinery expense in composting all materials on a good-sized commercial farm. While machinery improvements are rapidly being made which are reducing very greatly the cost of the whole business of composting, the task still remains an expensive operation and in some senses an "extra" one which must be counted in on the cost side of any farm economy.

At Malabar we have consistently practiced what Sir Albert Howard calls "sheet" composting. All the manure is kept under cover in the feeding sheds, even in the loafing-shed of the dairy barns, for a period of two to three months. During this period no fertility is lost either by "burning" or by leaching away and in the meanwhile the benevolent bacteria count has increased millions of times, fungi and moulds have flourished and the carbon content of the bedding has been broken down by the action of all these elements plus the action of glandular secretions and various acids, and the raw sawdust, straw or shavings have been converted into the finest kind of highly available fertilizer.

After two or three months, this rich, moist, trampled manure is either spread over the meadows and pastures or over other fields where it is worked into the soils by disk, tiller or Graham plow to a depth of eight to nine inches. As meadows and pastures are always the base of a new planting of small grains, the soil also contains a great amount of roots and other organic material. This, together with the already half-disintegrated manure, is mixed into the earth and actually makes a compost heap eight to nine inches deep covering the whole of the field. It is in this shallow compost heap that our crops other than grass and legumes are constantly grown with an immense increase of moisture and highly available fertility. In this simple fashion the composting is actually achieved without any particular elaboration of the natural processes and without any "extra" work. In more recent operations in which the Ferguson tiller or the Graham plow is used we have been able to increase the compost depth to as much as eighteen inches.

Out of the Earth, 68-69

Corn

We know now that it was economically foolish for us to grow corn at all, even on carefully contoured strips or even on our comparatively level ground, but we did not know it then and there was no one to tell us.

Corn and Middle West were terms which were inseparable. Corn was sacred. Corn unfortunately still is King in the minds of many Middle Western farmers just as Cotton was once King on the dilapidated lands of the Deep South. In our area a farm without corn was inconceivable. It was supposed that virtually no animal could do without it and that it was impossible to fatten a steer or a hog upon anything but corn. Yet corn was destroying the good earth of millions of acres of once good Middle Western land and countless farmers were actually raising corn at a loss and would have discovered the fact if they had ever taken the trouble to estimate the costs in terms of man-hours, seed, fertilizer, gasoline, taxes and interest, and the price they received either for the corn itself or the cattle they fattened on it at any but the highest yields per acre. And they overlooked entirely the slow destruction of the soil, which is the farmer's working capital, in terms of erosion and the destruction of organic materials and soil structure which arises from the constant plowing, stirring and fitting of soils which go with row crops.

Eleven years ago if we had not raised corn at Malabar we should have been looked upon as insane in our area or the neighbors would have said that we were too damned lazy to plow. Today more and more neighbors are following our pattern and by doing so increasing their profits, reducing work drudgery and costs and building up the capital of their land.

As a nation we inherited corn from the Indians, and it became, under a poor agriculture, like cotton, one of the most destructive factors in the general decline of our productive soils. I should be the last to advocate the total abandonment of corn which has a sound place in certain livestock operations and has a growing and eventually an even more important place in chemurgy for the production of alcohols, plastics and countless other products, the development of which is still in infancy. But the once common belief that corn is the most profitable of crops and indispensable in any livestock program and the indispensable backbone of our Middle Western rural economy is the sheerest hogwash.

Unfortunately it is economically a very destructive hogwash. It was once believed, and practice appeared to back up the belief, that only corn and hog- or beef-feeder farmers could be rich farmers and that therefore flat deep corn land was the most profitable land and brought the highest prices. Fortunately this kind of reasoning is beginning to change partly because cash corn-crop farming has virtually destroyed by erosion and depletion some millions of acres of good rolling land and run its owners into bankruptcy, and partly because we are beginning to find out that a well-managed farm program can be just as profitable without any corn whatever and is a much more stable operation since the costs are infinitely lower in terms of labor and fertilizer, and the prices for dairy products and to some extent beef are far more stable and dependable than the prices of corn and hogs. Moreover, even in many areas of deep rich soil, yields have been steadily declining and good drainage disappearing through an agriculture based upon corn, cotton, soybeans or similar row crops.

Out of the Earth, 166

We do the whole of our winter grain feeding during the ten or twelve hours we spend on a summer day filling the silo. On a farm such as Malabar, producing dairy cattle and milk, there is no need for corn whatever as the combination of oats and barley makes a much better feed than corn for dairy animals... Corn is the most expensive feed a farmer can employ.

Out of the Earth, 182

Cotton

The dethroning of King Cotton or at least his reduction to the status of a constitutional monarch is perhaps the most fortunate single economic happening in the history of the South. No tyrant king ever did more damage to a people.

Out of the Earth, 211

Democracy

Democracy, in any of its hazy countless sometimes phony forms, cannot flourish or even be maintained in an atmosphere of misery, starvation, illiteracy and ignorance. It cannot simply because these things in themselves infect and destroy the very structure of government by the people and leave the people victims of the first dictator-general, demagogue, criminal or psychopath to come along and take over power while victimizing the people in the process by persuading them that he alone can solve troubles which essentially are not political at all but material and economic.

A New Pattern for a Tired World, 18

Imposing democracy upon peoples who have not earned it and do not understand it is never successful, for the structure degenerates almost immediately into a dictatorship or oligarchy of a vicious and corrupt nature... Democracy in the sense of true representative government and in the sense of a republic is not something that can be given or bestowed, imposed or commanded. It is essentially a luxury which must be earned through literacy and prosperity, through wisdom and self-restraint, through knowledge and consideration and through fierce ideals of independence, liberty and the dignity of the individual man.

A New Pattern for a Tired World, 43

Dogs

We had come to have several dogs instead of merely one because when anything happened to one the sense of loss was too great. So we were always having new litters of puppies or buying new ones. Later we discovered that having more than one dog didn't make much difference because each one has its own personality and is an individual and when he dies, the sense of loss is not softened by the fact that he left behind several companions.

Pleasant Valley, 200

Big dogs, indeed, have no place in the life of demon housekeepers. Fortunately, all our household prefers dogs to an immaculate house. The five boxers sleep in my room which serves as office, bedroom and workroom and fortunately is on the ground floor and has many windows and two outside doors leading into the garden. Prince sleeps on the foot of my bed, Folly in a dog bed at the foot, Gina on the sofa and Smoky and Baby on chairs. Although Baby has long outgrown the chair he chose as a puppy and hangs over both ends, nothing will induce him to give it up. Each place belongs to a different boxer and if one attempts to take over the property of another, the fight is on. Now and then, other members of the family complain that my room is a little "high" and Nanny attacks it with Lysol, taking over usually while I am away and cannot protest. I am afraid that I prefer the smell of dogs to the smell of Lysol.

Last summer a guest observed, "I can't believe this house is new. It looks so old and well-worn. Nothing looks new!" to which George replied, "Dogs and children take care of that. It looked like an old house six months after it was built."

Pleasant Valley, 219-220

There is no more sociable dog than a boxer and there is nothing they like so much as visitors or a party. As they come rushing out they are likely to scare people to death, since they are ferocious in appearance, but they are in their hearts all amiability. In that respect they are ideal watchdogs on a place like Malabar where there are hundreds of visitors a year. No one can come near any building without the boxers knowing it and setting up an uproar, but biting is not a part of their natures. The golden retrievers were different for nothing could persuade them that a part of their duties as watchdogs was not to bite and on occasion they went beyond bluff and took pieces out of Charley Kimmel, the game warden, whom they know well, and out of two or three other visitors. In the end we gave them away, although they are the most beautiful of dogs.

The boxers, used to square dances and picnics and meetings, learned long ago that a group of automobiles meant a party and a party meant that they were going to have a feast of hot dogs, of steak bones, of pie and cake and doughnuts. No party ever had more welcoming hosts than the boxers and the two cockers on the occasion of farm festivities. Usually the next day meant indigestion for them and the consumption of great quantities of grass and zinnia leaves, which boxers seem to regard as a cure for indigestion. But apparently the party is always worth the indigestion.

Pleasant Valley, 222

I know that much of what I am writing sounds sentimental and much of it is. And so I am sentimental and so what? It is inevitable that anyone who likes and understands animals should be a sentimentalist. I think too that such people find in animals and especially dogs consolations and sympathy in time of hurt which no human, however close, can ever bring them. And there is much truth in the sentimentality about animals, much which brings a special warmth and satisfaction in living and a clue to much that is a part of understanding and of God. Some people will perhaps not understand at all what I am writing about and others will know, instinctively and rightly.

Malabar Farm, 176-177

Draft (1954)

On the human side, one is tempted to ask bluntly, What right has any politician or general to advocate the conscription of boys from Iowa, California or Ohio or where you will and send them all over the world to be killed, maimed, taken prisoner or at best to waste two of the best years of their lives in the quixotic and hypocritical assumption that: (1) it is part of a defense policy; (2) that it is worth sacrificing them to preserve the liberties of peoples who have never known liberty and frequently have no word in their languages to define such an abstraction?"

A New Pattern for a Tired World, 75

Korea is a first-class example of the fact that the American government, acting independently or as a kind of universally unpopular stooge for the U.N., cannot possibly run the whole world and dictate the policies of nations everywhere, without eventually ruining her economy and, through vast military operations, even losing her vaunted freedoms at home. Permanent conscription, drafting millions of unwilling and resentful young Americans to follow a stupid and confused policy everywhere in the world, is the first dangerous step in losing those freedoms.

A New Pattern for a Tired World, 222

Earthworms

At the same time that the purely organic school of agriculture has been growing up, there have been made some fantastic claims by the crank element regarding earthworms.

There can be no dispute whatever regarding the immense value of the earthworm in converting thin dead soils or soils low in organic material into living and productive soils, but since the earthworm, like all living organisms, must eat to live and must also have a certain level of moisture in order to survive, his existence and his propagation becomes extremely unlikely in soils devoid of organic material, sparsely covered by sickly vegetation and subject to drying and baking under sun and wind. His survival is therefore closely related to green or barnyard manures, mulches and decaying organic materials in general. The claims that a few earthworms introduced into a cement-like field covered by sparse vegetation will soon rehabilitate the entire field and create quantities of topsoil are as absurd as the old-fashioned chemical fertilizer advertisements which implied that a sprinkling of fertilizer on an asphalt pavement would produce bumper crops.

Out of the Earth, 65-66

Education

Jamie was, in his way, a symbol of the inflated reverence for schools and academies and universities which caused them to spring up like mushrooms everywhere in the Middle Western country during the second half of the nineteenth century. The whole inflated mass of educational institutions was born of a generation or two which, like Jamie had had little opportunity for education and so sought exaggerated advantages for their children and grandchildren...

Humbly he never saw that within himself lay the greatest and surest means of acquiring an education. He never saw that his own passionate curiosity about everything in the world and his own hunger for knowledge was a better means than all sorts of professors and academies.

In the few hours a day he had left from the stiff job of running a big farm and bringing up a large family, he read anything and everything. It would have been impossible for him to have gone uneducated, because he could not help himself. His passion for knowledge was like a disease.

The Farm, 56-57

It is one of the failures of our fundamental American philosophy that we confuse education and intelligence as much as we confuse plumbing and civilization. One ounce of intelligence is worth a pound of education, for where there is intelligence, education will advance and follow on its own, but where education alone exists, the results can be terrifying beyond even the realms of untutored stupidity.

Out of the Earth, 256

Erosion
Erosion is not a cause, it is a result of bad farming.

Out of the Earth, 123

No farmer in his right mind, hankering for a farm pond that will water his stock and provide swimming and fishing for the whole family, would build a farm pond which will silt up in a few years because he has not properly managed the land on the watershed above it. To have a decent, clear, good pond or tank you have to keep the rainfall where it belongs and prevent soil from washing away.

Out of the Earth, 126

Exploitation & Sin
The methods and tactics of the average farmer and cattleman have followed very largely the same course as those of the industrialists and bankers. Largely speaking they exploited the land as the industrialists exploited other natural resources, ruining one farm to move westward and claim another for a dollar an acre or for the taking, ruining this one in turn and moving westward again until at last they reached the Pacific and there was no more free virgin land save a little that could be drained or irrigated.

It can be said without fear of contradiction that no nation in the history of the world ever set about destroying its natural and real wealth at so appalling a rate.

A Few Brass Tacks, 50

The Great Southwest is booming, but booms must always be paid for one way or another at some time by someone; in the long run there is never any such thing as a "quick buck." Someone, perhaps a son or a granddaughter or a child unborn, will have to pay. We are already leaving a vast burden to future generations which will have no Eldorado to plunder as we have had. Perhaps one day they will have to work, as most nations in Europe and Asia work today, to buy the raw materials and the food which we still have in abundance. Perhaps they will have to spend, as Britain does, one-third of the nation's income to buy food for the people, or do without as India and China, where half the populations are born and die without ever having had enough to eat, even of the poorest food, for one day in their lives.

These disasters today seem far away. All of us alive today may be dead long before the first symptoms appear, so perhaps none of it matters; but if one has any real morality or genuine religious feeling and faith, as so many of us keep asserting loudly, we are hypocrites, for there is no worse sin in the eyes of God than stealing the heritage of children as yet unborn.

Flat Top Ranch, 7-8

Farm — Family Farm and "Farming As A Way of Life"

The Farm was the only sure refuge. There, at least, her children would have good food and a roof over their heads. There they would have the independence without which life was unthinkable.

The Farm, 297

Nothing in farming is simple.

Out of the Earth, 188

There is a good deal of sentimentality awash throughout the nation with regard to "farming as a way of life," a phrase which carries the implication that there is something especially satisfactory, at least spiritually, in farming in a primitive way as our ancestors did upon the frontier. The truth is that "farming as a way of life" is infinitely more pleasurable and satisfactory and profitable when it is planned, scientific, specialized, mechanized and stripped of the long hours and the drudgery of the old-fashioned obsolete pattern of the frontier or general farm.

There is also much loose thinking about "the family-sized

farm" and the idea that a specialized, scientific, business-like farm cannot be "family-sized." This is sheer nonsense, for the modern farm may be family-sized and still infinitely more satisfactory than the "family-sized" farm of the past in which there was no program, no plan, no pattern but only a scurrying, planless confusion in which a family was trying to raise a few dairy cattle, a few beef cattle, a few hogs, a few sheep, a few chickens together with 10 acres of this and 10 acres of that in a frontier pattern which no longer has any justification in a highly industrialized world where markets, distribution, mechanization and many other factors which did not exist on the frontier have altered not only the agricultural but the economic and even the sociological picture.

The specialized, scientific, business-like farm does not mean the single-crop or even the undiversified farm. It merely means that a farmer and his family do two or three jobs well on a planned, sensible basis rather than a dozen jobs planlessly, badly or inefficiently.

Out of the Earth, 251

A lot of things have changed on the farm today, but the essence of the farm and the open country remains the same. The freedom is unchanged and the sense of security and independence and the good rich food and the beauty that lies for the seeing eye on every side and, above all, that satisfaction, as great as that of Leonardo or Shakespeare or any other creative artist, in having made something great and beautiful out of nothing. The farmer may leave his stamp upon the whole of the landscape seen from his window, and it can be as great and beautiful a creation as Michelangelo's David, for the farmer who takes over a desolate farm, ruined by some evil and ignorant predecessor, and turns it into a Paradise of beauty and abundance is one of the greatest of artists.

Out of the Earth, 299

Farm Labor

It is impossible in a book written with intentional honesty not to comment upon one sad fact which has contributed frequently to failure, to mistakes and to ragged-looking fields from time to time at Malabar. This is the poor quality, the inadequacy and the lack of responsibility which is manifest in so much of American farm labor, even among what might be called skilled labor and college-educated young Americans. We have had at Malabar a long experience and opportunity for observation and comparison with the workers and young farmers of other nationalities, for we have had from time to time Danes, British, Swedes, French and Brazilians working with us for periods of months and occasionally years and we have had countless other native-born American boys and young men during the summer harvest season. In addition to these I have had experience with the North Italian and Brazilian workers at Malabar-do-Brasil. There is only one conclusion to be drawn ... that any one of the foreign-born workers is worth three average American workers.

This qualification of worth is not based alone upon the capacity to work or the cheerful willingness to put in long hours during the emergencies which sometimes arise in harvest time; it is based upon such factors as the use of brains, interest in what the worker is doing, pride of achievement and of doing a job thoroughly and well; it is based above all upon a sense of responsibility and the capacity to learn from day to day from the very jobs and tasks the worker is performing.

From My Experience, 48-49

The only pool of good agricultural workers from which the farmer can draw today is that infinitesimally small one made up of the kind of man who wants to be a farmer and would not work in a factory, putting nuts on bolts for eight hours a day, no matter what the wages. We have had and have this kind of man and when you can find him he is a treasure to be guarded.

From My Experience, 56

Farmers

"Some day," old Jamie said, "there will come a reckoning and the country will discover that farmers are more necessary than traveling salesmen, that no nation can exist or have any solidity which ignores the land. But it will cost the country dear. There'll be hell to pay before they find out."

The Farm, 342

Anything is better than standing still. The conservatism of the farmer is sometimes his worst handicap.

Malabar Farm, 36

A farm life is a good life.

Malabar Farm, 38

Happy and fortunate is the farmer who has plenty of sons and daughters who can work with him and possess maturity, intelligence and a sense of responsibility.

From My Experience, 57

The farmers and gardeners of the world, however poor or prosperous, whatever their nationality or race or faith, possessed a common basic philosophy which proved a bulwark against the uncertainty of existence and the periods of crisis which the men who lived in great cities lacked conspicuously and immeasurably.

The farmer, the gardener, is inevitably a pragmatist who believes in what works. This is so because he lives nearer to the basic and eternal laws of nature than any other element of society. These laws are a part of his daily life. He lives with them and in a sense by them. The rain, the sun, the ice and snow, the soil, the breeding of his animals, are constant and eternal reminders of the laws by which man must live whether he chooses to or not, those laws which, if ignored or tampered with, only encompass his own disintegration and destruction.

A Few Brass Tacks, 8

Farmers and fazendeiros everywhere will imitate the operations of a practical and profitable agricultural operation where they will often pass by the operations of a government experiment station.

From My Experience, 139

Fertilizer

The whole commercial fertilizer theory represented both the ignorance and the arrogance of the limited or greedy men, manufacturers and farmers and professors, who are perpetually seeking a short cut or a means of outwitting Nature.

Out of the Earth, 15

Some eight years ago I made in Atlanta, Georgia, two statements: (1) that what General Sherman did to Georgia was insignificant in relation to what the Georgians had done to their own state by the constant unvaried growing of the cash crops, cotton and corn; (2) that the average Georgia farmer spending $100 on commercial fertilizer realized only about $10 or less of actual value. Because of the exceedingly low organic content of most Georgia soils after a couple of centuries of single-crop, corn-and-cotton agriculture, the other $90 worth of commercial fertilizer very often went down the nearest stream along with the topsoil during the succeeding winter if the soil was left bare of cover crops.

The two statements made an uproar, the first among the old-time sentimental and shiftless Georgians or the ignorant small farmers and sharecroppers of whom there remain fewer and fewer each year. The second volume of uproar came from the National Fertilizer Association and finally developed into a controversy staged in the pages of their trade paper...

I was, falsely, accused of saying that commercial fertilizer had no value, which was and is certainly not true. I merely stated that its value was in almost direct ratio to the amount of organic material and consequently to the well-balanced moisture in any soil. During the controversy I pointed out that, in so far as the fertilizer business was concerned (as indeed in any business), a satisfied customer was a good and profitable customer, and that I had encountered many farmers who asserted that commercial fertilizer wasn't worth what they paid for it...

The fertilizer was certainly worth the money. The fault lay not with the fertilizer but with the farmer himself. Because of the poor natural conditions of his soils, he probably utilized at the most not more than 25 to 30 per cent of the value he had paid for.... I also pointed out that some of the magazine advertising of the fertilizer companies could actually be the basis of a suit for using the mails to defraud since it read as if all one had to do in order to raise a bumper crop on an asphalt highway was to sprinkle a little commercial fertilizer on the surface and broadcast seed.

Whether or not the controversy had anything to do with a change in the subsequent policy of the fertilizer companies I do not know. I do know that in succeeding years the companies have published countless articles on the value of organic material and have hired top-quality agronomists with a profound belief in organic material as the basis of all sound agriculture to carry on a campaign for a better basic agriculture.

Out of the Earth, 52-53

Floods

You do not stop floods at the mouth of the Mississippi or the Missouri but upstream in the forests, the cultivated fields and the grazing lands.

Out of the Earth, 124

Food & Money

Johnny's mother was an excellent cook and, like all good cooks, had a passion for the art. It was her greatest means of expression. She came of a family which had always been accustomed only to the best of fowls and finest of cuts and the most succulent of vegetables and fruits, for they came from the family's own barnyards and gardens and orchards. In the richness of the bounty, only the best parts of the sheep and pig and beef were eaten. The rest was sold and the "innards" were considered worthy only of the dogs. It was a family in which the tradition persisted that in hard times one might wear shabby clothes in a pinch, but one could never go without good food. In the kitchen, even at the most precarious financial moments which in Johnny's family came all too often, there was never any economy.

The Farm, 126

As every good cook knows, there is something special about food cooked over a wood fire ... something magnificent and miraculous in the case of steak and fish and coffee and sweet corn; and added to the wood-smoke flavor there was the sunlight and the open air and the wild smell of the abandoned clearing.

The Farm, 275

Food, according to the labor organizations, is the principal item in the living cost budget of city dwelling industrial and white-collar workers. It is the cost of food, increasing steadily since the Civil War, which sets off (according to labor economists) the demands for constantly increasing wages among industrial workers, white-collar workers and city dwellers generally, raises which are passed on in the prices of everything all of us buy including both industrial and agricultural commodities. What all of us need is not more dollars but dollars which buy more. That is the only way in which any of us ever gets a real raise in pay whether we are keeping books or making automobiles or producing hogs.

How better can a start be made toward stabilizing our economy on a productive, not a speculative, basis than by achieving a really productive, efficient agriculture with lower costs to consumer and higher profits to the producer? As with all else in our modern, highly integrated world, high production per man hour, per dollar invested, is the answer and never scarcity and high prices.

Malabar Farm, 7

I like to eat and eat well. I like not only good recipes and a great variety of dishes with plenty of herbs and spices and rich sauces, butter and cream, but I like them made out of first-class materials ... clean, succulent vegetables and fruit high in vitamins, in minerals, in flavor and freshness. Increasingly it becomes difficult to obtain this quality of vegetables and fruit. Eating in the U.S. has become increasingly a matter of convenience and labor-saving rather than of good materials or skill in cookery.

There are so far as I know only two ways today of having the top quality in fruits and vegetables ... either to grow them yourself or to drive into the country and buy them fresh from the grower, not from one of these roadside stands which buys its supplies wholesale in the city, transports them, wilting and even rotting, to the country roadside stand and then sells them to you in the deceit that they are "home-grown." Countless, if not most of the so-called "roadside stands" today operate on such a method of procedure and frequently the quality of the vegetables and fruits which you buy on such a stand is lower than that to be found in the chain store city market where at least refrigeration has played some role.

And so because I love soil and good eating, the vegetable gardens at Malabar have been maintained at full production from the very beginning. I like my peas, my sweet corn, my young string beans straight from the garden into the pot. I like my tomatoes sun-ripened and still warm from the sun. I like my potatoes grown in the best of soils so that not only are they clean and beautiful to look upon, they are also full of flavor, as different in flavor and protein content from potatoes grown in fertilized sand as day is from night.

But there was another element in the maintenance and development of the vegetable gardens at Malabar which crept in almost at once. That was concerned with the growing prevalence of disease and insect attack which one found everywhere in the U.S. and worse, the constant, universal and increasing use of inorganic chemical poisonous dusts and sprays with which nearly all the vegetables consumed are constantly sprayed, dusted and drenched ... vegetables consumed more or less directly from the field and vegetables that are quick-frozen and canned.

One of the things I discovered on returning from eighteen years of living in Europe was the fact that the garden pages of newspapers, the seed catalogues, the agricultural magazines and of course the pages of the chemical trade papers were filled with a constantly increasing array of high-powered inorganic chemical poisons. After a brief survey one was led to believe that it was impossible to raise any crop in the U.S. without saturating it at some time during its period of growth with all kinds of violent poisons.

All this came as a surprise to me for a number of reasons. One certainly was that in my grandmother's vegetable garden and even the vegetable gardens which I set up myself as a boy, all this array of violent poisons was unnecessary. There was virtually no disease and the attacks by insects, certainly of some species, were negligible. Another was that in all the years I had farmed in a small way and gardened in Europe it had been unnecessary to use anything to protect the growing plants but ordinary hydrated lime to prevent the snails and slugs from devouring a small range of vegetables and flowers.

From My Experience, 177-178

Free Enterprise

The worst enemy of free enterprise, indeed of democracy itself, is not the demagogue and the radical but the economic conditions which produce the wretched and discontented populations willing to listen to their harangues. Perhaps what all of us will have to learn — farmers, industrial and white-collar workers, small businessmen and industrialists, the last perhaps most of all — is that the economic welfare of the whole of the nation is the economic welfare of every class and every citizen as well. And I am not writing of booms and inflation, with their sick and illusory prosperity, but of a stabilized economy in which real and permanent prosperity exists, without booms and depressions. Such a real prosperity cannot be accomplished by social legislation, or any other palliative in terms of money, but only by sound planning and the investment rather than the spending of government and taxpayers' money and by undertaking measures which are based upon an economy of real wealth and provide real and independent economic security for all citizens who are able and willing to work. I know of no better place to make a beginning than in the breaking down of our great industrial-urban concentrations and by increasing the production of our great, potentially permanent bases of real wealth — our forests and our agricultural land.

A Few Brass Tacks, 221-222

Gardens & Landscapes

No house was decent or respectable which had not a fine garden. It was the last vestige of a profound belief that life was not worth living unless time was wasted upon what pleased the senses, even though there was no profit in it.

The Farm, 280

A garden, a landscape or even a whole farm, if it is to be successful by any standard, is essentially a creation and an expression of an individual or at least two or three individuals who feel alike toward it, who share the same aims and traditions; for tradition has much to do with the beautiful garden, landscape or farm. There should be a rightness in relation to the whole landscape, to the climate, to the country, to the regional architecture, to the type of soils, even perhaps to the existence of the natural birds and wildlife. If should have a relation to the past of the region, to history itself.

From My Experience, 76

I think it is imagination and a kind of vision which drives the good farmer and the good gardener to work all hours of the day in every kind of weather, often enough beyond his strength. Arthritic old ladies forget the agonies of their rheumatism in order to tend some tender plant or shrub; the old and tired farmer will work into the darkness far beyond his strength to keep his fields neat, productive and in order. This urge and drive has made of me as it has made of many a gardener, a kind of contortionist, this drive which forces one to stretch muscles and sinews into impossible positions, merely for the sake of a seedling or the pruning of a plant surrounded by other plants which must not be trampled or injured. Certainly it has done much to keep a figure which should have become large and heavy and rotund by nature in ordinary city life, and maintained muscles and a suppleness which are quite as good as they were at eighteen.

In his imagination every good gardener and farmer sees the

harvest with the planting of the first seed. As the earth covers it he sees the flowers, the rich grain, the beautiful grass that will soon be born from the seed. With each hoeing, with each weeding, with each cultivation he is driven by the vision. And the true gardener and farmer suffers with his plants and crops; if it is too hot and dry, he becomes ill and really suffers himself; if the plants are ill, he feels their illness in his bones. It is this vision and drive which keep the good farmer forever planting, forever hoping, persistent and undefeated in the face of flood, of drought, of every disaster...

The most satisfactory things about such a vision and such a goal are that one must work perpetually with nature and that the task is never really finished nor the vision ever really achieved. There is always something more to be done; and so I shall be well occupied until I die at last, I hope in the midst of that very landscape and garden I have helped to create. It is not a task or a vision with which one can grow bored, for one is living with the whole of the universe which, as all will agree, is fairly inexhaustible during the short span of our lives.

From My Experience, 79-80

It is a curious fact that the simplest farmer and gardener and the most intelligent, experienced and sophisticated of people have the same good and easy manners because both are likely to have a proper sense of values and the realities of human relationships.

From My Experience, 93

God

I am a very religious man and somewhat of a mystic. Certainly I have never been an atheist or even an agnostic. Broadly speaking I do not believe that it is necessary to know everything, or indeed anything at all, about God and that there are plenty of other things to occupy our time and energies without worrying too much about God. I am unwilling to conceive of God, if I think about Him at all, as a good friend who has a terrible job on His hands if His entire concern is claimed by the human race. That any of us should hold such a belief as that of the preoccupation of God with our puny ambitions, desires and miseries argues presumption and egotism in the face of anything so vast and terrifying as the universe — presumptuous, egotistical ants.

I am, however, deeply grateful toward whatever force has

made this word full of children and dogs, and trees and streams and valleys, and the makings of good food and drink and love in all its manifestations.

From My Experience, 341-342

Government

Economic pressures and the steadily declining purchasing power of the dollar have not only led to strikes and increasing demands for higher wages and prices but have created in the public mind a philosophy of turning toward government or the "state" to settle all troubles, economic, social, political and otherwise. It is a feeble philosophy and a dangerous one, based upon the assumption that there is something all-knowing, all wise about government when it is nothing more or nothing better than the men who go to make it up and inevitably brings with it, as its powers expand, the confusion, extravagance, red tape and inefficiency which afflicts all complicated administrative bureaucracy. Such a bureaucracy through the taxes levied to support it, inevitably eats into the savings, economic security and working capital of the nation, thus creating in a vicious circle more and more dependence upon government and steadily increasing inroads into the liberty and dignity of the people.

A Few Brass Tacks, 54

Possibly the most satisfactory form of government would be a perfect paternalism presided over by God who, we assume, is endowed with justice, wisdom, humanity, efficiency, honesty and indeed all virtues toward which civilized man aspires but which even in his finest manifestations, he has never quite achieved. Under such a paternalism we should indeed have a pleasant and ideal world with all worries and all political and economic responsibilities removed from our individual shoulders. But since we cannot have God to operate the machinery of government, we are forced to do the best we can, working together, to produce a government which provides us as nearly as possible with the blessings listed above. And we dare not risk paternalism lest, instead of God, we find ourselves being ruled by Hitler or Stalin.

A Few Brass Tacks, 239-240

Grass Farming

Gradually we began to produce less corn and more good grass, and as we did so, the rising profits began to show up on the farm books principally in the money we did not spend, the man-hours we did not need and the machinery we did not have to buy. For three years now we have not raised any corn at Malabar and it is unlikely that we shall ever again raise corn. For one year we have not raised any wheat. Our only present rotation is from heavy meadows of brome grass, alfalfa and ladino clover into spring barley or oats and back again into alfalfa, brome grass and ladino...

Our carrying capacity, winter and summer, of cattle has increased from the original 30 head which could barely get through with the feed raised in the first year or two, to a capacity of 275 to 300 head, and we are still 40 per cent from maximum optimum production and carrying capacity because much of our recently acquired land is only beginning to approach the productive capacity of land which we have had five years or more.

Most important of all, we have been able to prove that an acre of our land sown to alfalfa, brome grass and ladino brings in the same gross in terms of cash as that of the 90- to 100-bushel-an-acre corn farmer, and less than 5 per cent of the farmers growing corn in the United States raise as much as 100 bushels of corn to the acre. Moreover, our net profit in cash terms is at least two to three times per acre that of the corn farmer since the heavy grass costs us approximately one-seventh in labor and gasoline and one-fifth in fertilizer as against the labor and fertilizer of the corn farmer.

In a capital sense the gain is immense, for each year we are improving our soil and its organic content rather than tearing it down. Each year our soil becomes more productive and more valuable. Even upon our steep hills we have a zero record in erosion and less than 5 per cent water loss in the heaviest cloudburst. Each time we plow in a deep, heavy sod, each time we spread a load of barnyard manure, our land goes up in value, until today we could sell, on a Federal Land Bank appraisal basis, very nearly any of our land for three to four times its original value...

At Malabar we buy no nitrogen fertilizer because our legume sod program produces free nitrogen for any crop save possibly corn.

We buy no protein supplements or concentrates at $100 to $120 a ton since we manufacture sufficient protein for dairy cattle and beef feeders out of sunlight, air and water through our rich and heavy legumes.

All of this money which we do not spend simply shows up on

the profit side of the ledger.

It should be pointed out, as another means of measurement, that if we had the same acreage in corn as we have in grass and legumes we should have to employ a minimum of twelve men and twelve tractors at a very conservative estimate. Until the beginning of 1950 we have run Malabar and a fifty-cow milking-parlor with four men and five tractors and three high school boys who come in during the summer to make grass silage and bale hay and straw. If we produced corn silage to fill our seven silos we should have to have at least twice as many men and tractors, plus the hard work of making corn silage. When we went out of corn altogether after gradually cutting the acreage year by year, we sold one tractor, one corn picker, three cultivators and half our plows and harrows and fitting equipment — a capital investment representing about $5,000, in addition to all the other machinery required in a four- to five-year rotation general farm program.

Our gross return on the year has more than doubled as we moved into a specialized grass-legume-livestock program and the profits on any crop have risen on a similar scale and a good deal more than that on milk and cattle.

Out of the Earth, 169-172

Our operations are not based upon a hope of high prices but upon making a good profit by efficient and economical operations regardless of price. When the price of milk falls we are doing all right and when it is high we are making a great deal of money, on a basis of maximum production per acre of maximum-quality feed at minimum costs in fertilizer, labor and supplements.

Out of the Earth, 176

Groundhogs (Woodchucks)

[There] is a condition one can witness on farms throughout the United States in any area inhabited by the groundhog tribe, even upon farms which have been managed reasonably well. Keep your eyes open the next time you drive through the country or observe your own fields and very likely you will see the same thing — small spots in fields of hay, wheat or oats where the crop is greener, higher and more productive. Walk over to them and, unless the farmer has spilled some fertilizer, you will find that our friend the groundhog has dug himself a home and spilled subsoil over the topsoil. Our own groundhogs told us a great deal — that the mineral richness of our deep subsoils was very great and that the remaining topsoil was depleted to a point where, in the beginning, some fields would not provide yields which merited harvesting.

Out of the Earth, 100

One of the last things we should desire at Malabar is the total extermination of woodchucks. The holes they dig and their generous hospitality in sharing them with other animals make them a great asset in building game and wildlife populations. Their holes serve at all times, but particularly during the winter months, as shelter and refuge for rabbit, quail, possum, skunks, partridges and other animals and birds. Female raccoon, when natural tree dens are scarce or non-existent will house their litters in woodchuck holes.

Malabar Farm, 81

Hogs — "A Hymn To Hawgs"

Whoever has really looked into the eye of a shrewd old sow should feel humility. It is a bright clear eye, more like the eye of a human than the eye of any other animal. It looks at you quite directly, even with what might be described as a piercing gaze. The look sizes you up, appraises you and leaves you presently with the impression that the old sow has indeed a very low opinion of you, an opinion tempered by scorn and contempt and perhaps even a little animosity. Clearly she does not think that you amount to very much and that, given a difficult situation, she could cope with it far better than you could do. It is as if she said, "You think you can shut me up and confine me. Well, that's what you think! Ha! Ha! and again Ha! Ha!" And any farmer knows what she is thinking ... that if she really wants to get out she'll find a way. Sometimes, I have a feeling that she is thinking, "You think you know how to manage me and bring up my litters with all your disinfectants, your heat lamps, your violet rays, your antibiotics, your supplements, your inoculations, your vaccinations. Just let me alone and give me my freedom and I won't have any troubles nor will the pigs I feed."

From My Experience, 14

Among all animals there is none which has such a variety of sounds designed obviously for the purposes of communication as the pig. Waste your time as I do, leaning on the fence, and you will see among the pigs everything from a director's meeting to a ladies' discussion of the attractions of the visiting boar. There are the sounds which a sow makes when she feels it is time to feed her young, and there are the frightful squeals of discontent from her pigs when she will not give in to their demands and lie down on her side to let them feed. And there is what is distinctly the most ferocious name-calling that can occur during the equivalent of a hair-pulling match between two old sows. Pick up a small pig and he will let out the most hair-raising shrieks for help that will bring running not only his own mother but all the sows in the neighborhood. He is the most blatant of small frauds for the minute you put him down again on the ground the shrieks stop instantly and are replaced by the pleasant "oink! oink!" noises of a contented small pig.

From My Experience, 19

A hog is by nature the cleanest of animals and will never foul his own nest unless forced to do so by the laziness or ignorance of his owner.

From My Experience, 22

Unlike the stupid sheep which will lie down and die under adverse circumstances with no will whatever to live, the hog has an immense will to live and to keep his freedom.

From My Experience, 30

In all the experiments in raising hogs at Malabar we have been concerned primarily with health, simplicity and net profits to the average farmer. It does not matter that a farmer puts ten thousand hogs on the market if he makes little or no profit and if he is plagued by sickness and ills of all sorts. A farmer raising a hundred hogs with common sense may have a much larger net profit. The truth is that the whole technique of raising hogs as advocated by many "authorities" has become so complex and so complicated that both the margin of health and the margin of net profit has been greatly lowered for any farmer who attempts to follow out all their advice and instructions. Capital investment in elaborate housing and feeding installations make it necessary to raise hogs for years before the investment can be amortized. The costs of daylight lamps, of artificial heating, of veterinarian services, of inoculations and vaccinations, of expensive hog "mashes" and artificial chemical "stimulants" and a hundred other things have made of the

comparatively simple operation of breeding, raising and feeding the
most intelligent and self-sufficient of animals something which, if
carried out in all the details, not only devours the profits but greatly
increases the labor and in general produces a kind of nightmare not
only for the hog but for the farmer who attempts to follow all the
advice that is put out. Much of this comes frequently through high-
pressure advertising campaigns put on by chemical, farm equipment
and feed companies and frequently by "experts" who have never
possibly imagined themselves to be hogs or what a hog would like
in order to be healthy, comfortable and happy, nor have they ever at
the end of the year been forced to balance costs against profits. They
are men who regard hogs as something to be kept in a test tube rather
than as highly intelligent, self-sufficient animals. A little time
"wasted" leaning on the fence of the hog lot where the hog is happily
taking care of himself might be of profit.

The farmer who farms five acres of corn or barley to produce
what he should be producing on one acre will never make any money
in hogs. The more hogs he has, the more money he will lose. Only
a well-kept set of books will prove that to him, but the farmer who
farms five acres of land to produce what he should on one rarely if
ever, keeps books. That is why heavy farm supports are politically
necessary.

From all this the reader has perhaps gathered the belief that the
writer has a higher opinion of some hogs than he has of some people,
and in this I am compelled to say he would be quite right.

From My Experience, 32-33

House

It was always a fine thing to plant a house on a hill, for it gave
a man a sense of power and freedom and repose.

The Farm, 17

Old houses have an aura of their own as if the spirits of the past
had somehow left behind them some of the essence of their very
lives and characters.

From My Experience, 240

One knows when a house is loved and when it is not loved. One
can tell by the eaves, by the stairways, by the shrubbery, by the very
grass which grows around it.

From My Experience, 243

Indo-China (Vietnam -- 1954)

The battle in Indo-China is not altogether a battle against Communists and Red China. In it are engaged countless Indo-Chinese, of all the small individual nationalities represented in the Indo-Chinese area, who hate French domination more than Chinese domination and many who are fighting not for the Red Chinese but against domination and exploitation by the French. Yet there are even those, principally in the armed forces of the U.S., who would, if they dared, advocate drafting American boys from Ohio, Iowa, Kansas and elsewhere and sending them into this struggle where they or the nation itself have no proper place and where our intervention can only serve to do us tragic harm in the long run.

A New Pattern for a Tired World, 60

Industrial Revolution

No change in the history of the world has ever come so rapidly or with such devastating effects as the brief industrial revolution with steam power, the telephone, the telegraph, the railway, the automobile, the airplane, the radio and countless other developments which have shrunken the world and made neighbors, however unhappy or perilous, of all of us. This headlong change has led us, especially in America, to confuse plumbing and automobiles, which have to do only with the body, with civilization, which has to do with the mind, the spirit, the soul and with man's relation to his fellow men. It has led man into a conceit in his own ingenuity which may in the end achieve only his destruction.

A Few Brass Tacks, 10

Inflation

I have lived with the money of many people and many nations in times of revolution, of war, of inflation, and year by year my respect for money, as anything more than oil in the ball bearings of commerce, has declined. I have seen the German mark valued at approximately four marks to the dollar and at many millions of marks to the dollar. I have seen men pay as much as ten million paper marks for a newspaper and I have seen a farmer in a small German town exchange a single wheelbarrow load of potatoes for enough money to pay off in one day the mortgage which he and his father had struggled for two generations to pay off — until money became cheap and real wealth, as represented by the wheelbarrow

242

load of potatoes, became scarce and increasingly valuable and barter became the sole means of exchange. I have seen the printing presses of France working day and night, under the stress of an inflationary spiral, until income from the savings of a whole middle class was wiped out and one got used to seeing nothing but new bank notes — because in a time of rapidly rising prices there was never enough money in circulation from day to day to carry on the payment of rising wages or meet the needs of ordinary transactions in a grocery store between the merchant and the customer.

A Few Brass Tacks, 17

No one is a greater victim of the illusion of money as wealth than the industrial worker in his constant struggle for higher wages. In the whole of our society only the farmer who is in debt and a few shrewd and nimble speculators ever really benefit by inflation. The farmer, under inflation, receives increasingly higher money prices for what he produces and if he is a wise man, he does not, under inflation, seek to expand horizontally by acquiring more land when the cost of land rises with the steadily lessening purchasing power of his dollar, but rather to expand vertically by increasing production upon the land he already possesses and thereby augmenting his income and profits both by increasing his production and through the benefit of higher and higher prices for what he produces. If, as is frequently the case, he has mortgages or old debts established at a time when the purchasing power of the dollar was high, he can pay these off with the inflated dollar (or any other currency) at a fraction of what the loan or the debt originally cost him. This has been common practice in all countries throughout the world in periods of currency inflation. It is essentially the story of the German farmer who paid off his long-standing mortgage with a wheelbarrow load of potatoes.

A Few Brass Tacks, 62-63

When the whole income of a millionaire from interest money on investments in mortgages or urban real estate or industrial stocks, or even government bonds, could not buy food for the household for a day, the farmer could barter a duck for shoes for the whole family or trade a sheep for an automobile. Each morning the German countryside provided a spectacle of bankers and industrialists and millionaires driving into the country to offer jewelry or automobiles or works of art in exchange for eggs, milk and other necessities. The farmer did not want and would not accept millions of marks in currency or in government bonds in exchange for real wealth which he produced from the real wealth which was his good agricultural land.

Inflation is also the worst enemy of those members of society who have invested money in the stocks of banks, industries or even government bonds in order to provide for themselves an income from the dividends of those investments. As prices rise and the value of the dollar declines, the returns from investments shrink proportionately until a point is reached at which an invested income of ten thousand dollars a year will not buy a loaf of bread and the investor who has perhaps counted upon this income for his old age, is left penniless holding great bundles of bank notes or stock certificates or government bonds more valuable to start a fire in the stove (if he can afford to buy fuel) than as a means of buying food, or clothing or shelter or anything at all. That is what happened in Germany and a little later came very nearly to pass in France when the money-investing middle classes were virtually wiped out of existence.

Your industrial wage-earning or salaried employee finds himself in the same situation, since wages or salaries are his income, from the labor which is his capital, unless wages and salaries are perpetually raised and even then he remains a victim since these raises eventually force up in turn the prices of whatever it is he produces, and lower the dollar value of wage or salary in terms of purchasing power.

The stability of the farmer and his real wealth in the face of inflation is reflected in the fact that under extreme or ultimate inflation agricultural land alone represents a wholly stable and desirable investment. At such times no one wants to buy urban real estate since it produces returns only in a currency which has little or no value. Valuable banking and industrial stock and even government bonds go begging since the returns from them are equally valueless when they can buy nothing, but agricultural land becomes more and more precious as real wealth and the creative renewable source of more real wealth.

In France and other European countries, with a long experience in wars, inflations and deflations, it has been at times almost impossible to buy good agricultural lands at any price. The reasoning can best be demonstrated by an incident out of the author's own experience. He sought to buy a small farm in France and finally offered approximately five times what it was worth to the old woman who owned it (an offer he was able to make since his income was largely in dollars and the franc, inflated both at home and abroad, brought him approximately forty francs for every dollar — another manifestation of the vagaries of money). When he asked the old woman why she would not accept such an offer, she replied, "I could take the money, but what could I do with it?"

Events have since proven her right, for at the time of writing, the value of the franc stands not at 40 francs as at the time of the sale, but at 120 francs to the dollar. In other words, if she had taken the money and locked it up, it would have shrunk by now to one-third the amount she locked away, or if she had invested it even in government bonds, her income from these bonds would have shrunk to a third; and the end of French inflation is not yet in sight. Meanwhile, she has the small farm. It has real wealth and what it produces can always be exchanged for money at prices which equal the value of the franc at 120 to the dollar, or in the black market for several times the value of the franc at 120 to the dollar. When and if the franc ever approached during inflation the vanishing point which the reichsmark reached in the twenties and the barter system returned, the old woman would still be secure and even impregnable for she could exchange potatoes for clothing and chickens for medicine, clothes or other commodities she might need.

During the long threat of wartime and postwar inflation, much buying of agricultural land has taken place among individuals and even family trust funds and public foundations as a hedge against the possibility of unlimited inflation in the future. In fact, a survey would probably show that, save for certain areas of very rich agricultural land, most of the buying has been done not by farmers but by city dwellers and investment organizations of one sort or another — all of them seeking to stabilize the value of their money by investing it in real wealth.

The farmer, badly burned after the last war by horizontal expansion at inflated prices, has been cautious. In this buying the motive has been neither speculative nor profit on investment for returns but for the anchoring of liquid money in real wealth unaffected through inflation and deflation by the vagaries in the value of the dollar. Many individuals, fearful of the prospects of the coming decade, have bought farms simply for security, for a shelter and food if and when the time comes when the buying power of the dollar becomes negligible or nonexistent, as it may well become through higher and higher taxes, lack of money with any real purchasing power, scarcity of industrial production, deficit financing and all the other evils which arise when the manipulation of money is used in an attempt to cure profound economic ills.

A Few Brass Tacks, 65-69

Johnny Appleseed

He existed. He was no invention of Greataunt Esther. He lives in the traditions of the whole Western Reserve — a voice crying in the wilderness, unkempt, unshorn, and unwashed, a demented fellow who in the Palestine of two thousand years ago would have been honored as a prophet. Like John The Baptist, he lived on locusts and wild honey, clothed in the skins of wild animals and bits of cast-off clothing. He wandered from settlement to settlement and cabin to cabin, preaching and singing, never staying more than a night. Winter and summer were alike to him. He gained his name from his habit of planting wherever he roamed, on hillsides and in valleys, by streams and on the edge of virgin forests, the seeds of apples which settlers had brought from the East. When the trees they brought with them began to bear, he begged for the seeds of their first fruit, and the Colonel and his family used, half-humorously, to save the seeds of the apples they ate in the long winter evenings and put them into a paper bag to give to Johnny Appleseed when he came in one night at sunset to sleep in the mows of the great barn. Wherever he went he planted, too, the fennel, esteemed as a cure for the fever and ague which rose to attack the settlers' families when their plows turned for the first time the rich black virgin loam of all that fertile country.

He lay down one night to sleep in a thicket and never wakened again. He was, in his way, the prophet of the New Country. He preached always that it was the promised land and that one day would be the richest spot on God's green earth. He was vindicated, but centuries sooner than he had believed. His legend lingered after him, and in one of the pretty parks of the Town there is a little obelisk raised to his memory. But there are other monuments, too, for in the hedgerows here and there all over Ohio and Indiana there still linger ancient apple trees, old, rotten, worm-eaten, hollowed by flickers and woodpeckers, sometimes blackened by the smoke of factories, grown from the seeds thrust into the rich earth more than a century ago by Johnny's crazy hand. And on hot summer days when one can see the corn pushing its tall tassels upward, the smell of fennel is everywhere.

The Farm, 103-105

Korean War (1954)

One "police action" war such as the tragic blunder in Korea should have taught us that little or nothing is accomplished beyond involving ourselves more and more deeply in the web of perpetual police actions and wars in every part of the world. The Korean situation has not been settled and will not be settled until we withdraw entirely from an area in which we have no right to be and leave the peoples of that area to work out their own problems, which in the end they and only they alone must do in any case.

A New Pattern for a Tired World, 74

Land

It should never be forgotten that the middle class which owns something and shares in the benefits and general wealth of a nation are the greatest champions of freedom, economic, political and spiritual. France, with all its characteristic indivdualist political vagaries, is still essentially a solid nation, and resists and survives crisis after crisis, wars and occupations of territory because so many Frenchmen have little shops and villas and small bits of land.

A New Pattern for a Tired World, 205-206

Legumes

As in the case of lime and the neglect in emphasizing its catalyzing properties, so we have often overlooked perhaps the greatest and most valuable quality and characteristic of nearly all legumes — that they are one of the few families of plants which can grow and will grow even lustily in soils totally devoid of organic material and at the same time provide a valuable crop and create organic material for us in great quantities. One cannot grow corn in soils low in organics or even wheat or oats or barley with profitable yields, but one can grow legumes abundantly provided the mineral balance exists or is established. And the legumes have as well the great and, to the farmer, precious power of producing great quantities of highly available nitrogen out of the air itself without any cost to the farmer. Moreover, there are other powers possessed by legumes and in particular by alfalfa and the sweet clovers which have not been sufficiently investigated. Among these is, without much question, their power to break down gravel and coarse soil particles into consistencies and chemical combinations in which mineral fertility becomes available not only to the legumes themselves but to other plants and notably the grasses which grow in affinity with them after a very short period of time.

Out of the Earth, 71

Lime

In the year we took over the Bailey Place, one 10-acre field of wheat already planted on the farm was not worth harvesting ... (So terrible was the prospect that when I told Max Drake, first manager of the farm, that I had just bought the Bailey Place suddenly and unexpectedly, tears came into his eyes. The restoration of that land to even the lowest sort of production seemed hopeless. The hills were known widely as the poorest land in the township.) The wheat, which would have yielded less than 5 bushels to the acre, was mowed down and left in the field. Its potential organic content was worth more to us than the crop itself. Two years later on that same field we took 33 bushels of wheat to the acre and four years later we took 52 bushels.

We accomplished this gain, wisely, not by the use of vast quantities of commercial fertilizer (we used only 200 pounds to the acre of 3-12-12). We did it by the use of organic materials in as large quantities as possible, by lime, grasses and legumes and an enormous mine of old barnyard manure we found accumulated in the barns and barnyards of the farm.

All this organic material went on the field plus lime and commercial fertilizer. The lime was perhaps the key element, for it made it possible to raise that greatest friend of the farmer, the whole family of legumes. The lime not only sweetened the hard acid soils but permitted the legumes to grow and provide nitrogen and green manure, and the legumes in turn did many wonderful things below the surface of the soil which we could not see. The principal function of the commercial fertilizer was as a "starter" for the seedings of legumes and grasses. It provided the first step in the process of putting "dead" unproductive soil back into circulation.

In recent years, in the emphasis upon lime and ground limestone as the key to raising legumes and rich grasses, we have tended to overlook another great virtue of lime — its power as a catalyst to make other minerals and elements of fertility available to crops. In sour soils the minerals and elements go into chemical combination with aluminum and iron, the chief elements of most soils, in which form they become locked up and unavailable to crops. That is the reason why most sour land is regarded as poor land and many farms acquire the reputation of being "worn out" when they are not worn out at all. Their natural fertility is merely locked up in unavailable form. Nearly all elements and minerals have a much greater chemical affinity for calcium (lime) than they have for iron or aluminum, and once lime is added, they go into chemical compound with calcium (lime), in which form they are highly available to crops of almost every kind.

Out of the Earth, 54

On the land we rent from the Muskingum Conservancy District there are two large fields separated by a county road which for two generations has been surfaced with limestone or with conglomerate glacial gravel. The prevailing winds blow at right angles to the road across the two fields carrying the dust away from one and across the other. Although the two fields had been treated the same by their former owners and had eventually been abandoned, the fertility of the field which received regularly the blown powdered limestone and the mineral dust from the disintegrated gravel, through the years since the road was first surfaced, has always been from 20 to 30 per cent greater. It is also notable that the pheasant and rabbit population is found nearly always on the side of the road where the deposits of mineral dust had been laid down for years.

Once my partner, resenting the dust which sometimes covered the crops on the leeward side of the field, suggested inducing the county commissioners to oil or tar the roads. I promptly vetoed the proposal, observing that we were getting every year many dollars per acre worth of the most valuable minerals in highly available form without spending a penny. Sometimes visiting farmers ask whether we do not resent the clouds of dust which rise on hot dry days from our graveled farm lanes to blow across the fields. The answer is "No." The tires of the visiting automobile act as a kind of fertilizer factory, pulverizing and spreading across our fields, together with wind action, a mixture of minerals from potash to phosphorus through such valuable trace elements as manganese, cobalt and a score of others.

Out of the Earth, 225-226

Machines

Machines are not in themselves the solution to a perfect agriculture; they are as good as the intelligence of the man who uses them and there is no implement in the whole category of farm machinery which cannot actually create losses and damage when used stupidly or carelessly.

From My Experience, 297

Man, The Nature Of

Active people, being driven by a force stronger than themselves, seldom grow bitter, since bitterness can be born only of indolence and inactivity and brooding.

The Farm, 256

In most of the panaceas offered either from the extreme Left or from the extreme Right, one element seems to have been almost wholly overlooked and that is the consideration of the nature of man — that he is a creature which must move upward toward a greater realization of his capacity and his dignity as an individual, that he must have gods in which to believe and results which justify, regardless of illusion, his faith in those gods, that there is in any man, save for the physiologically handicapped and debased, a desire to work and to create which is the foundation of his neighbor's respect for him, and what is more important, his respect for himself.

A Few Brass Tacks, 6

Man is not naturally a cynic; he wants pitifully to believe, in himself, in his future, in his community and in the nation in which he is a part.

A Few Brass Tacks, 3

A man may have five automobiles in his garage and bathrooms with mauve matching toilet paper and still be an utter barbarian; indeed such emphasis upon material things is likely to make him so. Many of our most notorious gangsters have been perfect examples of this state of mind. On the other hand a poor man living in one room without means of transportation and only an outdoor privy may be a high type of civilized man.

A Few Brass Tacks, 235-236

The complete man is a rarity. Leonardo was one and Michelangelo and Shakespeare and Balzac. They lived; they brawled; they had roots; they were immoral; they had vices as well as virtues; they were totally lacking in preciosity and the pale, moldy qualities of the poser or the seeker after publicity and sensation. The complete man is a happy man, even in misery and tragedy, because he has always an inner awareness that he has lived a complete existence, in vice and virtue, in success and failure, in satisfaction and disappointment, in distinction and vulgarity. Not only is he complete; he is much more, he is a man.

The older I grow the more I become aware wistfully of that goal of completeness. It is not something that can be attained by wishing or even by plotting and determination. The man who sets out deliberately to be a complete man defeats himself, for from the beginning he is of necessity self-conscious, contriving and calculating. He becomes the fake, the poser, the phony. Some attempt to turn their own inadequacies into a defense by affecting a sense of snobbery or superiority. In this sense a writer like Henry James is pathetic. So are many writers of our own times with their lacy preciosities, their affectations, their pomp and pretensions, their fundamental shallowness and decadence.

From My Experience, 8

Man is merely a part of the universe, and not a very great part, which happens to be fortunate principally in having evolved such traits and powers as consciousness, reflection, logic and thought. The wise and happy man is the one who finds himself in adjustment to this truth, who never needs, in moments of disillusionment and despair, to cut himself down to size because it has never occurred to him, in the beginning or at any time, to inflate his own importance whether through ignorance, morbidity, egotism or undergoing psychoanalysis (which is merely another name for one of the age-old manifestations of brooding impotence and frustration of the incomplete man).

From My Experience, 10

I am afraid it is true that teachers, like good cattlemen and good farmers and good engineers and good cooks, are born and not made. So essentially are most really good people.

From My Experience, 11

Considering the general insignificance and unimportance of man, the pleasures of agriculture are perhaps more real and gratifying than the pleasures and even the excesses of the purely mathematical mind (which are certainly not pleasures to be underestimated).

From My Experience, 12

Often enough the successful man who comes up the hard way is the one who ruins his own children's lives by removing from their existence the very elements which make for character and a sense of responsibility — all in the desire that his children should have "all the things he never had."

From My Experience, 53

Knowing what you want and sticking to it is one of the great forces of life, and often enough it is a force which proves almost irresistible in a world in which most people never know quite what they want or are forever changing their minds about the goal.

From My Experience, 338-339

Market Gardening

For years we had simply given away or fed to the pigs or plowed in the surplus vegetables, but the increasing numbers of people who wanted to buy them not only interrupted our work (for we did not want to be disagreeable) but gave us the idea of perhaps organizing the whole thing and making it simpler not only for the buyers but for ourselves. And so we backed into the whole business of market gardening and a market stand, which has become perhaps the most profitable undertaking per acre of all the projects at Malabar Farm.

We have also made a specialty and increasingly followed the policy of raising and marketing vegetables which cannot be found or are rare in the average city market and are varieties which are no longer planted by the big market gardeners for the general market. We have been producing Bibb lettuce for years, long before it was known outside the most expensive and excellent restaurants frequented by the gourmet and we experiment constantly with new varieties of vegetables which are sometimes superior to the old ones. We have a whole following of customers who come to us to get okra and the tiny red and yellow tomatoes and Italian paste tomatoes and white pearl onions, and there are customers so addicted to the happy and healthy habit of watercress that they will come from a great distance simply to get it dark green and fresh out of the icy, swift-flowing spring water...

Not only have they [various soluble fertilizers containing many minor elements] improved the general quality of market produce but the rapid growth has given us the advantage of supplying the early home-grown market when the prices are high and the profits greatest...

The prospect for further expansion lies ahead of the market for the boys have uncovered an excellent market at good hotels, restaurants and even hospitals throughout the area. Chilled fresh vegetables can be delivered fresh each morning with the minimum loss of freshness, sweetness and general flavor and we are able to provide a great variety of things which are difficult to find in the general market. The vegetables have not been shipped through a commission warehouse or knocked about a central market for hours and sometimes days, but come fresh from the garden, chilled thoroughly by cold spring water.

From My Experience, 312-318

Marketing

What good was it to pack apples carefully wrapped in paper, to ship to the big markets of the East, when shipping and the middlemen left nothing for the farmers, and often enough the middlemen took precious dollars off the price because the apples arrived bruised and damaged, a charge which the farmer could never know was true? What good was it to raise wheat for a price which made it sounder economics to feed it to the hogs than to send it to market? Why have a fine dairy when it showed no profit at the end of the year and the men who owned the canned-milk plant grew rich and built fine houses? Why grow potatoes for a dubious profit of a few dollars a field? Why? Why? Why?

The Farm, 331

Manure

It was once commonly and universally believed that all barnyard manure was alike and contained the same fertilizer values. We know now that barnyard manure can vary as much as vegetables in its mineral content according to the kind of soil from which it comes originally in the form of forage. In other words, poor land and poor farms with soils of depleted or unbalanced mineral content produce poor manure and rich soils produce rich manures because the cattle cannot utilize all the minerals coming to them through the forage off rich soils. This factor of course has little to do with the "inoculating" values of manure which carries benevolent bacteria, fungi, moulds, animal secretions, hormones, enzymes and other elements which undoubtedly affect the germination of seeds and set to work reactions within the soils which make the mineral content more available to succeeding crops. Nor has it, of course, much to do with the value of the organic material represented by the manure which is very great.

Out of the Earth, 183

That most valuable of fertilizers, barnyard manure.

Out of the Earth, 187

Money

We shall never learn by turning backward and we shall never find the answer by following the soothsayers and demagogues who promise paradise overnight or those whose panaceas are all founded upon money or the manipulation of money. Man's problems are not and have never been solely material problems, nor can they be solved by inflations and deflations or the manipulations of currencies. When they become so, as they threaten to do in our trying times, civilization dies to be revived again only when man through misery and defeat and disillusionment touches bottom and begins again. For civilized man, for those leaders who have influenced the long journey upward of mankind, money or rewards in material were not the great and ultimately desired rewards. When they become so, man dies spiritually and his civilization dies with him.

A Few Brass Tacks, 11

In one sense, at least — the economic one — the New Deal will have passed having had little lasting effect upon the grave and deep problems which confront us in our complex, modern industrial society. The principal reason for the failure probably lies in the fact that nearly all the countless remedies attempted were in terms of the manipulation of money which can for a very brief period have the effect of a tablet of benzedrine but in the long run, like benzedrine, can only create a demand for more and more of the same treatment while the whole system deteriorates internally.

A Few Brass Tacks, 35

Mushrooms — "La Chasse Aux Morilles"

As maple syrup is the symbol of the dying winter and the last of the snows, the morel is an assurance from Nature and God that the last of the cold spring rains has fallen and the season of heat and exuberant growth is at hand. Like the bull thistle, the nettle and the dandelion you will find the morel growing only in rich country on good land and rarely on poor and worn-out land. It loves fertility and moisture and you will find it only on the borders of rich pastures, in the virgin woods or under ancient apple orchards.

The hunt for morels is as great a passion with real gourmets as the big game hunter's search for rare specimens and the excitement is not unrelated. I have never shot anything but lions, tigers, panthers and Indian bison, all among the world's most dangerous animals, and then only out of politeness and with no pleasure whatever in the killing. The particular victims were dedicated to me, and considering the effort and expense of organizing the hunt and the ritual which accompanied it, it would have been in bad taste not to have done the shooting and to have pretended some pleasure and excitement in the process... I can say quite honestly that hunting morels is at least equally as exciting as pursuing big game. It is a much less expensive sport and, as a gourmet, I much prefer the result of the chase. Also it can be conducted within the limits of my own property.

When the violets and the Dutchman's-breeches and the squirrel corn begin to flower and the wild ginger of the early settlers begins to thrust its rich lush leaves and queer stunted dark red blossoms through the leaf mold, it is time to look for morels. When the trillium comes into full bloom and begins to turn pink, the season is over and the best one can hope to find is a stray morel, which somehow came along too late and has begun to dry up, ready to spread its spores to the wind to provide morels for other years.

From My Experience,146-148

Abundance follows winters when there has been much rain and snow and the ground is filled with moisture to the point of wetness. Yet if the spring is slow and the rains cold, the hepaticas, the bloodroot, the wild ginger, the trilliums and all the others will come and go with scarcely a morel to be found. There must be moisture and heat almost as strong as that of midsummer.

The hunter knows also that old orchards are good for finding the King, that the deep woods are the haunt of the dogpecker and that the Black King and the Little King may be found almost anywhere there is fertility or virgin soil. He also knows that all morels seem to like the vicinity of ash trees, whether in the forest or on the edge of a meadow...

Even the most honest and truthful of men will turn liar when questioned on his return with a great catch of morels.

From My Experience,167-169

Nature

Neither in agriculture, nor in economics, nor in human history does anyone ever succeed in creating a plan and then imposing a plan or theory. In all the progress of mankind, in all his discoveries, one thing grows out of another in perfect continuity, based upon observation and the utilization of what has been observed, always within the limits and benefits of natural law.

Pleasant Valley, 161

Man cannot himself escape nature. Neither can he ever subdue her or attempt to exploit her endlessly without becoming himself the victim. In this country we have on the one hand witnessed the spectacle of a people destroying by exploitation as rapidly as possible the very sources of their prosperity and well-being — and on the other hand an attempt by superficial methods founded upon socialistic principles to set things right by experimenting with the buzz saw of economic laws. In the long run one method is as futile and destructive as the other, one tearing out the very base of the whole structure, the other further weakening a structure which has already begun to totter and shake.

Pleasant Valley, 244

In Nature there is no such thing as a single crop; indeed Nature abhors the single crop and the single crop has been the most destructive single influence in American agriculture. The evils of single-cropping extend even into the area of legumes, which undoubtedly flourish better and provide more and better forage when they are grown with grasses.

Out of the Earth, 74

No force on earth will give such a response and such a reward as Nature when you understand her and work with her.

From My Experience, 81

Then came the war and all thought of continuing the struggle was abandoned and Nature was permitted to have her way. For nearly five years the garden went wild and in doing so produced what Nature wanted. Once we yielded to her, she rewarded us handsomely...

Once we turned Nature loose, and let survive what belonged there and pleased itself there, she presented us with one of the loveliest gardens, especially during the exuberant Ohio spring.

From My Experience, 85-86

New Agriculture

In the picture of modern agriculture — the New Agriculture — in a complex, highly intricate and integrated national economy, the question of proper land use plays an important role, not only the proper land use of the individual farm, but of the county, the state and the nation. On a farm it means simply using the land according to the best, most profitable and often most obvious use... Roughly the plan works out thus:

(1) We are in hill country with little or no level land. The soil is light but minerally rich. It is not land suited to corn but when properly handled grows the finest hay, grass silage, and pasture in the world. Many farms in our region were completely ruined in the past by trying to raise corn and hogs on hills. (2) The first step in achieving proper use of the land was doing away with the old, square fields and establishing an agriculture upon the contour around the hills rather than up and down them... (3) One hundred and forty acres of rough and rocky ground, not even suitable to permanent pasture and already in timber, was put into efficient wood-lot management with all cattle fenced out and seedlings allowed to grow into valuable timber. (4) A considerable acreage of steep land and low-lying land was put into permanent bluegrass pasture, limed, fertilized, clipped and treated as a valuable crop

with a high-carrying capacity of livestock. (5) A large acreage of less steep land was put into strip cropping given over to a rotation of hay, silage and pasture production alternated with wheat and oats. (6) The fairly level land was worked intensively in a corn, oats, sweet clover rotation. (7) Gradually the corn acreage has been reduced and the whole area has become, outside the woodlots and permanent bluegrass pastures, a grass, small grain farm with the prospect of corn being eliminated altogether, putting the intensively farmed oats, corn, sweet clover area into grass and buying what corn we need from the flat prairie lands to the west of us where corn is a specialty. The flat-land Iowa farmer can produce corn more efficiently and more cheaply than we can, while we have the advantage over him in grass, hay silage, and pasture production so long as we do a good job of it.

Malabar Farm, 53-54

To be sure, the whole of the New Agriculture, so far removed from the old conception that "anybody can farm," is not dependent alone upon the factors of soil fertility and the resulting good nutrition, although consideration and understanding of soil is its base. There are many other elements: (1) the new and more productive strains of crops developed by the plant breeder, although these are of no avail unless the quality and fertility of soils is the first consideration; (2) vast new improvements in machinery and mechanization, although these, too, are secondary to soils and may only serve to destroy the fertility of soils twice as fast as before if they are employed by the bad and ignorant farmer; (3) insecticides, dusts and chemical sprays which have done much to alleviate both disease and the attacks of insects, but on really good, living, productive soils the necessity for which is greatly reduced and in some cases obviated altogether; (4) developments both in irrigation and drainage, but again the need for both can be greatly reduced in most cases and sometimes be obviated by simple consideration for the element of organic material and its relation to the moisture factor, erosion and poor drainage...

Essentially the New Agriculture is concerned with soils and the related factors of good nutrition, health and optimum production both in quantity and quality, and this is as it should be. In the past soil was all too often overlooked or was made victim of every sort of short cut and panacea to force artificial rather than natural fertility. Most of the time that path led to disaster in terms erosion, poor drainage, lowered production in quantity and quality and seriously lowered nutritional value in foods both for beasts and humans. It might be said that in one sense medical research is following the same pattern as the New Agriculture — that is, turning to fundamentals through the emphasis on preventive rather than curative or "patent" medicine, and in doing so is making remarkable discoveries similar and closely related to those made in the New Agriculture. Indeed, some of these discoveries are very nearly the same in both fields since they are so closely related and so interdependent.

But perhaps the most important element in the New Agriculture is the fashion in which it reaches out into almost every field of science and deals with the fundamentals of human existence whether it be war and peace, or economics, or health, or the problem of feeding a world which, at the old and the prevalent levels of agriculture, is overpopulated to the point of starvation in many areas. Men and nations, as the tragic happenings of the world reveal each day, are dependent primarily upon the soil for their very existence. In the era of the Industrial Revolution this truth came very near to being forgotten, but today both nations and people are being reminded of it day after day through bitter and tragic experience.

Out of the Earth, 47-48

Fortunately there are great changes in progress, arising principally from the younger generation which has been given a different point of view regarding agriculture. Largely speaking, their point of view represents the New Agriculture in which the farmer is part businessman, part specialist and part scientist rather than the old, wasteful, ignorant, frontier agriculture or even an agriculture in the four-year rotation general farm pattern. This change will come about eventually through the force of economics alone since the older patterns are profitable neither for the individual nor for the nation. Moreover, they imply two other defeating factors — an overburdening investment in different kinds of machinery and long hours of drudgery.

Out of the Earth, 250-251

"Oakies"

The plight of the "Oakies" immortalized by Steinbeck in "The Grapes of Wrath" was not caused by the shiftlessness of the individual farmer or the harsh behavior of banks and land corporations; it was caused by the ruinous policy of the government in restricting homesteading of federal lands to a quarter-section to the individual. Most of the land opened for settlement was in reality grazing and cattle land. In addition, the vagaries of a climate where floods and droughts frequently alternated made farming a hazardous affair indeed. In order to make a living (which was not possible from grazing on 160 acres), most of these settlers raised cash crops and the climate quickly did the rest, and much of the land threatened to become desert until it was turned back into larger holdings of grazing land.

Flat Top Ranch, 18

Ohio

This was the kind of country to which he belonged — a country, gentle, smiling, well-watered and fertile, out of which man might make a new paradise if he were good and wise enough.

The Farm, 16

Day after day it grew warmer, and all about the cabin the woods broke into a glory of wild flowers — hepaticas and spring beauties, violets purple and yellow, the white stars of trilliums, bloodroot; and last of all, beneath the forest trees came the white of the dogwood, like the beauty of thick white clouds caught and entangled in the lower branches of the great oaks and beeches. Surely a land so full of beauty was a blessed land.

The Farm, 18

Even in the beginning it became apparent that despite any desire in our part or any amount of nostalgia, Nature simply did not want the kind of carefully tended and ordered garden that one had in Europe. This was no ancient ordered countryside with centuries behind it of care and work and tending; this Ohio country was still wild country, exuberant, vigorous, primitive and only a few generations away from the forest wilderness.

From My Experience, 84-85

Organic vs. Chemical

During the past few years there has grown up, principally in England and in this country, an extreme school of thought which decries all chemical fertilizer as destructive both to soil and to health. It is as extreme as the old school, now utterly discredited, which taught that it was possible to farm and get good yields from the continuous use of chemical fertilizer alone. In our experience at Malabar, we have been unable to go along with either school of thought the whole way for a number of reasons, some born of observation and some based merely upon available knowledge and common sense.

The truth, it seems to us at Malabar, lies somewhere in between the two schools. Certainly no abundant profitable agriculture can be maintained without organic material which is still the chief factor in the availability and value of both chemical fertilizer and the natural fertility of soils, yet it is not always possible to build up soils by the use alone of organic manures, green manures and composts made off those soils if they are, as in many cases, naturally deficient in certain elements.

Nature laid down her soils in haphazard ways and, except for two or three soil types, few of them contain perfect balance of minerals. Occasionally one encounters soils which are almost totally deficient in certain minerals or trace elements or in some rare cases these may exist in chemical combinations which make them unavailable to the plants growing on such soils. Some of the world's poorest soils are virgin soils because of their lacks and imbalances, and in such cases no amount of green manures or other natural fertilizers grown on these soils and composted from them will correct the deficiencies or imbalances. In some form or other the lacking minerals must be brought in from the outside, and the cheapest and quickest way is through the use of chemical fertilizers employed reasonably.

Even in soils high in organic materials, the use of chemical fertilizers can be abused and, as agronomists have discovered, the excessive use of chemical fertilizer even in one year's application can do serious harm. The excessive use of commercial fertilizer over considerable periods can and inevitably will do great damage even in the presence of abundant organic material. There is no doubt whatever that excessive use of chemical fertilizers will destroy much of the living factor in soils represented by earthworms, bacteria, fungi and moulds and so in the end actually convert living soils into dead ones. Moreover, it is possible to saturate soils with auxiliary and undesirable elements such as sulphur to a point where the soils become not only unbalanced botanically but actually poisonous to the plant life and possibly even to animals and humans.

Many theories have been put forward and some research has been done in the field of this soil "poisoning" through the use of chemical fertilizer and its relation to various glandular and digestive derangements and even to the mysteries of cancer, but it is difficult, I think, to find anything very definite or wholly convincing one way or another in this respect. It is hazardous however to take an uncompromising stand either for or against such theories because so little is known, so little has been proven and the element of co-ordination and cause and effect in such cases has been so little studied.

Out of the Earth, 64-65

There are one or two other factors involved in the organic-chemical fertilizer dispute. The first at least is purely economic and related in particular to the case of the farmer working to restore to fertility badly abused farm land of high potential fertility. The average farmer cannot sit about waiting to build up his land to profitable yields by the slow process of composting alone. In most cases he must obtain as quickly as possible yields which will pay for his taxes and interest, purchase his seed, fertilizer and equipment and still show at least some small degree of profit. Here is where chemical fertilizer can hasten the process in two ways: (1) by quickly providing him with reasonable yields; (2) by enabling him to produce rapidly considerable quantities of green manures and even barnyard manures (by increasing livestock carrying capacity of his land along with his income) which he can turn back into the depleted soils to raise their quality and production.

Not long ago I had a letter from a friend who belongs to the rigid, uncompromising "organic" school. He wrote that he was very proud of the record he had made in raising wheat production by organic methods alone. He boasted that he had raised his production from an extremely low level, after seven years of composting and the use of organic materials, to a production of 20 bushels to the acre. As a matter of simple economics the average farmer would be in the hands of the sheriff if he failed to do a great deal better than that in a long period of seven years...

The immense values of organic material to productive soils is indisputable and it is safe to say that, outside truck gardens, the greatest and most serious deficiency in the soils of the United States today is organic material. It is also probably the greatest limiting factor in high continued production and in the prosperity of the ordinary farmer. But again, it is not the whole answer to balanced and living productive soils but only a part of the whole pattern. Among my truck-gardening and hothouse-growing friends there have been many instances where, in their efforts to maintain the high organic content so valuable to them, they have overdone the process and produced soils that contained too much organic material, turned sour and produced a sickening odor which could not possibly be given off by any healthy balanced soil. There can scarcely be enough propaganda made in this country in behalf of organic material. On the other hand, exaggerated claims made for organic material to the exclusion of all other factors may prove unreasonable, uneconomic and unsound and lead many a farmer into difficulties.

Out of the Earth, 67-70

Organic material of any kind mixed into the soils produces miraculous results.

Out of the Earth, 282

One of our constant struggles at Malabar is to avoid becoming kidnapped by the organic extremists and even the cranks. I have observed earlier in this book and will probably observe again that at Malabar we are not now and never have been extremists or cranks. If we find the need for chemical fertilizer, largely to produce lush cover crops and green manures, we use chemical fertilizer in considerable quantities and with excellent effect. If we find that it is necessary to use an insecticide or a fungicide, we use them although we will always choose the organic forms of rotenone, nicotine and pyrethrum or Bordeaux mixture, all of which are comparatively harmless to animals and humans. In *Out of the Earth* there are many pages devoted to the rather senseless battle between the chemical fertilizer "quick-buck" people and the organic extremists.

From My Experience, 183

From the beginning we have had a common aim and interest ... to produce the finest of plants and vegetables, as nearly as possible free from the need for dusts and sprays, and to carry out and even perhaps create a program in soils and gardening which would produce not only the economic advantages of high production per acre but the equally important ones of quality, both in flavor and nutrition. Behind all this lay the over-all aim of Malabar which might well be painted over our doorway together with the phrase, "Come and see for yourselves."

From My Experience, 190

At Malabar we are inclined to be reluctant and to hold back in the use of any dust or spray until absolutely necessary, even in the case of such mild vegetable poisons as rotenone, nicotine and pyrethrum. These may indeed be virtually harmless to humans and to animals but they are known to have a strong toxic effect upon insects and in the case of rotenone even upon fish.

It is therefore reasonable to suppose that even a mild insecticide such as rotenone could also have a serious toxic effect upon certain living soil bacteria and even upon earthworms and other beneficial living organisms which are essentially a part of any truly healthy, living and productive soils. If this could be true of a comparatively weak vegetable poison, how much more destructive to good soil conditions must be the effect of arsenic and high-powered inorganic dusts and sprays which are used wholesale today. It is not impossible that the resistance factor in many commercial, vegetable-growing operations has been greatly reduced through the destruction by wholesale use of poisons of the living organisms of the soil which are a part of any really sound, permanent and healthy agriculture. Such a condition could easily set up a vicious circle in which the steady destruction of living organisms gradually diminished the availability of fertility and served in turn to reduce the capacity of the soil to produce fast-growing, vigorous, resistant plants. In order to correct this weakened condition, more and more poisons in increasing amounts are then used and in turn accelerate the whole process of reducing a good soil to a condition of sterility in which it becomes merely a sterile medium in which to grow things instead of a living and healthy soil in which the process of birth, growth, death, decay and rebirth is in constant operation. Some such vicious circle may well account for the increasing infestation of disease and insects and declines in production and quality on many hard-worked vegetable production and farm areas throughout the country.

From My Experience, 227-228

We have no liking at Malabar for consuming in our daily meals quantities, either large or minute, of poisons universally recognized as lethal or of poisons such as arsenic or DDT which the system does not eliminate in any normal fashion but which accumulate gradually and slowly within the human body. Nor do we have any desire to act as laboratory specimens for the testing of viciously poisonous inorganic chemical by-products dumped on the market without proper tests or research into their lethal quantities, poisons advertised as so violent and viciously effective in destroying insect life that the operator is warned to use a gas mask while handling them. Whether they do real harm and serve in a general way to impair the health of the whole nation and to create an increase in the degenerative diseases of middle age, I do not know at this stage of the game nor does anyone else. One thing is certain — that used as they are in the production and processing of our foods to the amount of millions of pounds a year, they can do no one any good.

From My Experience, 231-232

Peace

It is doubtful that the world will make much progress toward real peace and genuine prosperity so long as nations and international relations are subject to constant intervention and at times domination by the professional military caste or so long as vital decisions and policies are influenced, controlled or kept from the people by military men or appointed bureaucrats or bureaus which have no direct responsibility to the people. It is exactly by this process of gradual encroachment, of obscure, concealed and indirect authority, without corresponding responsibility, by the technique of crisis and terror, concealment and secrecy that the liberal or mildly socialistic governments of central Europe were translated gradually into bureaucratic and oligarchic Nazi or Communist dictatorships in which the people themselves had less and less direction, force and authority in government, and truth and fact became distorted into the psychological atmosphere of a nightmare and all freedoms became lost.

A New Pattern for a Tired Planet, 15

Permanent Agriculture

It is only now, more than two centuries since farming really began on the North American continent, that we are beginning to get a genuine and permanent agriculture. To be sure, in certain small and restricted areas such as the Pennsylvania Dutch country and scattered Amish settlements, a sound and enduring and productive agriculture has long existed. Here and there throughout the nation there have always been isolated good farmers; but such areas and individuals represent only a minute fraction of 1 per cent of the agricultural and livestock areas of the nation; and it must be remembered that these peoples and individual ranchers have a special point of view toward the land; they do not look upon it as something to be mined as one might mine coal and exploit oil, nor do they ever believe, as did and do so many farmers and cattlemen, that their land owes them a living. They believe that their land is something to be held in trust to God, which will give them security and a good living during their lifetimes, so long as they care for it, and must be passed on to their children as rich and productive as they found it, or even more so.

Flat Top Ranch, 3

Plant Health

The healthier and more productive and faster-growing the plant, the less likely are the wholesale attacks of disease and insects.

From My Experience, 191

Ponds

Our ponds are each one a spot of beauty, a small universe teeming with life. The big herons visit them and the lovely red-winged blackbirds build their nests in the rushes along the borders. They are the delight of the big fierce Toulouse geese and the tame mallards. They are the source of much music in the night from the peeping of new young frogs to the booming bass of the big Louisiana bullfrogs which we put in as tadpoles years ago and which now measure as much as eighteen to twenty inches when stretched out. In April their borders turn green and gold with lush foliage and flowers of the marsh marigold, and later they are bordered with the blue Siberian iris and the purple and gold of the native wild flags. At night the muskrats move across the surface in the moonlight and the raccoons and foxes and possum come down out of the thick woods to drink and catch unwary frogs, leaving the imprint of their small paws in the wet mud along the banks. And there are the scavenging mud-turtles and a few big destructive snapping-turtles which the mallards avoid by shrewdly never taking their young onto the ponds until they are well grown. And there are countless birds, the swifts and barn swallows which skim low over the ponds in the blue evenings, to catch the insects hatching from their depths, and the flocks of goldfinches which finally mate off and build their nests from the down of the purple thistles growing in the damp ground. And in spring and autumn there are the visits of the wild ducks which join our mallards and feast off the richness of the farm ponds and the neighboring fields for three or four weeks at a time. For a lonely farm pond provides life and fascination...

In a way, a farm pond is a symbol of life itself. It is a bright spot on any farm, a whole universe in which the laws of nature operate under the close and intimate gaze of the interested. One can find in farm ponds and along their borders almost everything. They change with the season, awakening from the frozen, silent sleep of winter, going into the beginning of spring and the fierce breeding life of early summer. They provide skating in winter and swimming in summer and good fishing for three seasons of the year. For the children they are a source of inexhaustible delight. And like the fishponds of the abbeys and castles of medieval Europe and the Dark Ages, when all the world fell apart in anarchy and disorder, they provide not only food for the table but peace for the soul and an understanding of man's relationship to the universe.

Malabar Farm, 85-86

Preventive Medicine

It is undoubtedly true that if in the West we had adopted the Chinese method of paying doctors for their services we should have made much greater progress in the direction of preventive medicine, for the Chinese pay their doctors only while the patient is in good health, and when he becomes ill, the payment ceases until the patient has recovered. The same system would undoubtedly have done much to allay the clamor for socialized medicine. Perhaps the greatest fault of our medical science has been its almost total emphasis upon curing a patient after he has become ill rather than upon preventing him from becoming ill in the first place.

Out of the Earth, 85-86

Production

The old economic problem which lies at the root of so many of the ills connected with our agricultural prosperity and living costs, is that of using constantly more and more acres to produce less and less food.

Malabar Farm, 248

What we need is an agriculture of less acreage and greater and more efficient production, an agriculture following the rule of agriculture in Denmark, Holland and Belgium and most of France where each acre produces the potential maximum without loss of soil fertility. Under such an agriculture, regardless of declines in market prices, there are no poor farmers. At worst a farmer can hold his own, at best he is a rich man. That rule is followed by probably less than 10 per cent of the farmers in the United States and that 10 per cent are the ones who are well off in times of depression as well as of prosperity. Of the remaining 90 per cent both profits and purchasing power are steadily declining and have been declining for the past hundred years, perceptibly or imperceptibly, until a large percentage are today producing little more than they consume with a narrow and steadily declining margin of purchasing power. At least two or three million live near the level of a Chinese peasant, with virtually no purchasing power at all.

A Few Brass Tacks, 102-103

In dealing with statistics of food or indeed of any agricultural production, the total production is not important in relation to farm profits or in relation to the purchasing power of the agricultural segment of our society or in the cost of food to the consumer. The only real measure in relation to our economy is the production per acre and the cost of that production.

A Few Brass Tacks, 104

Propaganda

The average citizen in every nation and most of all in the U.S. is bombarded constantly by propaganda and press releases designed to cloud his judgment, appeal to his prejudices, fill him with deliberate misinformation for a calculated purpose, and generally sell him down the river.

Government during the past generation has become itself one of the greatest propagandists, all the way from the professional elements in the armed services, who hire thousands of press agents at taxpayers' expense to sell their own particular bill of goods, down

268

to the smallest bureau which sends out mimeographed sheets concerning the wonderful humanitarian work it is doing and how indispensable this work is to the welfare of the nation and the world, and above all how indispensable it is for the political party in power to be continued in office. One of the great evils of bureaucracy is that it tends increasingly to become self-perpetuating at the expense of the country. The armed forces represent our greatest bureaucracy and our most powerful all-pervading lobby.

A New Pattern for a Tired World, 1

As in the case of Europe, so again the Average American lazily or ignorantly maintains a vague physical picture of Russia which resembles his own U.S. and again he falls victim to the military and bureaucratic propaganda which constantly presents Russia as a vast, rich, united, powerful and productive world power which it is not.

A New Pattern for a Tired World, 67

Profits

Any practical farmer knows that the profits on 100 bushels of corn grown on one acre are much greater than on 100 bushels of corn grown on five acres. The reasons are simple and should be apparent to any layman — that the costs in fertilizer, seed, labor, time, taxes, interest and wear and tear on machinery is approximately five times as great on the 100 bushels of corn grown on five acres than it is upon the 100 bushels grown on one acre.

A Few Brass Tacks, 107

The farmer cannot look for steadily rising profits from higher and higher prices... The increased profits can and must be found not at the top but at the bottom of the production market, in more efficient planning and management and better forage and feed produced at low labor and fertilizer costs through grass and legume programs and higher feed yields per acre...

The farmer who constantly expects his prices to save him from his own laziness, ignorance or lack of efficiency is a doomed man and will prove to be more and more so in the coming years.

Out of the Earth, 180-181

When a pencil and paper were brought into use (a process neglected by too many farmers who frequently raise crops at a loss without knowing it), the new plan became not only reasonable but actually profitable. It was simply to use first-cutting hay rather than straw as bedding for the cattle at Malabar.

Out of the Earth, 187

Revolution

Revolutions, except in the Latin American sense, are caused more by economic depression and oppression than by any new ideology. People in rich countries, endowed with real wealth wisely developed, do not need liberty and freedom from dictatorship. They already have it.

A Few Brass Tacks, 56

Political ideologies are born of economic conditions and follow rather than precede economic crises of which the results or even the character are not at once clear or perfectly understood.

A Few Brass Tacks, 61

The Russian Revolution and the French Revolution were not revolutions for anything or to establish any theory; they were revolutions against oppression primarily economic and secondarily political, powered by the energy and numbers of those suffering the oppression.

A Few Brass Tacks, 126

Russia (1946, 1954)

Russia, if and when she develops wisely her immense natural wealth, will lean more and more toward unrestricted Western democracy and the rewards of individual enterprise in one form or another, because she will be able to do so.

A Few Brass Tacks, 56

Her problem is to find a form of political peace and order under which her people can work to develop, wisely if possible, the sources of her real wealth and power. Although Soviet Russia (and a generation or less from now it might be no longer a Soviet league of Marxian governments but a vast federated democratic empire in the sense of Western democracy) is a comparatively weak nation so far as military power is concerned and a nation with a future as yet undetermined and politically uncertain, when she speaks the world listens.

A Few Brass Tacks, 59

Russians are men first, Russians second and Communists third and Communists only for a fleeting period in the long range of history.

A Few Brass Tacks, 238

The Iron Curtain was devised for two purposes: (1) to prevent Russian citizens from discovering how much better off than they were the peoples of all Western Europe and indeed all the rest of the world save Asia and the Middle East; (2) to prevent outside nations and peoples from discovering how wretched and unstable were conditions inside Russia...

Actually Soviet Russia is in the same afflicted state as the ancient Czarist empire, and suffering from the same maladies — abysmal living standards for the great mass of her people, secret police, exile and concentration camps, forced labor, militarism and the vicious necessity of suppressing the rights of free speech or the right to assemble, of playing always upon the love of the homeland and the menace of invasion by European nations. In this shrunken world of course, the U.S. has been added to the enemies against whom the Russian people are protected by their government. There still exists the same passion to expand by establishing viciously exploited buffer states, with the same consequences that the more she expands the more rebellion and hatred she invites and the weaker and more unstable she becomes.

A New Pattern for a Tired World, 71

Science

The discoveries of all science are not in essence discoveries at all but simply the understanding bit by bit of the laws and balances by which the universe operates. In agriculture and animal husbandry and even to a large extent in medicine and veterinary science, this approach has frequently either been overlooked or the form of the pattern has been distorted by the kind of specialist who attempts to find all the answers in his own narrow field. Those who seek short cuts and panaceas and Swamp-Root-Snake-Oil operations and spectacles for hens are important only because they delay and confuse and sometimes block the process by which the truth can eventually be discovered. It is probably true that the coordinating scientist with the mind of the Renaissance and the pen of a Darwin or a Huxley can make the most valuable contributions in extending and enriching the knowledge of man with regard to the universe. It is only such a mind which can, standing upon the firm multi-pillared foundation, erected by the modest and sound specialist, construct the whole of the edifice.

Out of the Earth, 95-96

Silver & Gold

Even the fact that we in the United States have nearly three-quarters of the gold of the world buried at Fort Knox in Kentucky does not make us a rich nation. That gold, like most of the world's silver, may one day be more valuable as a metal used in the manufacture of our intricate modern machinery than as wealth or as the backing for currency. Indeed, I am not certain that this is not already true save for the fictitious value given it by the age-old superstitions regarding gold as wealth. We, during the Second World War, approached very nearly a point where copper, tin and even lead became more valuable to the needs and the economy of the modern world than silver or gold.

A Few Brass Tacks, 19

One cannot survive upon a diet of silver or gold but there comes at times a moment when a single egg becomes more valuable to a starving man than all the gold in Fort Knox.

A Few Brass Tacks, 20

Of silver it could be said that it is real wealth in so far as it is a metal useful in the manufacture of machinery but as currency it is worth exactly what it will buy, no more and no less. Intrinsically, a silver dollar is worth more than a one dollar bank note only because the silver in it is worth more as industrial raw material or real wealth than the paper in the bank note. This difference becomes apparent when all money, metallic or paper, becomes sufficiently debased.

A Few Brass Tacks, 21

Soils

In midsummer the earth cannot be left untended, least of all by a bridegroom who himself wants sons.

The Farm, 53

There is no more good virgin soil in this country and most of the rich virgin soil that existed in the beginning has been farmed long enough for it to take on the stamp and character of the men who have owned and farmed it. What I am trying to say is simply this — that if a good man or good men have farmed soil for a hundred years or more, it will be rich and productive land. On the other hand, if shiftless greedy men have exploited it, there will be little left that is any longer worth anything either to the owner or to the nation.

Pleasant Valley, 145

There is much that we still have not discovered or understood. In the field of experiment and research alone there exists a whole unexplored world of great fascination, for in a cubic foot of good productive soil one can find the pattern of the laws which govern the universe — laws before which political ideologies, manipulations of currency, short cuts, and all manner of man-made dodges become singularly silly and puerile.

Malabar Farm, 8

There is no satisfaction like watching the earth grow richer because of what you do with it.

Malabar Farm, 33

It is appalling how little we know as yet of the processes taking place within the soil.

Out of the Earth, 57

The soils which are easiest to work are not necessarily the richest or the most productive soils. Most muck soils and soils with a high sand content provide good mechanical mediums in which to grow vegetables but it is rare indeed that such soils are not unbalanced, minerally poor and frequently actually deficient in many of the minor elements important to the growth and nutrition of plants, animals and people.

The muck soils, while they may be easy to work, are frequently almost entirely composed of nitrogen and carbon and require the constant use of fertilizers of wide variety in order to produce mature plants or healthy animals and people. Soils which are actually peaty in quality are not only poorly balanced but they are subject to rapid oxidation and deterioration when repeatedly plowed and cultivated. In many areas, after years of operation, these soils presently disappear altogether; they have simply become oxidized out of existence, a process which cannot happen with truly good and well-balanced soils since such soils are composed not mainly of carbon but of a wide variety of the actual minerals which feed plants, animals and people.

From My Experience, 180

Many a heavy clay soil, with the fundamental mineral balance and "meatiness" of soil will produce much finer vegetables and fruits in the long run than the short-cut sandy, or the muck soils, and in the long run at a much lower cost.

From My Experience, 181-182

The greatest fault of American agriculture today and the reason for the poor income and high costs of production for many a farmer, is merely that of soil structure, which is tied so closely not only with the availability of natural fertility but of chemical fertilizer as well, and above all with the absorption and conservation of rainfall and moisture (a factor that has become increasingly important in the present drought cycle).

From My Experience, 200

In our experience at Malabar the regeneration of soils and the actual production of new and highly productive topsoils have been greatly speeded up and the costs reduced by employing a combination of rugged grasses and legumes with modern power and deep-tillage machinery. Both elements, the mechanical and the natural, were required, working together to achieve the result desired. This is quite outside the other benefits such as drainage, control of erosion both by wind and water, the checking of water losses, better soil texture, bacterial life, etc., etc.

From My Experience, 306

Ordinary soil tests on many soils will frequently show large quantities of a given element but do not reveal whether this element exists in a chemical combination which makes it highly available to the crop or whether the soil texture is such that it will absorb and conserve the rainfall and moisture which are necessary to the availability and the activity of the soil bacteria and other living elements vital in making both natural and chemical fertilizers available to the crops. There is much we still do not know regarding the microbiological relationship to availability.

Out of the Earth, 198

At the base of all of this lies the basic truth, so often set forth by Dr. H. H. Bennett of the U.S. Soil Conservation Service ... that poor land and poor agriculture make poor people and poor nations. It is a kind of vicious circle with one evil influence operating potently upon the other to increase the pattern of degeneration both in soil and people.

Out of the Earth, 286

The roots of deep rooted plants are the greatest of all soil builders not only because of the organic content which they provide but because they serve as well to break up hard, intractable subsoils, provide penetration for moisture and oxygen and in the case of deep-rooted legumes bring nitrogen into the lower levels of the soil.

Out of the Earth, 308

Starting Farming

How, indeed, does one get started in farming and ranching today without capital? The simple answer is that one does not get started.

Among city people even today there is a kind of childish idea that if a man wants to start farming, all he has to do is start farming. And among farmers, sometimes good ones who have inherited nearly everything they possess and should know better, I have heard occasional sneers at the men who made their money elsewhere and invested it in farms. Where would some of these farmers be today if their land, and very often their livestock, their machinery, and the house they live in, had not been left them without any capital investment whatever on their part? A great many of them would certainly not be in the farming or ranching business today.

The fact is that few things are more difficult than for a young man to get started on his own as a farmer. Scores of young men and young couples come to Malabar Farm each year to ask, "How can we get a start at farming with little or no capital?" The only honest answer I can give them is a short and harsh one, simply, "You can't." For a young man to get started today on even a small farm of average fertility within decent markets, a capital of forty to fifty thousand dollars is needed to purchase the land, the machinery, and the livestock necessary to a profitable operation. Not so long ago, one could have said to such a young man, "Borrow the money to buy yourself a team, a plow, and a harrow, and the government will give you rich virgin land for nothing." But those days are past.

Flat Top Ranch, 16-17

275

Subsidies & "Surpluses"

It is abundantly evident that in a world where at least two-thirds of the population suffer from malnutrition and hundreds of millions live at a starvation level, there are no surpluses. There is only poor distribution and the high prices caused by an unproductive agriculture which limit consumption of high-protein foods.

Malabar Farm, 216

Farmers, the greatest of individualists, are the worst enemies of government supervision and control, yet when prices begin to fall, farm organizations are the first ones to come running to government for restrictions, price floors, mild forms of subsidy, parity prices, etc., to protect a minority group artificially by creating scarcities, and the high prices which in turn create both surpluses and lower living standards. The individual farmer would do much better to increase the quality and efficiency of his farming so that he could produce wheat at fifty cents a bushel with a profit rather than dollar-a-bushel wheat at a loss which can only be cured by subsidies or by raising the price of food — a raise which in time, after being passed through wages and manufactured commodities prices, comes back and hits him in the face.

A Few Brass Tacks, 38

Of all the means of aiding our sick agriculture, subsidies are probably the worst, with government buying of agricultural commodities in order to support prices (actually a form of subsidy) playing a close second. Both represent the perfect example of trying to cure fundamental evils by the use and manipulation of money, the process of applying poultices on the exterior of the abdomen to cure a stomach ulcer. They solve nothing and only tend to preserve and augment the original and fundamental evils.

A Few Brass Tacks, 129

Corn, like wheat and cotton and tobacco, is one of the principal sources of our national surplus problem and of the burden that falls upon the neck of the taxpayer who must pay out millions in good tax money for support prices allotted, generally speaking, almost entirely to single cash-crop agriculture.

The reckoning in regard to such a policy is certain to come one day (and a day not too far off) because there are in the United States only about eighteen million farmers, including all the people who own as little as 3 acres of land or produce as little as $350 in total crop income per year and there are about 133 millions of other citizens who are growing weary of paying high food prices and, on top of that, hundreds of millions to subsidize in one way or another the single-crop cash-crop farmer in order to keep consumer's prices high. The city population and the general public are beginning to find out about such things, and the strongest farm bloc, even by log-rolling in Congress, will be unable eventually to pass on to the city consumer the burden of a greedy, ill-managed and generally poor agriculture in the form both of high prices and taxes. When single-crop subsidies are removed we shall begin to have a good agriculture, self-supporting and independent, which will stand on its own feet, conserve the fertility of our most important natural resource and make a far greater contribution to our national welfare and economy than our agriculture is making today.

Out of the Earth, 167

Subsoil

We were, after the first year of a seeding, scarcely using the long overworked, depleted and leached-out topsoil at all but were drawing upon the fertility of the deep subsoils which had not been utilized since the forest had been cut off the land more than a hundred years earlier. After the first year of a seeding the roots by-passed the topsoil and went deep, finding there not only all the mineral fertility the plants needed but a fertility which was in good balance. Under the deep-rooted legume and grass program we were, after the first year, scarcely using the topsoil of our farm at all save in growing ladino clover and our native bluegrass and white clover...

Each time we plowed in one of the deep-rooted heavy sods ... minerals, now in organic form and therefore highly available, drawn from deep down were mixed with the worn-out topsoil. This factor accounted for the astonishing jumps in yield of oats and wheat and, in the beginning, even of corn, which occurred when a manured, deep-rooted sod field was plowed and new crop seeded. Actually we were and are farming those Wooster Silt loam soils from three to twenty feet deep after more than a hundred years of farming them only eight to nine inches deep. And in the process we are undoubtedly recovering some of the fertilizer used by our predecessors on the same land which, in an area of abundant rainfall, had leached down through the loose gravel loam into deeper strata of the soil.

Out of the Earth, 103

We do not pretend that every subsoil would give the same results ... But there are in the United States millions of acres of such soils and millions of acres of them today are lying idle as abandoned "worn-out" farms, not because they are really "worn-out" but because they have been farmed only eight or nine inches deep for generations and because the residue of minerals which has not been depleted has simply become unavailable to plants because of poor farming and the lack of lime, organic material and commercial fertilizer "starters."

Out of the Earth, 108

Unions

All efforts by organized labor to unionize farmers have been dismal failures, and will continue to be so, since nearly all farmers and even tenants, are individual proprietors and not employed labor. There are, however, great possibilities for better understanding between farmers and organized labor in the establishment of co-operatives, with the farmer on one side as the producer and union labor on the other as consumer.

Malabar Farm, 29

United Nations

If the United Nations Organization can serve as a means, as machinery, toward solving economic problems, and distribution of food and raw materials and markets, it will have a purpose. If it serves only to prop up and preserve archaic systems of imperialism and an economy based on the manipulation of money or to attempt to settle border "incidents" arising from more profound economic maladjustments, it will have served no purpose and go down in futility as the League went down when it became merely the instrument of the money economy, processing, imperialistic nations of western Europe.

A Few Brass Tacks, 286-287

Forcing the emetic of a United Nations, conceived wholly on a political basis with reformatory overtones, down the throat of the world while ignoring economics, raw materials, markets and food, can only cause the patient, as might be expected, to vomit.

A New Pattern for a Tired World, 42

Every time we act as "police agents" for the United Nations (and we appear to be the only active "police agents" of this organization), we are automatically acting in behalf of those very forces which are suspect and hated in Asia.

A New Pattern for a Tired World, 61

Water

We already knew from long experience what the cold water of the spring could do for the freshness, the crispness and the tenderness of vegetables brought in from the hot sun-drenched garden. In a short space of time, the vegetables left in the cold water of the old stone troughs seemed to change. The wilt from the hot sun on the salads gave way to an icy crispness. The cucumbers were quickly chilled through and the sun-ripened melons achieved a coldness that no refrigerator could possibly produce. The Pascal celery became so crisp that if dropped to the floor, it shattered like glass. This was not the dead cold of the refrigerator but the living cold of the spring water, gushing out of the primeval rock.

From My Experience, 250-251

There is something beautiful in the sight and sound of running water, not from a tap or a faucet, but out of the rock or from the kind of beautiful fountain which in Italy becomes doubly beautiful with the arrival of the hot dry summer.

From My Experience, 253

Wealth — "Real Wealth"

Inherited wealth may create a strange paralysis which destroys the value of everything and corrupts its possessor with a strange enchanted dullness.

The Farm, 342

Real wealth is primarily the natural resources of a nation — its forests, its minerals, its oils, its agricultural land, the health, the vigor, the working capacity and the ingenuity of its people. Without these things, any nation becomes a poor nation economically and a weak nation militarily and politically. Once these resources have been wasted or used up, it will not matter how much gold is buried in Fort Knox nor how many thousand bales of bank notes are printed by the Treasury; the United States will inevitably become, like nations in the past suffering the same exhaustion of real wealth, an insignificant and unimportant nation with its people surviving at a very low standard of living. The only alternative would be for the nation to become a banking-processing nation like the United Kingdom with all the insecurity and perils which the late war have made evident as accompanying such a money economy.

A Few Brass Tacks, 23

Weather

City folks rarely understand what disasters and what delights weather can bring to the farmer. In their physically limited and protected lives, rain means merely that the buses and street cars will be overcrowded, or a hot spell means only that they will be uncomfortable and will grumble, louder perhaps than the most discontented farmer. Weather does not mean to them floods or droughts which may ruin their income and destroy the rewards of a whole year's work, with whole fields ruined perhaps for years to come. It does not mean the loss perhaps of hundreds of cattle snowed in on the range.

Weather for the farm is rarely the right weather. If you need rain for the corn, the pastures and the new seedings, it may be a disaster for the hay cut and drying in the field or for the grain that is just dry enough for combining. If you have good hay making and harvesting weather — bright and hot and dry — it may be bad for the corn and the pasture. Weather is the principal reason why the farmer has gained the reputation of being a "grumbler." Rarely is the weather right for everything. On those days, not more than half a dozen times a year, when the weather is right, the good farmer is the happiest man in the world and would not change places with any man.

Malabar Farm, 403

Weeds — Nature's "Cover Crop"

At Malabar we have learned many things, some of them small and subtle, peculiar to our own soil and affecting us alone, some of them fundamental and important, not only to ourselves but to others. Some discoveries were the result of deliberate experiments. More often they were made by accident and the result simply of an eye which observed what went on under our feet and all about us.

There was a summer three years ago when a wet season prevented the final cultivation of the corn. The corn was well grown but far from free of weeds. The important fact was that it was above and ahead of the weeds. At first the weeds distressed us but as the hot, dry weeks of August and early September came on, I began to discover a remarkable thing — that where there were weeds in the corn rows, the soil beneath was moist and cool; where the corn was free of weeds, the soil was hot and parched and dry. Where there were weeds, the corn grew stronger and higher, the ears were larger and the grains weighed more. Much the same thing happened the following year with almost identical results...

The discovery and the observation were contrary to traditional and accepted beliefs — that weeds took moisture from the growing corn and that weeds of any sort or size impaired growth. Clearly in the case of our cornfields something had gone wrong, not with Nature but with tradition.

That weeds absorbed water and transferred moisture in the air we could not deny nor did we doubt it. Therefore it was necessary to discover how and why the soil beneath the weeds was still moist despite the added drain upon the moisture and why in the parts of the field that were free of weeds the soil was dry, dusty and caked. Shade, obviously, was one answer; the soil where weeds were mixed with the corn was more protected than those parts of the field where the corn alone provided a shifting, variegated shade and permitted evaporation through the force of the sun and wind. But further observation made evident another discovery which proved to be a far greater element in the fact of more moisture and better growth in the weedy portions of the field. We discovered that after a rain or a heavy thundershower, the water ran off the cleanly cultivated portions of the field and accumulated in the low spots. The corn in the low spots had too much water; that on the higher spots had little or none at all because it ran off. In the weedy corn, in the same field, on the same sort of mildly rolling land, no such thing occurred. No water accumulated in the low spots, no water ran off. It stayed where it fell.

At the Zanesville, Ohio, Soil Conservation Service station we found a part of the answer to the story of moisture. It was simple enough, no more than this — that most of the rain which fell during the hot, dry weeks of late summer came with violence in the form of thunderstorms and cloudbursts, in drops which fell heavily upon the bare soil. Each drop, by its size and the impact upon the surface of the ground, sealed the surface of the earth and made it virtually impermeable to the heavy rainfall that followed. As a result, in the portions of the field where the corn was free of weeds the rain ran off to accumulate in the low spots where it half drowned the corn. Often enough on the higher ground a new rain would penetrate less than an inch.

In the parts of the field where the ground beneath the corn was weedy, the heavy drops of water never reached the soil, as great globules of water. Striking the corn and the leaves and stems of the weeds, each heavy drop was shattered and the rain reached the earth below, not in great dashing drops, but as a gentle, misty rain, like the rain to which northern and central Europe is accustomed. The parched, water-hungry soil was not sealed by the impact of the heavy rain; it drank up all the moisture as it fell, as a sponge absorbs water. There was no runoff water; it all stayed where it fell, evenly distributed over the whole of the weedy area. The tests on Zanesville experimental plots showed that where heavy rains fell on hot bare soil in midsummer as much as 70 per cent of the water ran off, seeking a lower level. On the plot next to it, covered by vegetation, 100 per cent of the rain remained where it fell.

Now the serious farmer need not deduct from the above that we advocate the cultivation of weeds with the corn; he may deduct if he likes that we at Malabar have no great objection to weeds in the corn provided the corn is kept clean until it is above and ahead of the weeds. And he may deduct also that we have no objection, after the corn picker has passed over the fields, to having in addition to the corn fodder a heavy amount of organic material left by the weeds to plow or disk into the soil for its lasting benefit and the benefit of the crop that follows. Many a good farmer sows rye grass between the rows of his corn for exactly the same purpose.

Pleasant Valley, 155-158

Weeds, mowed down, were an actual benefit to the grass legume seeding because the additional mulch which they created served to keep the ground cool and moist during the hot dry months on those eroded hills exposed constantly to wind and sun.

Out of the Earth, 62

Wildlife
Where there is both good cover and good well-balanced soil of

high available fertility, there you will always find the big populations of wild game, and where you find plenty of field mice, pheasants, quail and other birds, there, too, you will find the foxes, the catamounts, the owls and other predatory animals and there, too, you will find the balance in Nature operating as it should, to the benefit of the farmer, the hunter, the fisherman as well as to the wild life itself.

Out of the Earth, 226

Bumblebees, like pheasants, shun poor, worn-out land, and their population increases as the land is returned to fertility.

Pleasant Valley, 285

Work

Rarely does the good farmer long for any immortality better than the rich fields he has left behind him and the healthy, intelligent children who will carry on his work and his name. If there is an after-life that is pleasant and comfortable, so much the better, but he hopes that it will not be an after-life in which there is no work, for it is by work of hand and brain that he has lived a full, rich life, which leaves him at the end ready to lie down and fall asleep in the quiet knowledge and satisfaction that what he has done will live on and on after him into eternity.

Out of the Earth, 8-9

Writing

In this age fiction writing is simply a way of making a living and for my money not a very satisfactory or even self-respecting one. There are better and more satisfying things to do. One degree sillier are the writings of those who write importantly about novels. Once when a person said to me, "Oh, I never read novels!" I was inclined to regard him with snobbish condescension as a Philistine. Now I am not so sure.

From My Experience, 4

When I look back now, the vague and visionary idea I had in returning home seems ludicrous and a little pathetic ... I wanted a place which, again vaguely, would be like the medieval fortress-manor of France where a whole community once found security and self-sufficiency. In a troubled world I wanted a place which, if necessary, could withstand a siege and where, if necessary, one could get out the rifle and shotgun for defense.

Today, fifteen years later, we at Malabar have not achieved these romantic dreams nor have I won the escape into the boyhood past which brought about the decision to return. A return to the past can never be accomplished and the sense of fortified isolation and security is no longer possible in the world of automobiles, of radios, of telephones and airplanes. One must live with one's times and those who understand this and make proper adjustments and concessions and compromises are the happy ones. In the end I did not find at all what I was seeking ... I found something much better ... a whole new life, and a useful life and one in which I have been able to make a contribution which may not be forgotten overnight and with the first funeral wreath, like most of the writing of our day, but one which will go on and on...

Perhaps it will turn out that I have left some contributions not only to the science of agriculture, which is the only profession in the world which encompasses all sciences and all the laws of the universe, but to the realm of human philosophy as well. None of this could I have done within the shallow world of a writer living as most writers live. Without implying in any way a comparison or any conceit, I am sure that Tolstoy understood all this on his estate at Yasnaya Polyana, Voltaire at Ferney, Virgil on his Tuscan farm; indeed most writers since the time of Hesiod who felt sooner or later the illusion and the futility of fancy words and sought some sturdier and earthier satisfaction.

From My Experience, 6-7

15

Bromfield's Brazil

By George DeVault

"We set out in Carlito's car not along the back highways, which themselves are none too good in Brazil, but up over the mountains along a wild trail which at times seemed suited only to goats," Louis Bromfield wrote in From My Experience *of his first visit in 1953 to what would become Malabar-do-Brazil.*

"Carlito's car was a Studebaker, and a true workhorse built high enough to clear the rocks and bumps, able to weather alike the foot of mud or foot of dust which seem to be the only two states known to Brazilian roads which are not paved...

"The season was the end of summer when the Brazilian sky is at the most beautiful. It is a very special sky which from the tops of the hills appears larger than sky elsewhere in the world. It is a special blue in color, and of great brilliance, which becomes bluer as the sun sets and night comes on until presently the blue fades into darkness and the stars come out like diamonds on velvet.

"As we reached the top of the last hill before descending the steep slope down to the winding river, the whole of the valley lay spread out below us and suddenly it struck me that the whole landscape was very like Pleasant Valley among the woods, hills and rich fields in far-off Ohio."

T he huge jetliner is nearly empty. Only about 30 passengers are on this evening's non-stop flight from Atlanta to São Paulo, Brazil. And three of them — thin young men with long black hair and dark nervous faces — "are being deported," the Varig flight attendant casually informs the other passengers. This is not tourist season. Carnival — dancing from midnight to 5 a.m. for four nights in a row — has been over for a month. It is March 22, the start of what passes for winter in the Southern Hemisphere. But that's OK. The destination is not the bright lights of São Paulo, the word's fastest growing city with some 16 million inhabitants. The purpose of this visit, it says on the visa application, is to "visit friends on their farm."

What I didn't tell the Brazilian consulate in New York City is that I have never actually met these "friends." We have traded a handful of letters and spoken on the phone exactly twice. I know them mainly from 40-year-old photos in books that were published when I was still a small child.

The friends are Ellen Bromfield Geld, her husband Carson, their children and grandchildren. In my well-worn copy of the 1955 *From My Experience*, there is a gray snapshot of a tousle-haired two-year-old. He stands jauntily spread-legged in shorts, a white shirt and saddle shoes in a garden. "The author's grandson, Stevie, who already speaks three languages in the polyglot community of Malabar-do-Brasil," is how Louis Bromfield describes him in the book. On another page, Ellen and Carson appear in a Joe Munroe photo taken at Malabar Farm in Ohio. Stacks of milk cans tower in the background as Ellen, her short blonde hair pulled back in a pony tail, grooms a calf that has been cropped out of the photo. Carson, standing patiently to her left, holds a coiled lariat attached to the unseen animal. The cutline reads, "Donna Elena" and "Don Carson" Geld, the author's daughter and son-in-law, who operate Fazenda Malabar-do-Brasil." Their faces are young and eager, hopeful and carefree. But more than 40 years have passed since those photos were snapped. Little "Stevie" is now in his early 40s, a year or so younger than I. Ellen and Carson are in their 60s. "What will they look like now?" I wonder as I doze off after dinner. "We'll find out in a few hours." The plane drones on into the night over the Caribbean Sea and Atlantic Ocean, the Equator and the Amazon jungle of Brazil's vast interior.

Morning comes all too soon as it does on all overnight international flights. The plane banks and circles down into the heavy fog that blankets São Paulo, just as the bright orange sun bursts over the "Serras do Mar," mountains of the sea, a few miles to the east. It is 6 a.m., local time, but 4 a.m., according to my body's internal clock.

After clearing Passport Control and Customs, I pick up six bottles of tequila that Carson asked me to bring — Cuervo gold, not silver — and head out into the nearly empty lobby of Guarulhos International Airport. Suddenly, a thin gentleman with graying hair steps in front of me.

"Car-sone ... Geld?" he says hesitantly, looking up at me with questioning eyes.

"Ruy?"

"Si." Ruy (pronounced Ru-ee) is Steve Geld's man Friday. Carson said Ruy would meet me at the airport, and here he is. It's early morning, but subtropical heat and humidity slam me in the face as soon as we step out of the terminal. It looks and feels a lot like South Florida. Ruy's car is parked at the curb nearby. It is a gray, Brazilian-made Chevrolet, complete with a CD player and car phone. I peel off my sport coat, grab my camera and Ruy merges smoothly into bumper-to-bumper rush hour traffic on the freeway at 70 miles per hour. São Paulo spreads out on all sides of us.

Ruy speaks three languages (Portuguese, Italian and Castilian Spanish), none of which match my English, Russian and snatches of German and French. But using a few international words, hand gestures and other signs we communicate well enough. He soon points to the brown Tietê River, which neatly divides the 6-lane freeway down the middle. He lowers his window a crack and holds his nose. I immediately get the message. The river is an open, stinking sewer. The Tietê, the river that bandeirantes followed into Brazil's interior in search of emeralds, gold and slaves, runs west from the mountains around São Paulo, then north of the Gelds' farm until it empties into the Paraná, which flows south through Uruguay and Argentina before emptying into the Atlantic at Buenos Aires. Bright, clean modern buildings — high-rise apartments and office buildings, new car dealerships and shopping centers — blanket the heart of the city. The smooth highway is crowded with more Chevies and Volkswagen beetles, which are also made in Brazil, plus countless diesel-spewing trucks and buses. Billboards tout everything from Mercedes Benz automobiles to Russian-made Ladas. Service stations and shops are everywhere. Closer to the outskirts of São Paulo, all vacant land is covered with squalid tarpaper shacks. They crowd under freeway bridges and blanket the hillsides. Brazil is as poor as it is beautiful. Most of its citizens are illiterate, uneducated and dirt poor. They flock to the big cities of São Paulo and Rio de Janeiro in hopes of a better life.

Once we're free of the city, a whole new world opens up to us. Every rise and curve in the highway reveals sweeping vistas of wild hillsides and rolling fields of incredible beauty. It's hilly like the San Francisco Bay area and lush green like the east side of the big island of Hawaii. Where the thick vegetation has been torn away by erosion or new construction, the soil is as red as any found in Georgia. People sell persimmons or jugs of wine along the roadside. Sugar cane is as common as corn in Iowa. There are banana trees, eucalyptus and 30-foot tall clumps of bamboo. And everywhere there is thick grass and cattle, all kinds of cattle — mottled brown Gir, the great horned Guzera, gray Hindu cattle known as Brasil, red Sindi and the great white Nelore that we "yanquies" call Brahmas. Pastures and idle fields are dotted with what appear to be huge "anthills" three to five feet high. They are the handiwork of subterranean termites that feed on the roots of grass. And the residents of just three to four termite hills in a single acre can eat as much grass as one cow. The hills are as hard as cement. The only way to kill the termites is to smash their hills open with a sledge hammer and pour in poison.

Traffic is getting lighter, the countryside more open. Ruy heads north toward Alphaville. His spedometer pushes past 80. We are on a thoroughly modern superhighway, complete with a dozen toll booths at one spot outside of the city. This road is only 10 or 15 years old. It obviously didn't exist when the Gelds moved to Brazil in the early '50s. In fact, there were only a few hundred miles of paved roads in the whole country back then. And barely 1 million people lived in São Paulo. What an incredible sight Brazil must have been: Thick, endless jungles full of jaguars and bandits, gold and diamonds, unlimited opportunity and adventure. It was a new frontier, as challenging and potentially rewarding as any the United States ever had to offer.

Ruy exits the freeway at the sign for Porto Feliz and turns onto the two-lane blacktop road for Tietê. The road winds up, down and around fields, farms and lush tropical forests. Finally, about 60 miles west of São Paulo, Ruy turns left onto a dirt lane and stops under a huge, hand-carved and painted wooden sign. "Fazenda Pau D'Alho Criador de Gado Sta. Gertrudis," it proudly proclaims beside the carved head of a droop-horned Santa Gertrudis bull. Garlic Tree Farm, Breeders of Santa Gertrudis cattle. This is it. We have arrived. It is a little after 8 a.m. The farm is in full swing. Ruy drives past a small field of tall, blue-green corn. The lane follows the outside edge of a mature pecan grove. The trees are loaded with nuts. His car raises a small cloud of dust against the cloudless, electric blue sky as Ruy stops beside a low white barn with a red Spanish tile roof under several large trees.

In the small field to the left are five men. Four of them are bent over, chopping doggedly at the thick grass with heavy metal hoes that are wider than the length of a big man's foot. The fifth man is moving back and forth quickly among them, offering friendly advice and encouragement. He is also checking on their progress and the contents of half a dozen 100-pound woven plastic feed sacks that the men are carefully filling with cuttings of the grass.

Unlike the others, he is dressed more like a cattleman than a fieldhand. He's wearing faded blue jeans, a white short-sleeved dress shirt and well-worn Western-style work boots. He is a cattleman. His full head of hair is gray now and his waist is a bit thicker than in the 40-year-old photographs, but there is no mistaking the clear eyes and resolute stance. This is Carson Geld.

Although born and raised in New York City — Brooklyn, to be exact — Carson knew from an early age that he was destined to be a farmer. Carson's father, Harry, was an apple buyer in the old Washington Market in New York City. He dreamed of buying a little apple orchard in upstate New York, but died before he could realize that dream. Starting at age 14, Carson worked summers making hay and harvesting grain on a farm in Cooperstown, N.Y. He later majored in agronomy at Cornell University.

The grass Carson now holds in his hand, Tifton 85 Bermuda grass POI, is his newest toy — and a promising new cash crop. "We plant one piece one meter apart. In three months, it will fill in all the space in between," Carson explains enthusiastically after a firm handshake and a minimum of small talk. He rattles off the history of how the first of his Tifton came back to Brazil in a suitcase, its 23 percent protein, ability to withstand temperatures as low as 21 F and a long list of other redeeming qualities. Carson has 10 acres in grass now. His publicity campaign is just starting to spread word of the supergrass throughout Brazil, which is as large as the United States without Alaska. His telephone rings night and day. "I should be on the road promoting the grass. I may have to hire a salesman," Carson says. He is selling the grass by the bag and also working on selling franchises.

But something even more urgent is driving Carson today: "The auction." It's only two days away now. This is not just any auction. It is the Gelds' annual "Novilno do Futuro," their heifer of the future auction of bred heifers that kicks off the cattle auction season in the state of São Paulo. The Gelds sell breeding stock from their herd of 200 registered Santa Gertrudis cattle. Other breeders will bring their cattle to the auction and buyers will come from all over Brazil. In all, there will be some 40 cattle in the auction, which is preceded by a huge cookout and cattle show and judging. The world-class judge, H. Martin Seyfferdt, has been flown in from his home in South Africa just for this show. It is a big, BIG deal. And there are still a million and one things to do to get ready for the auction. The last thing Carson needs right now is a visitor with endless questions.

He is saved by the sudden barking of the dogs. The three boxers — Boris, the oldest and the ringleader, Moses and Zeca — that have been rooting around the pecan trees and fencerow are now tearing across the pecan grove, racing to intercept a station wagon that is hurrying up the bumpy drive in a cloud of dust.

"Here's Ellen, back from market," Carson says. She is returning from nearby Tietê. The back of her car is packed with wooden crates full of fresh green beans, tomatoes, peppers and onions, all destined for a huge salad for the hundreds of hungry people who will be attending the auction. Like her father, Ellen is a writer and a farmer. She always writes for a few hours in the morning. She has published seven books, five fiction and two non-fiction, is revising the manuscript of an eighth and has plans for yet another novel. When her writing goes well, the rest of the day is great. But when her writing does not go so well — or when other duties keep her away from her writing — the rest of the day can be pretty awful. Ellen has not been writing this morning, but she is still smiling that warm easy smile of her youth. Ellen resembles the old photos even more than Carson does. She is not one for idle chitchat, either. Not today! She is much too busy. Like two determined generals preparing for a major battle, she and Carson trade the very latest intelligence on preparations for the auction — the placement and timing of deliveries of ice, beer, the big top circus tent, sound system, tables and chairs. Ellen, still sitting in her car, mentions coffee and needing some help. I toss my camera bag in the back of her car and we head on up the last leg of the U-shaped lane to the house. The lane is completely canopied by trees. Majestic pecans create a huge block of cool shade on the right. Two rows of assorted acacia trees with frilly, dark green leaves line the grassy shoulders of the lane. A large pasture gently slopes downhill to the left behind four stands of barbed wire. Every single one of these trees were planted by Ellen and Carson after they cleared the land of 80,000 worn-out coffee trees.

The barking boxers dart back and forth in front of the car, sometimes rolling on the ground just ahead of the front wheels. Ellen is talking, yelling at the dogs out the open window and swearing as we move slowly up the bumpy lane, through a grove of young citrus trees and into a 3-car carport. It is just one corner of a large, low building with thick white walls and a red tile roof that is largely hidden by a wild tangle of flowering vines. The door to Carson's cattle office is to the left.

We lug the crates of produce down a flagstone walkway and into the large kitchen. Two Brazilian women are already hard at work there, cooking on the 6-burner bottled gas stove, loading the heavy duty dishwasher and cleaning pots in the large double sink. The fourth dog, Henry the bassett pup, supervises it all from his command post on the red tile floor under a small table to one side. The crates go on the large wooden worktable in the middle of the long room. The kitchen is no place to talk, so I carry a crate of beans out onto the porch, recalling Louis Bromfield's firm stance on visitors: "Guests should be useful or stay out of the way," and "Them that works eats." Ellen follows with two mugs of steaming black coffee. The porch is also protected by a red tile roof and framed by vines. The view faces west, across the sparkling blue water of an in-ground swimming pool. It's backed by a line of gray-trunked coconut palm trees, and weathered 4-rail fence topped with a strand of barbed wire. Plump red cattle graze peacefully on the rolling pastures beyond.

With the crate of beans on a low bench between us, we settle down on weathered wooden chairs in the shade and begin snapping beans, drinking coffee and talking non-stop. It's almost as though we've known each other for years and are just picking up where we left off the last time. There is a lot of catching up to do. Good conversation, especially about farming, children and dogs, books and writing, flows as freely as the coffee. Ellen has as many questions as I do. She wants to know all about me, my wife and children, and the book project that brought me to her farm. But she is even more curious about the changes taking place today in Russia where my family and I recently lived for a year publishing Rodale Press' *New Farmer* magazine in Moscow. Finally, the talk turns to Ellen's father, how she and Carson came to Brazil and why her father was so unhappy about the move.

"Louis Bromfield did not trust his children. The farther apart they were the better they got along," she says, matter-of-factly. It's familiar territory. She has been over it many times before. Although Ellen talks comfortably and well about her family history, she writes about it with even more eloquence. Here, from *Strangers in the Valley* (1957), is how she describes her father's reaction to the news that she and Carson are taking their baby and moving to Brazil:

"It was a rather uncomfortable feeling, far from eased by the incredulous, tight-lipped expression on my father's face that dogged us for the duration of our stay at Malabar. After a silence-shattering, "My God, just what do you intend to live on?" he must have decided to abandon our salvation by rational means, for he never mentioned our financial status again. But that fateful expression trailed us all our days and, without any verbal effort, said everything.

"I cannot say exactly why we decided to leave the permanence of the little house, Switzer's creek and the ancient elm tree at the end of Carson's stay in the army. Perhaps it was because we wanted to take part in the building of a new frontier in the Western hemisphere. Or perhaps we felt, as my father had once felt, that our world had become too limited. Louis Bromfield's shadow was a large one in Pleasant Valley; I think we wanted to get out from beneath it and spread our wings at a distance.

"Ironically, for he did not approve of our dreaming — it was my father who first put the idea of Brazil into our heads. I can remember him coming home from that land with fabulous tales of men who owned small empires of virgin forest and plains, who had created fortunes from coffee and cattle in a few short years and in their own territory bore all the power and wealth of little kings. And when the Brazilians came to Malabar we heard the stories over again, greatly magnified and glorified so that, in our eager and innocent imaginations, Brazil became a magic word, the last and most promising frontier on earth.

"On the merit of these tales, Carson and I began to create in our imaginations a fazenda in the richest of all valleys, the Parabia, with a fine rambling house built in a rectangle enclosing a patio filled with tropical birds and plants, with fertile, abundant lands to till — a virtual paradise in which expense seemed a minor detail. We often think back now, look at one another and laugh, then blush deeply at the immeasurable depth of our naiveté.

"But perhaps at times naiveté is a good thing, for it gives one a false courage. Had we known how cold Brazil can be to a stranger with no money in his pockets, we might never have packed up and left the security of Pleasant Valley, Ohio, nor done it with only enough money to pay our passage to Brazil and our own living expenses there for two months. And yet that is what we did...

"In those days the idea of being marooned only troubled us at night as we lay alone in thought, looking out at a benevolent sky through the branches of the elm... America and Pleasant Valley promised us security for the rest of our lives; Brazil didn't really promise us anything."

Without knowing a word of Portuguese, Ellen and Carson moved to Brazil in 1953 with their year-old son, Stevie, 16 bags, a rocking horse, a few bags of seed and a border collie named Jo. They had no jobs and little money.

Louis Bromfield's Brazilian friends seized the opportunity to start up the Malabar-style farm they had been trying to sell him on for years. They hired Ellen and Carson to manage the place. "Daddy didn't think we could possibly do it, just because I was his daughter," Ellen recalls.

He should have known better. Perhaps because she was Louis Bromfield's daughter, Ellen, with Carson beside her, had the drive, determination and just plain ornery stubbornness to actually reclaim a farm from the jungle. But the task was still a lot more than the young couple had bargained for, as Ellen explains in *Strangers in the Valley*, which details their first year at Malabar do Brasil: One of their first tasks was to make livable a farmhouse that had literally been falling apart for 50 years. It was in such bad shape that stonemasons refused to go inside for fear the walls would collapse on them. There was no electricity. Water was a constant problem. While rebuilding the well, a Brazilian friend was overcome by exhaust fumes from a portable, gasoline-powered pump. Carson drug the big man out of the well and after giving him artificial respiration for two hours, finally revived Armando. Fields were overgrown with weeds that had run wild for 10 years. Livestock consisted mainly of ants, rats, termites and ticks. The laborers who came with the place didn't want to work and soon left. Equipment was in such sorry shape and parts and repairs so unreliable, that much of the planting, cultivating and harvesting had to be done by hand. At times when there was simply nothing they could do about breakdowns and delays, Carson settled down with a good book until the needed parts, implements or workers arrived. It was the same stress-relief approach he perfected at Cornell University: While everyone else stayed up all night drinking coffee and cramming for exams, he went to a Marx Brothers movie. The library at the farm grew rapidly. Other problems they encountered in their first year included a dead horse in the water tank, armed cattle rustlers, drought and flood, hordes of mosquitoes carrying Yellow Fever and, last but not least, Macumba, a dreaded Brazilian voodoo curse.

But they stubbornly stuck with it and when Bromfield visited the farm again in March of 1954, they were able to show him good crops of corn, rice, soybeans, peanuts and vegetables. "You and Carson have made this a beautiful place. I want to come back year after year," he said. But he went away and I never saw him again," Ellen writes.

One thing she fails to mention until the very end of the book is the fact that during most of that first year, while they were literally chopping a farm out of the jungle and living the life of true pioneers, she was also pregnant with her first daughter, Robin Lizabeth.

Would they do it again? "Oh yes, definitely," says Ellen. "It suits us. We can see our ideas on everything. It's fun to be a part of it all."

Malabar do Brasil continued to grow and improve for the next few years. Then Louis Bromfield died in 1956. "After daddy died, people lost interest in it," Ellen says. Malabar do Brasil was sold. It is now a dairy.

Despite the loss, Ellen and Carson stayed in Brazil. Carson worked as the first Purina feeds dealer in Brazil. Then for four years he managed a large farm for the Anderson Clayton company, producing soybeans, cotton, peanuts, sunflowers and castor beans. Ellen stuck with her writing and managed their growing family. Politically and economically, however, the situation in Brazil went from bad to worse. Anderson Clayton finally abolished its fazenda "with the stroke of a pen," as Ellen likes to put it. And Carson was out of a job.

"It turned out to be a major stroke of luck," she explains, snapping the last of the beans beside the pool. "The time was right. It was a year or so before inflation took off. Carson started working as a technical editor at a rural magazine in Tietê."

It was 1961. The couple had managed to save enough money

for a down payment on 240 acres of worn-out coffee land just outside of town. The place was "a shambles," much like Brazil's government itself throughout the early '60s. The country was on the verge of revolution and, some predicted, civil war. Fearing nationalization of all business or a pro-Communist government, friends urged Ellen and Carson to live in town and buy dollars — not land. But it was the lure of land — the dream of putting down deep roots on a place of their very own — that drew Ellen and Carson to Brazil and kept them there. They closed the deal on the old coffee plantation and set about building their dream home.

But political unrest also continued to build. In 1964, Brazil's military leaders fearing a Communist take-over, toppled the president. The head of the army became the new president. Congress gave him sweeping new powers that included the ability to rule by military law and suspend political rights. Did the Gelds ever think about leaving? "Never!" snaps Ellen, without hesitation. "The clashing forces never met. It was a laughable revolution." But it was a revolution, nonetheless. The economic, political and other changes it brought through the rest of the decade made life in Brazil even more of a challenge, which seems to be the stuff on which Ellen and Carson absolutely thrive.

They looked at land as much as 350 miles to the west. With the money they had saved, Ellen and Carson could have bought several thousand acres deeper in the interior. "It was cheaper, but we would have had to invest even more," Ellen says. "There were no schools for the children. The roads were poor and there were burned trees standing all over the place. They're gone now, of course."

But what Ellen and Carson were seeking then was land — and a life — that they could live and enjoy now, rather than sacrificing for some vague goal in the distant future. So while Carson's magazine job paid their living expenses, the couple borrowed money from a bank to buy equipment, build a house, barns and make other improvements. For two years, the family lived in Tietê while their house was slowly being built at what they now proudly call Fazenda Pau D'Alho, Garlic Tree Farm. It is a good and proper name because some garlic trees, which Brazilian folklore holds to be the best indicator of good land, do grow there naturally. When crushed, the leaves of the garlic tree smell just like garlic, which is why some unscrupulous Brazilian real estate salesman carry a few cloves of garlic in a pocket while showing land to prospective buyers.

Their gamble paid off quickly and well. Although nearly worn out, the feeble coffee trees produced enough of a harvest to pay off the land. Most of the 40-year-old trees were then cut and sold as firewood and the Gelds began repairing the soil erosion caused by 40 years of coffee cultivation on the rolling land that, except for patches of bamboo and palm trees, looks a lot like northeastern Iowa.

"There was nothing but raw land when we moved here. No buildings, no trees. We had to plant and build everything," explains Ellen. "We put it into pasture. We decided to go into breeding stock because this is a small place and we could not make enough raising beef." Land they bought for $100 an acre now sells for up to $3,000 an acre, due largely to growing development pressure from São Paulo as more and more wealthy and middle class Brazilians buy farms and build homes or vacation cottages in the country. Farther to the west, even better land costs up to $5,000 an acre.

The house they built is exactly the house of their dreams, "a fine rambling house built in a rectangle enclosing a patio filled with tropical birds and plants." It was first sketched out while they were living at Malabar in Ohio. The U-shaped, one-story house has thick brick walls that are painted white and topped with red Spanish tile that is now blackened here and there with mildew, flecked with green moss and laced with old thick flowering vines. The house frames a large flagstone patio that is bordered by an incredible array of tropical trees and flowering plants. Brightly colored birds are everywhere. Screened French doors painted dark green open onto the patio from all sides. The doors have no locks and, except at night when the dogs are shut up inside, "are always open for the comings and goings of dogs and children and absent-minded people on half-forgotten missions," Ellen writes. "The house has become a part of everything around it until it no longer matters which is the front door and which is the back."

Inside, the spacious house is cool, dark and inviting. The living room with its flagstone floor, red brick fireplace and cathedral ceiling with exposed, dark beams, has seen a lot of living. It is comfortably furnished with heavy, unmatched furniture. The walls are lined with books, including Ellen's seven books and many signed first editions of Louis Bromfield's works, plus Bach, Brahms and other classics on CD. There are drawings and paintings, including one of Bromfield at Malabar in Ohio, and the usual assortment of mementos gathered over a rich lifetime. Deep scratches from the toenails of generations of much-loved dogs identify the doors to all of the bedrooms. The children's rooms are intact much as they left them with posters and favorite photos on the walls, books and other keepsakes crowding the shelves. Both walls in the long hallway leading from Ellen and Carson's bedroom to the living room are covered with scores of framed photos of children and grandchildren.

An old TV set and a VCR are tucked away in a corner of the boys' old rooms. The rooftop antenna provides poor reception. They could follow son Steve's lead and hook up to the cable. Steve even has HBO at his fazenda some 20 miles away. But Ellen and Carson do not watch that much TV, so they just don't bother. Life moves at a different pace here on their fazenda. There is a definite Brazilian inclination toward the basics and the things that really matter most in life. Until about 1990, for example, they did not have a telephone. "Carson had a phone in his office in Tietê and that was enough," Ellen explains. "The children loved it. They thought that Brazil was Fazenda Pau D'Alho and when they went away from it they were in for a surprise."

Fazenda Pau D'Alho is the center of the universe for Ellen and Carson and they spend as little time away from it as possible. They don't go out to restaurants much, probably because Ellen is such a wonderful and inventive cook, preparing everything from moussaka to London broil with seemingly no extra effort. Ellen hardly ever goes into São Paulo and visits Tietê only occasionally. Carson makes the long drive to downtown São Paulo maybe once a week for Santa Gertrudis Association meetings and other cattle business.

For exercise, Ellen and Carson work hard and regularly in their large vegetable garden behind the machine shed. They keep a big pile of cattle manure nearby and do all of the tilling and cultivating by hand, using the same style of heavy hoes that have been used for centuries in Brazil. Carson, who Bromfield once said simply had to look at a machine for it to collapse, seems most at ease and productive with the hand tools. That's not too surprising. Carson first learned to farm with horses, a scythe and a dump rake during World War II. For entertainment, he and Ellen have everything they need right on their fazenda — dogs, cattle, wildlife, children, grandchildren and nature's constantly changing show of clouds, sunrises and glorious sunsets.

This evening before cocktails (scotch on the rocks for Carson and rum for Ellen) and dinner, we stroll up the back lane past the cattle barns. It's almost dark. A big truck is backed up to one end of the barn. Two heifers are balking at being loaded inside. Ellen averts her eyes, quickens her pace so that we hurry past the place. The heifers, Carson explains in a low voice, are headed for the butcher. They will be the main attraction at the cookout at Saturday's auction. Neither Ellen nor Carson says much the rest of the walk. It's obvious that all of their animals mean an awful lot to them, which may explain why these cattlemen don't eat much beef.

By the next morning, preparations for the auction are in full swing. Cattle trucks, tipping wildly from side to side as they lumber up the rutted lane, are steadily filling the barns with bulls and bred heifers from other area breeders. A bright yellow and blue circus tent ringed with bold stars now covers a 150-foot long oval beside the milking shed. The show ring, handling chutes, sound system, signs and banners are all in place. Eighty tables with white linen tablecloths are set up under the big top, awaiting centerpieces of fresh-cut flowers. The centerpieces usually come from a florist. But flower prices are now so high that Ellen is doing it herself this year. We spend most of the morning picking crate after crate of Swedish ivy, white blossoms and green foliage from the terraced beds and borders around the house and patio. Then we clean out the last of the sunflowers from the vegetable garden. Ellen starts filling 80 small clear glass globes with flowers and arranging them just so on a long table in the shade on the patio, as more supplies, cattle and visitors continue to arrive.

By evening, everything is ready and perfect. The only unanswered question is, of course, the weather. "That looks pretty damn black out there," Carson grumbles, watching heavy, dark clouds roll in from the south.

Saturday morning dawns dark and dreary. The sky is ominously overcast. Slight sprinkles wet the dust on the cars and trucks as they fill up row after long row in the pecan grove. The sun fights fiercely to break through the clouds and, by late morning, wins a partial victory. Thin wood smoke and the smell of sizzling meat fill the air as hundreds of slender bamboo spears loaded with chunks of homegrown beef are spread atop the cooking fires. The 25-ounce beers are disappearing rapidly from the tubs of ice. Bottled soda and wine are flowing freely at several refreshment stands. Next to the milk house, bingo cards are selling well. Grand prize is two round-trip tickets to the United States on American Airlines and two nights at a Miami Ramada Inn. There is also a lottery on the new Fiat sedan on display just outside of the bigtop. Two federal police officers in a VW beetle patrol car keep an eye on things from a respectful distance. Squealing children and barking dogs run everywhere. It's a big circus, a fair — and a feast! With appetites whetted by the enticing smells wafting through the pecan grove, scores of people line up for "chiroskos" long before the juicy kebobs are ready. Only the Santa Gertrudis banners around the show ring and the lines of patient cattle tethered at one end of the pecan grove stand as reminders of the real purpose of the event.

After everyone has eaten and drunk their fill or at least taken the edge off their appetite and thirst, it's show time. Cattle handlers all wearing white T-shirts with the silk-screened logo of the auction and matching baseball caps begin leading different classes of cattle into the show ring. First come the bred heifers, all guaranteed pregnant. Then the bulls. Every animal that is shown must be sold afterward to the highest bidder. That's the rule. Despite the party atmosphere, this is serious cattle business. You can tell by Carson's official appearance in khaki dress slacks and his white straw cowboy hat, complete with pins that bear crossed American and Brazilian flags and tout "A Taste of Texas," "Ohio State Parks" and "Santa Gertrudis." The most serious of the lot, however, is Judge Seyfferdt. He puts the cattle through a demanding performance inside the show ring, having the handlers circle them clockwise, then counterclockwise, up and back, right and left. He pokes and prods, squints close-up at some features and moves way back to compare others. Then he has the animals stand and stretch and do it all over again until he decides on his favorites.

Outside the show ring, the party continues. Only a few people in the rows of folding chairs keep a close eye on the action in the ring. Everyone else is eating and drinking, talking and laughing and having a grand old time. Sitting in the second row, Ellen is at the heart of perhaps the largest and most lively crowd. No wonder. She is suddenly surrounded by her children and some of her 13 grandchildren. There is Steve in a baseball cap, blue checked flannel shirt and blue jeans. His thick hair is mostly gray now, but he still has that same jaunty air of the little boy standing in the garden. And the same easy, loud laugh and wide grin of his mother. Steve's oldest boy, who is somewhere off in the crowd with his cousins, is going off to college next year. He's thinking about Cornell. Where else? Both Ellen and Carson studied agriculture there. In fact, that is where they met. Steve and two other Geld children went to Cornell, while one each went to school in Colorado and Wisconsin. All three of their boys work for farm-related businesses that involve everything from orange juice and soybeans to cattle feed. Robin, the Gelds' first child born in Brazil, lives with two boxers in São Paulo where she writes screenplays and short stories, and translates and edits a variety of materials. The other children all live in rural areas. Kenny, the youngest son, is here with his wife and young children. Christina arrives with her toddler and newborn. Michael, who lives more than 600 miles away in the interior, can't make it this year. The only other ones missing are Ellen's sisters, Anne and Hope, who both live in Montana. They're missing quite a party.

Even the judge is blown away by the whole affair. "This is completely unique, actually," Seyfferdt says, as he begins announcing his top selection. "Usually, these sales are held in towns with show rings, not on farms. I've seen nothing like this anywhere else in the world. I am impressed." The finish is not as good for the Gelds as in some other years, but their bull still places second and one of Steve's heifers comes in third. That is still good enough to help boost prices a bit at the auction.

Inside the cavernous auction tent, everything and everyone is ready to go. Waiters, volunteers for a nearby school for "exceptional children" with developmental and physical challenges which benefits from the auction, are circulating among the 80 tables, freely pouring Chilean red and white wine and Johnny Walker Red scotch. There are also six bottles of tequila for anyone who is interested. The sound system is blaring. Sinatra is belting out "New York, New York," and the BeeGees are "Stayin' Alive." The crowd is in a really mellow mood. But the auctioneer is unable to start. Something is wrong in the auction ring. Some kind of animal is running amok. Patches of tan, brown, white and black fur flash by as the creature dives, burrows and romps wildly through the thick golden straw.

"Hen-REE! Hen-REE!" A droop-eared head suddenly pops up from the middle of the straw. "Who, me?" the eyes ask, innocently. Henry, the bassett pup, is stealing the show. A ring worker leads

Henry out of the spotlight to a thunderous round of applause, and the auction is under way. With all the drama, passion and intensity of a Broadway musical on opening night, it builds over the course of two hours to a shattering climax that leaves everyone exhausted. Not all buyers and sellers are completely happy with the prices. They seldom are. But no one is really complaining, either.

The bulk of the crowd drifts back toward the cars parked in the pecan grove, preparing for long drives home. A surprising number, however, find their way to the house. There, the party is just beginning anew. Live, from Fazenda Pau D'Alho — it's Saturday night! There is plenty to eat, plenty to drink. Friends and family quickly fill the living room and spill out into the night on the patio. It's time to mambo — and samba — and twist and shout! And party on down, as the younger generation takes control of the CD player and aims the speakers out of the windows toward the patio. Tom Petty is having his "Last Dance with Mary Jane," Cheryl Crow is drinking another beer at noon on Tuesday on "Santa Monica Blvd.," Lynyrd Skynyrd is extolling "Sweet Home Alabama" and the Eagles are stuck in "Hotel California," the acoustic version, of course. In years past, as many as 200 have stayed for the festivities. This year's crowd, though formidable, is only about one-quarter that size. There are people from easily half a dozen different countries.

Dancing on the patio lasts way past 11 p.m., with Ellen and Carson gyrating with the best of them. Finally, about midnight those who must still drive home begin making their goodbyes. The children who are spending the night find their way back to their old rooms. Guests repair to their quarters and the quiet night envelopes the farm.

S unday morning dawns bright and clear and early, as the grandchildren clamor noisily for breakfast at grandma and grandpa's house. More than a dozen chairs crowd around the dining room table. Three generations of the family are present. Conversation, questions and good-natured arguments, jokes and curses explode in English and Portuguese, with young and old slipping easily in and out of both languages. Soon as breakfast is finished, children and grandchildren scatter in all directions. Some head for their own homes, while others linger around the farm. Four-year-old Sofia appears a little later at the wheel of the Gelds' big Massey-Ferguson tractor. Her father, Kenny, supervises from his perch on a fender. He is having as much fun as she is.

By late afternoon, Ellen and Carson almost have the farm to themselves again. The children and grandchildren are long gone. Only the singing sound of a milk pail fills the air as old Aristides, who "retired" from the farm six months ago, milks the two dairy cows by hand. The sun breaks out of the clouds. Shafts of warm, golden light fall onto the cattle grazing on the far hills. Part of the herd moves toward the barn. First one cow, then two, three, four. Finally, there are 24 fat red cattle, followed by little white birds that eat ticks off of their backs in the pasture where the big top stood. I slip through an opening in the rail fence to get some better photos.

Suddenly, the cattle all turn and begin trotting back out into the pasture. At first, I think the clicking of my old Nikon has spooked the herd, starting a stampede. The real culprit soon becomes obvious. Carson is yelling at the top of his mighty lungs as he strides quickly toward the panicky cattle: "Hen-REE! Hen-REE!!" A droop-eared head pops up from the tall green grass. The wide brown eyes aren't so innocent this time. They don't ask, "Who, me?" Henry can't be bothered now. He is busy. This little puppy has work to do. Henry quickly lowers his head and continues charging the cows. Carson closes in on him. And the good life on the land goes on exactly as it should in Bromfield's Brazil.

16

Malabar:
A Place of Learning

By Ellen Bromfield Geld
Fazenda Pau D'Alho (Garlic Tree Farm)
Tietê, Brazil Jan. 3, 1996

I cannot remember the exact circumstances, perhaps they were too painful, in which we announced to my father that we had decided to give a try to living in Brazil. I only know that he was thoroughly appalled and that it would take him several years, punctuated with chiding letters of remonstrance, to come to terms with it. That's how parents are; how we are.

Yet I also know now that what lay behind our going were the ideas our parents on both sides had transmitted to us in the course of our growing up. "First of all," both Jenny Geld and Louis Bromfield had often been heard to say, "try to live by doing the things you like. That way your precious time will never be wasted."

It was that kind of thinking indeed that caused us to decide to go. And though he considered us insane at first, eventually my father would come to admit with a certain pride, that much of the fault was his own. For certainly we would not have made such a decision had we not one night sat until the small hours on the porch at Malabar Farm, listening to a conversation between himself and the Brazilian Carlito Aranha — two men from very different worlds who nonetheless when they talked about farming, set each other's minds afire.

Like my father, Carlito had taken over an old, eroded and depleted farm, in his case planted up and down hill to thousands of coffee trees. Tearing out the old coffee, he had set about using everything he had read, and learned to rotate legumes with corn, rice and vegetables, plant a vineyard and balance his crops with the raising of hogs, chickens and dairy cattle. It all came together in a highly successful farming operation that indeed, out of its bounty, had given many a sharecropper the chance to acquire land of his own.

As he'd worked and read, Carlito had seen, through his reading of Louis Bromfield's books, how deeply his thoughts coincided with those of the author. No wonder, then, that when he came to visit Malabar, the two sat up talking all night and we, as we listened, were caught in the spell.

"After all," we said at the time, "we have decided to try to make a living from farming." And listening to the two of them talk, it seemed to us then that Brazil, almost as much of a frontier as the United States had been half a century earlier, must be the best place to go.

Luckily that childhood advice, taken at face value, served us well. For eventually we did acquire our own place in Brazil where we've had a good life, raised our children and continue to live — breeding cattle and grass-farming in the shadows of wide spreading pecan trees.

To try to seek a living by doing what you like was one of many ideas that I have always thought of as my most important heritage from my father. Others I have extracted from my memory in times of need, such as now, to be reconsidered, interpreted, embellished upon.

How often in my childhood, for instance, did I hear it said that agriculture is probably the most complex profession in existence? And how often I have seen that this is true, encompassing as it does something of almost every other profession from mechanics and the complicated architecture of farm buildings to practicing genetics and even doctoring.

It is as well ever changing; so that in order to adapt what is going on in the scientific world, one must also always be aware of what happens around one every day in the world of the farm.

Nowhere could this have been more obvious than at Malabar. Growing up there, helping with the haying, the planting, the care of animals, our attention was constantly drawn to details. Did we see how the alfalfa roots penetrated deep into the soil, aerating and helping the earth's nutrients become available to the grain that was to follow?

Did we see how a productive animal is one that lives in the circumstances that best suit it? On range our chickens had no need of antibiotics. On pasture our cattle grew well, bred well and calved well for they also could walk well and feed according to their very specific routine. All they needed was good pasture. "Always remember," my father would say, "that cattle take from the land just as crops do. Therefore pasture needs to be thought of as a crop which also needs to be renewed, fertilized, grazed with great attention to its capacity."

As the years went by, at Malabar we kept a par of new developments. I think Louis Bromfield was among the first to switch from the moldboard plow to the disk plow and then to the chisel as it became obvious that, by cutting through the soil instead of turning it over, you avoided hardpan and left invaluable organic matter where it could be of use.

Eventually he had to admit that the division of labor was too great for us to be able to maintain a variety of livestock, so my father turned to cattle. Yet he remained convinced to the end of his life, just as I am, that livestock provides a necessary balance to crops.

No matter if we produce more than the cattle can consume; they consume what they need and we sell the excess. The manure that we collect provides a bonus in fruits and berries, corn, squash, tomatoes and beans, which in turn make our lives more secure and definitely more delightful to live.

How we loved at Malabar to help with the canning of tomato juice, peaches and plums and jellies of every variety to be used the whole year round. How we do so here too at Fazenda Pau D'Alho, where there is no greater pleasure for ourselves and our children and grandchildren than to pick limas or eggplant or lettuce, fresh and clean from the garden. Indeed how much better one's time is spent walking beneath the trees to the vegetable garden, planning to make zucchini fritters for supper, than driving along a strip to the rattle, push and shove of a supermarket.

These are concepts that became ingrained in our lives as we grew at Malabar, along with the knowledge that everything, from healthy soil in a well-tended field, to a clear running stream, to the native forest that shelters the springs that feed it, are essential parts of a whole, else nature would not have provided them.

For this, during all those years, my father was constantly preoccupied with the narrow track relentlessly pursued as agriculture came to be looked upon as an "industry" with a "scientific" solution for everything. The cleaner and larger the fields, the greater the input of chemicals and big machinery, the more specialized the produce, the more efficient.

For this as well, as we grew up and watched, we saw countless American farmers fall by the wayside, in debt for machinery and

inputs they could not afford. While others -- badgered by governmental programs of subsidies and quotas -- turned their landscape
into a sterile one of closed, air-conditioned houses surrounded by
livestock factories, towering silos amid the monotony of endless
acres of grain. That was the official model. If one sought official
advice, no other choice was offered.

Yet common sense and experience must have told a good many
people that such could simply not be. And sitting here behind my
computer, looking out toward the trees and pastures of Pau D'Alho,
I am again overwhelmed at the thought of the energy and imagination Louis Bromfield put into proving it.

In all this, most fortunate was the fact that, working out
scientific and practical concepts on his own land, he was able to
write of them in such a way that people could share his experiences
and make use of them, adapting them to their own conditions,
whatever they might be.

Here in Brazil, Carlito Aranha was but one of many whom
we've encountered as, selling our Santa Gertrudis heifers and bulls,
we've traveled the length and breadth of a country as big as the
United States. Among them I think in particular of Manoel Henrique
Perreira who, like Carlito, inherited a fazenda so depleted and
eroded that banks were reluctant to give him crop loans. Nono, as
his friends call him, had balanced his rather dull and theoretical
agricultural studies at The University of Parana by reading all Louis
Bromfield's farm books. He had as well looked into the most recent
practices in no-till planting.

On his battered, hilly land, Nono began to rotate his wheat and
soybeans and corn with lupine and vetch -- these latter to form a
mulch in which he seeded his conventional crops. He began to
winter his cattle on rye grass, the straw of which he also incorpo-
rated into the mulch before spring planting. Within five years, his
topsoil had regained its original degree of organic matter. In his
permanently covered soil, he can now plant up and down hill
without danger of erosion. His cost of tillage and fertilizers has been
reduced by half, while his overall productivity in grains has risen
from 10,000 kilograms to 14,000 kilograms per hectare, the highest
in Parana, the greatest grain producing state in Brazil.

Knowledge of his success is such that he is on call everywhere
in South and Central America to describe his experience, and help
others to adapt to this particular method, which Brazilians call

planting in the straw.

It is, of course, the same concept my father used and divulged in that time when universities and departments of agriculture were recommending and backing open tilling, single crop, high intensity fertilization and spraying. These high tech, scientific methods certainly produced high results on experimental farms, but in the end they also caused the problems of compacted soils, pollution and the instability of an agriculture dependent on single crops that farmers face today.

The difference between then and now is that sustainable agriculture's worth is gaining recognition even in bureaucratic entities which are always the most reluctant to face the results of error, the need to retool and change gear. Because of this, the more enlightened schools, such as the Ohio State University, now have departments of sustainable agriculture. Yet one doubts they would have, had not people like Louis Bromfield and Nono Perreira, who lived their farming every day, proven the sense and practicality of what they were doing.

For truly, what is sustainable agriculture if not a sensible manner of working with all the resources that nature possesses to put our scientific achievement to better use? Thus in a soil made more friable by chisel plowing and the maintenance of organic matter, the need for fertilizer is reduced. On land covered by a mulch of the last crop's straw, run-off is cut down, rain water is better absorbed and the use of herbicides cut to a minimum. Rotation avoids disease even as it enriches the soil with the bacterial help of legumes. These are facts, proven by years of hard practice of which profit and stability have been the result.

But even as we practice, as usual we are learning. New methods arise out of old. Though man has been here for thousands of years, research has only begun to pay due respect to the forest for all it must contain. The Brazilian forests, for instance, from which such wonderful Indian names of plants spring to mind - *ipecacuanha*, *genipapo* and *indaya*.

Amid the incredible, endless intricacies of the earth, the plants that grow out of it and the creatures that feed upon them, we have only made a small dent, concentrating as we have on a few grains and fruits. Only now are we beginning to look upon pure sunlight as the best form of energy. And at last -- instead of continuously consuming and throwing away until there's nothing more and nowhere left to throw -- we are seeking ways to recycle, make use of resources that grow more precious as the world grows smaller.

Particularly in farming, at the source of most things, new methods need somewhere to be tried in real situations where their workability can be shown to and taken advantage of by people who make a living from tilling the land. This is especially true of people who, if they tried optimum input on single crops grown right up to the front door, would go broke and possibly die of boredom in the process.

And that is why, whenever I think of Malabar Farm in Ohio, I think of it essentially as a place of learning.

Oh, I know that thousands troupe through The Big House yearly to gape at the room where Humphrey Bogart and Lauren Bacall spent their wedding night. But that's all right, it is part of Malabar's character, and heaven knows in a world blighted by sameness, character is something we can never have enough of. Just as is the beauty of a house that, splendid as it is, fits so homely and comfortably into its more than splendid setting.

And when I think of that setting, I realize each time how privileged we were as children to be able, whenever the mood struck us, to take a walk through the woods. Once when I was visiting the Park, someone showed me most of the paths that had been chosen as riding and walking trails for visitors. And I was amazed to see that most of them were indeed the paths we had followed as children, picking blackberries and raspberries in season, or pretending to be pioneers or Indians "settling" in the old cabin up Ferguson Way, or peering out like Pocahontas from the sandstone cliffs overlooking Pleasant Valley.

Remembering this, I think of the countless children who have missed so much by *not* having had such an opportunity and hope that Malabar can give it to them every now and then. Or I think of people who have never taken a quiet walk through the country, but whose spirits might be so much better soothed and renewed by such an experience than by prowling through a spiritless shopping center with never enough money to satisfy needs that money can't buy.

In this sense, like any natural preserve, I see Malabar as a link between city folk and nature of which all of us are a part and upon which we ultimately depend for our survival. Not just physically, like ants, but spiritually as people who must have beauty in their lives or become -- even without realizing -- ill for the lack of it.

That is what natural preserves are for, to remind us of harmony and balance and the value of greenery and birds and animals. And why they are needed even in the midst of the greatest of cities, if there is to be tranquillity as opposed to the desolation that ugliness imposes upon our lives.

And yet the great difference about Malabar is that, while one can take a walk in the woods there, ignoring all else if one likes; one has only to look about to see in a thousand ways, the harmony between its woods and waters and its pastures and fields. Each is complimentary to the other. Each has need of the other to create a whole.

From beneath ancient trees, out of sandstone formations within the great hill called Mount Jeez, for instance, a spring flows through a bed of water cress and on down to fill a pond where bass abound and from which water is drawn for a vegetable garden at the hill's end. For those who want to gather practical meaning from this beautiful and natural orchestration, it is only necessary to see how it would be if the forest that secures the hilltop were destroyed, and how that would affect all the parts. How soon the pond would be silted in and the spring would most likely disappear.

As it is, cattle graze on the densely matted grass that holds the hillside and drink clear water from the spring's trough. And just as the spring also supplies fresh, clear water for the house beside it; so as it flows through another trough in the springhouse, does the water cool vegetables and milk on its way. Milk that, when I was a girl, we turned into butter and cheese, just as we do nowadays at Pau D'Alho.

Here on our place in Brazil, the butter and cheese and vegetables as well as a couple of pigs to eat waste from the garden, are another part of my heritage from Malabar, Ohio. One that makes it impossible for me to look at jaboticabas or acerolas on a tree without feeling an instinctive urge to preserve. The whole are part of a farm program that requires a good deal of work, but no great expense. Two Santa Gertrudis cows from our breeding herd give us all the milk we need, and the soil of the garden is rich with manure from the barn. All these provide us with fresh, delicious food and plenty left over to supply those who work on the fazenda, as well as a child day care center in Tietê nearby.

Certainly, they do away with a lot of waste and greatly reduce our food expenses. But as much as anything, there is no way to calculate the pleasure they give us. For though I don't much like washing vegetables, I'd rather do that than get into a car and go to a supermarket. And the rest is all creative: "Dr. Bromfield's tomato juice" for Bloody Marys and spaghetti sauce, dill pickles and Jalapeno peppers with garlic in oil to be eaten with the beans. Ahh, how well I remember, on his visits to Brazil, my father's standing over the woodstove, cooking mango chutney with peppers and onions and ginger, and Carlito Aranha's asking if that was a concoction to kill flies. Though once he ate it with pork, he was ready to make it himself.

Such things as these I visualize as part of learning in a sustainable farming program at Malabar Farm, just as we have taught them to countless farm girls in Brazil. Part of a program such as 4-H has long carried out in the United States that includes young people in competitions in everything from canning to raising steer. For farming is a life which, if it is not creative, can be drudgery. But if it is creative, it can have no equal in pride and pleasure.

Because it has Louis Bromfield's vigorous, inspiring memory behind everything that is done there, Malabar is unique. For this, quite simply, no other place can be better suited to be what he described in his book, *A Few Brass Tacks* as a pilot farm, a place where the work of universities can be translated.

Thinking of its lush, hillside pastures, I visualize a program based essentially on grass farming and livestock. If it isn't geared to making profit, it isn't performing its task of providing people who live from farming with ideas they can use on their own land.

Linked with Ohio State, I see it providing internships for students who nowadays more than ever -- as many of them may not be from farms -- need to live what they study in order to put it into perspective. I think of practical studies that will not only turn out technicians, but farmers who actually desire to make a living by owning a piece of land and working it.

I imagine these interns coming not only from American Universities but everywhere in an international program in which students from Brazil or Russia or Australia can gain a different perspective even as they take advantage of the wonderful, up-to-date and growing Sustainable Agriculture Library administered by OSU's Dr. Clive Edwards.

Or I see them learning as they work in the vegetable garden, producing truly fresh vegetables to be sold from the stand below the springhouse. As they care for the cattle, seeing for themselves how sturdy animals can be fattened on grass at less cost and better advantage to the human diet. Or learn by experience how the aerator breaks through the cattles' plodding tread; and the chisel plow cuts deep, leaving the trash in place; how crops grow healthily out of the mulch-protected soil.

For it is all very well to read about these things, but lucky is he who can see with his own eyes as well, talk with his companions in the field about how a well-drained soil, rich in organic matter, makes fertilizer more easily available to plants.

In the same way, I imagine farmers coming to spend the day going over the farm, talking and exchanging ideas; taking home material from the library when they leave. Perhaps even taking time, when a less pressing winter provides it, to attend this or that seminar given by visiting speakers.

Finally, I think of farmers and city folk and environmentalists meeting and mingling at Malabar in an atmosphere conducive to comprehension. For how absurdly harm is done by misinterpretation and incomprehension among people who obviously must have the same end in view -- that of keeping our planet a richly varied, healthy place to live on.

Therefore at Malabar, where it can be so easily seen how the forest lends itself to the field, I imagine one day walking tours and talks being given on riparian conservation or selective logging, or how a conservation easement works. Other such walking and talking could be applied to such subjects as layered agriculture, the value and proliferation of cattle birds, the enormous role of pasture on lands not suitable to cultivation.

Every year, universities offer instructive tours led by professors in the broad fields of environment and agriculture. Why should not Malabar be a stopping place?

As these thoughts come to mind, it occurs to me that I would discourage the idea of having specialized guides with memorized spiels to do the showing and telling. Better the actual students and employees taking turns, I expect. For you don't have to be Louis Bromfield to put a point across. It is enough to be someone like Nono Perreira who enjoys people and is actually living and doing the thing he likes. I know this because, even more than selling grass and cattle and pecan seedlings here at Pau D'Alho, we enjoy the opportunity it gives us to meet all kinds of people, walk with them over the fazenda, talk about the things that come to mind. THAT, in the end, is what is important because it brings the whole thing close to home and to life.

Yes, I can see, the more I write, the more I think and get fired up about Malabar, how useful it can always be in a world where the exchange of ideas and living evidence are so essential -- especially in a world in which people are increasingly inclined to sit isolated in their little air-conditioned boxes, literally afraid to confront what goes on outside; convinced, as we can become, of the inevitability of a landscape blighted by identical motels and shopping malls amid forests of neon signs.

I know the world must change and I cannot predict how it will be for my grandchildren. But something more that I gained from my father's thinking was a profound need for continuity in order for life to make sense to me. Not continuity in terms of inheriting material things. My father had his farm, I have mine, our sons have theirs. That too is a part of what he taught us, the pleasure and accomplishment of doing our own things in our own way.

And yet there is that thread that makes me want to pass along the knowledge of what was best in the world I grew up in, so that it may be of use in theirs. Therefore, though I know inevitably there will be fewer farms and more people will live city lives, still I don't want them to lose the sense of what nature alone can offer.

Instead of great concrete jungles of inner city decay surrounded by strips and junk heaps, I hope they will be able to live in smaller, more compact yet beautiful cities such as Seattle where there are countless parks, and greenery is within the city as well as without. Where nearly everyone has his patch of shaded garden, inhabited by birds and squirrels. A city from which he can get out into a countryside, unmarred by acres of parking lots; occupied instead by old and revered trees.

For in the end it seems to me that perhaps half the psychosis, addiction to drugs and other forms of despair that exist, have much to do with lives from which beauty is absent. From which the sense of peace and harmony that comes from having nature near at hand has been excluded. These are important things, perhaps the most important, for without them and the richness they engender, our planet cannot survive. Such are the ideas I learned at Malabar; the ones I would like to see passed on to any who can make use of them.

Appendices

How to Visit Malabar Farm Today

Guided tours of the 32-room Big House, preserved just as it was at the time of Louis Bromfield's death, are offered year-round at Malabar Farm State Park in Ohio. Contact the park for daily hours. Cost is $3 for adults and $1 for students age 6-18. Children under five are admitted free. The park offers hiking trails, 12 miles of bridle paths, fishing, 15 campsites, plus sledding, ice skating and cross-country skiing in winter. Bromfield's books, including his agricultural classics, are available at the park bookstore. Contact:

Malabar Farm State Park
4050 Bromfield Road
Lucas, Ohio 44843
Phone: (419) 892-2784

Where to Eat at Malabar

Home cooked meals are available seasonally (usually May 1 through Oct. 31) at Malabar Inn, a stagecoach inn built in 1820, which is also located in the park. Call ahead for exact details. Malabar Inn does not offer overnight accommodations. Bromfield used the 2,000-gallon per hour spring beside the Inn to cool vegetables at his bustling produce stand, which he called "The Roadside Market to End All Roadside Markets." Tough guy actor James Cagney once sold vegetables there for days while visiting Malabar. Contact:

Malabar Inn
3645 Pleasant Valley Road
Perrysville, Ohio 44864
Phone: (419) 938-5205

Books by Louis Bromfield

The Green Bay Tree, 1924
Possession, 1925
Early Autumn, 1926 (Awarded Pulitzer Prize, 1927)
A Good Woman, 1927
The Strange Case of Miss Annie Spragg, 1928
Awake and Rehearse, 1929
Twenty-four Hours, 1930
One Heavenly Night, 1931
A Modern Hero, 1932
The Farm, 1933
Here Today and Gone Tomorrow, 1934
The Man Who Had Everything, 1935
The Rains Came, 1937
It Takes All Kinds, 1939
England, a Dying Oligarchy, 1939
Night in Bombay, 1940
Wild is the River, 1941
Until the Day Break, 1942
Mrs. Parkington, 1943
What Became of Anna Bolton, 1944
Bitter Lotus, 1944
The World We Live In, 1944
Pleasant Valley, 1945
A Few Brass Tacks, 1946
Colorado, 1947
Kenny, 1947
The Wild Country, 1948
McLeod's Folly, 1948
Malabar Farm, 1948
Out of the Earth, 1950
Mr. Smith, 1951
A New Pattern for a Tired World, 1954
Animals and Other People, 1955
From My Experience, 1955

314

Books about Louis Bromfield

1. Anderson, David D., *Louis Bromfield*, New York: Twayne Publishers 1963. 191 pp.
2. Brown, Morrison, *Louis Bromfield and His Books*. London: Cassell & Co. Ltd.1956. 166 pp.
3. Carter, John T., *Louis Bromfield and the Malabar Farm Experience*. Mattituck, NY. Amereon 1995. 104 pp.
4. Clinker, B. Keith., *Louis Bromfield — A Bibliography*. Mt. Vernon, Ohio. Owl Creek Books 1992. 16 pp.
5. Geld, Ellen Bromfield, *The Heritage — A Daughter's Memories of Louis Bromfield*. N.Y.: Harper 1962. 205 pp.
6. Gramly, Allene Holt. *Louis Bromfield*. Mansfield, Ohio: Appleseed Press 1987. 28 pp.
7. Little, Charles E. (ed.), *Louis Bromfield at Malabar — Writings on Farming and Country Life*. Baltimore, Md.: Johns Hopkins University Press 1989. 239 pp.
8. Redman, B. R., *Louis Bromfield and His Books*. N.Y.: Stokes. 1929
9. Ward, Howard J., *Louis Bromfield*. N.Y.: Harper 1956.

Books by Ellen Bromfield Geld

Strangers in the Valley, 1957
Brazil: Portrait of a Great Country, 1959
The Jungley One, 1961
The Heritage — A Daughter's Memories of Louis Bromfield, 1962
The Garlic Tree, 1970
A Timeless Place, 1971
The Dreamers, 1973
A Winter's Reckoning, 1976

George DeVault is an editor at Rodale Press Inc. in Emmaus, Pa. He began his journalistic career at age 15 as a photographer for his hometown newspaper, *The Delaware Gazette* in Delaware, Ohio, and went on to work as a photographer and reporter at *The Columbus Dispatch*, in Columbus, Ohio, and a reporter and later assistant city editor at *The Fort Lauderdale News and Sun-Sentinel* in Florida. For 10 years he was editor of *The New Farm* magazine and, since 1991, has served as editor of the Russian-language *Novii Sadovod i Fermer* (New Gardener and Farmer), the last magazine started by Bob Rodale. He also edited *Booker T. Whatley's Handbook On How To Make $100,000 Farming 25 Acres*, *Backyard Market Gardening* by Andrew Lee and Peter Henderson's *Gardening For Profit*, which was also published by The American Botanist. He is a contributor to *Successful Farming*, *Farm Journal*, *Top Producer* and *Organic Gardening* magazines. He lives on a small organic vegetable farm near Emmaus, Pa., with his wife, two children and two dogs.